S0-AFQ-780

$\bar{z}$	conjugate of z	(6.2)
ρ or $|z|$	rho, absolute value or modulus of z	(6.3)
θ	theta, argument of a complex number	(6.3)
z^0	the complex number $1 + 0i$ or $(1, 0)$	(6.5)
$z^{-n}, n \in N$	$1/z^n$	(6.5)
$z^{1/n}, n \in N$	nth root of z	(6.5)
$\{a, b\}$	the set whose elements (or members) are a and b	(A.1)
$\in$	is a member of, is an element of ($\notin$, is not a member of, is not an element of)	(A.1)
$\{x \mid \ldots\}$	the set of all x such that $\ldots$	(A.1)
$\cup$	the union of	(A.1)
$\cap$	the intersection of	(A.1)
$\varnothing$	the null set, the empty set	(A.1)
H	the set of irrational numbers	(A.2)
J	the set of integers	(A.2)
N	the set of natural numbers	(A.2)
Q	the set of rational numbers	(A.2)
R	the set of real numbers	(A.2)
$\sqrt{a}, a \geq 0$	the nonnegative square root of a	(A.2)
$\approx$	approximately equal to	(A.2)
$|a|$	the absolute value of a	(A.2)
$<$	is less than	(A.2)
$\leq$	is less than or equal to	(A.2)
$>$	is greater than	(A.2)
$\geq$	is greater than or equal to	(A.2)
(a, b)	the ordered pair of numbers whose first component is a and whose second component is b	(A.3)
$f, F, g,$ etc.	names a function or a relation	(A.3)
$f(x)$	f of x, or the value of f at x	(A.3)
$\overline{P_1P_2}$	the line segment whose endpoints are P_1 and P_2	(A.4)
P_1P_2	the length of line segment $\overline{P_1P_2}$	(A.4)
$\mathscr{R}$	a relation	(A.6)
$\mathscr{R}^{-1}$	the inverse of relation $\mathscr{R}$	(A.6)
$\overrightarrow{AB}$	ray with endpoint A and including B	(A.7)
$\angle ABC$	angle ABC (the vertex is at B)	(A.7)
$\perp$	is perpendicular to	(A.7)
$\triangle ABC$	a triangle with vertices A, B, C	(A.8)
$\cong$	is congruent to	(A.9)
$\sim$	is similar to	(A.9)

TRIGONOMETRY
An Analytic Approach

Fourth Edition

TRIGONOMETRY
AN ANALYTIC APPROACH

Irving Drooyan
Walter Hadel
Charles C. Carico
Los Angeles Pierce College

Macmillan Publishing Co., Inc.
New York

Collier Macmillan Publishers
London

Copyright © 1983, Macmillan Publishing Co., Inc.
Printed in the United States of America.

All rights reserved. No part of this book may be reproduced or transmitted in any form or by any means, electronic or mechanical, including photocopying, recording, or any information storage and retrieval system, without permission in writing from the Publisher.

Earlier editions by Irving Drooyan, Walter Hadel, and Charles C. Carico copyright © 1973 and 1979 by Macmillan Publishing Co., Inc. Earlier edition by Irving Drooyan and Walter Hadel copyright © 1967 by Macmillan Publishing Co., Inc. Portions of this material have been reprinted from *Essentials of Trigonometry,* by Irving Drooyan, Walter Hadel, and Charles C. Carico, copyright © 1971 by Macmillan Publishing Co., Inc., and from *Algebra 2 with Trigonometry* by Irving Drooyan, Walter Hadel, Herman Hyatt, Charles C. Carico, and James Hardesty, copyright © 1970 by Macmillan Publishing Co., Inc.

Macmillan Publishing Co., Inc.
866 Third Avenue, New York, New York 10022

Collier Macmillan Canada, Inc.

Library of Congress Cataloging in Publication Data

Drooyan, Irving.
   Trigonometry: an analytic approach.

   Includes index.
      1. Trigonometry, Plane. I. Hadel, Walter. II. Carico, Charles C. III. Title.
QA533.D75 1983-   516.2'4   82-15295
ISBN 0-02-330350-6   AACR2

Printing: 12345678   Year: 34567890

ISBN 0-02-330350-6

PREFACE

This fourth edition of *Trigonometry: An Analytic Approach* reflects sixteen years of classroom experience with the earlier editions. As in the previous editions, the circular functions, which are pairings of real numbers with real numbers, and their properties are introduced in Chapter 1 and are the basis for a mathematical characterization of periodic phenomena. This approach gives early importance to those aspects of trigonometry that students, who plan to continue their study of mathematics, will need in calculus.

This edition, like the previous editions, is designed for use in a one-semester or one-quarter course in trigonometry. Although it is assumed that students undertaking the study of trigonometry have had prerequisite work in algebra and geometry, Appendix A includes a review of topics in these subjects that are needed as a background for the course.

In this edition we have rewritten some textual material, and the sequence of topics has been changed to improve the presentation. In particular, the circular functions are introduced in Chapter 1 using geometric notions. In addition, portions of material in this text have been rewritten so that instructors can easily adjust their classroom procedures both for students who use a calculator and for those who do not. Although the use of a calculator is optional in many sections, particularly in solving triangles, we continue to give special attention to the exact function values of 0°, 30°, and 45° and integral multiples thereof. Careful instructions are given in the exercises when to specify exact answers or when to specify decimal approximations which are obtained by using a calculator or tables. Answers to all examples and exercises that include degree measures of angles appear in decimal form. Table III also provides such measures.

Appendix B now includes instructions on the use of linear interpolation in conjunction with tables for those students who do not use a calculator.

All exercise sets in this edition have been revised as necessary to insure that they are carefully graded with respect to degree of difficulty. In addition, many new exercises have been added. To aid in making assignments, the exercises have been graded. Exercises labeled A provide routine practice and are sufficient for a basic course. Exercises labeled B contain more challenging problems and provide the instructor with flexibility in making assignments, depending on the time available and objectives of the course.

As in the previous editions, the subject matter of the text is continually reviewed through the use of Chapter Summaries and Review Exercises. Items in both the Summaries and Reviews are cross-referenced to the appropriate section of the text, as is the list of symbols inside the front cover. A detailed summary of the important topics in the text that appears inside the back cover can serve as a convenient reference chart for students completing assignments or studying for examinations.

The answer section at the end of the textbook provides the answers (including graphs) to all odd-numbered exercises of each exercise set and to all the exercises in the chapter reviews. Answers to even-numbered exercises are included in the Instructor's Manual.

We gratefully acknowledge the encouraging and helpful comments from the reviewers of this fourth edition: Paul Gormley, Villanova University; Stanley Guverud, Milwaukee School of Engineering; Lee Hart, University of Missouri, Kansas City; Shirley Huffman, Southwest Missouri State University; and Corinne Newell, Texas Southern University.

A special thanks is extended to our production supervisor Elisabeth Belfer for her outstanding professional help in the preparation of each edition of this book.

Woodland Hills, California
                                                          Irving Drooyan
                                                          Walter Hadel
                                                          Charles C. Carico

CONTENTS

APPENDIXES

1 CIRCULAR FUNCTIONS

Trigonometry (from the Greek, meaning "triangle measurement") was used as early as the second century B.C.E. to find the lengths of sides of triangles and the measures of angles in such fields as astronomy, surveying, and navigation. With the development of the sciences, including physics and engineering, the study of mathematical models, which can be used to describe periodic phenomena such as alternating current, pendulum oscillations, and wave motion, has become an important part of trigonometry. These models appear as functions that are called *periodic functions*. The most common periodic functions are the *circular functions,* which we consider in this chapter, and the *trigonometric functions,* which we consider in Chapter 3.

A summary of prerequisite topics of algebra and geometry is to be found in Appendix A. You may want to review that material before beginning this chapter and refer to particular topics as necessary during your work in this course.

1.1 The Cosine and Sine Functions

In this section we will define two functions in terms of the coordinates of a point on a circle of radius one, a **unit circle.** In particular, the point will be the terminal point of an arc with initial point at (1, 0).

Lengths of Arcs on a Unit Circle

Consider the graph of $x^2 + y^2 = 1$, a unit circle with center at the origin. We shall assume that there is a one-to-one correspondence

1

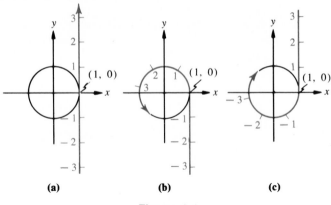

(a)   (b)   (c)

Figure 1.1

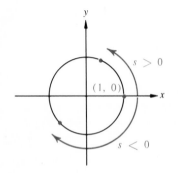

Figure 1.2

between all arcs with initial point at (1, 0) on this circle and the elements in the set R of real numbers. The correspondence can be visualized as shown in Figure 1.1, where the line can be thought of as "wrapped" about the circle, either in a counterclockwise direction or in a clockwise direction. If the terminal point of the arc is considered to be in a counterclockwise direction from the initial point, a *positive* real number is assigned to the length of the arc; if the terminal point of the arc is considered to be in a clockwise direction, a *negative* real number is assigned. At this time we will use the variable s to represent the lengths of such arcs, as shown in Figure 1.2, where $s \in R$.

The radius of a unit circle is 1. Hence the circumference, given by $2\pi r$, is equal to 2π. The distance halfway around is π, one-fourth of the way around is $\pi/2$, and so on. Selected end points of arcs (viewed in a

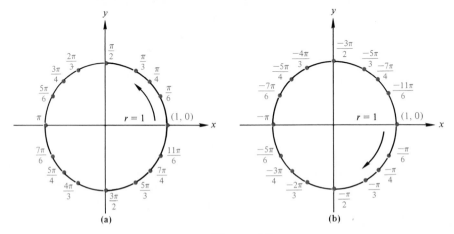

(a)   (b)

Figure 1.3

counterclockwise direction) on a unit circle with initial point at (1, 0) and their corresponding arc lengths in units of π are shown in Figure 1.3a. Selected end points of arcs (viewed in a *clockwise direction*) and their corresponding arc lengths in units of π are shown in Figure 1.3b.

In our work we will often need to know the quadrant in which the terminal point of an arc lies. It is usually more convenient to use multiples of the irrational number π as the basic unit of measurement, unless otherwise noted. However, when we use decimals we will use $\pi \approx 3.14$, $\pi/2 \approx 1.57$, $3\pi/2 \approx 4.71$, and $2\pi \approx 6.28$.*

Examples

a. The terminal point of the arc with length $11\pi/12$ lies in the second quadrant because $\pi/2 < 11\pi/12 < \pi$.

b. The terminal point of the arc with length 4.2 lies in the third quadrant because $3.14 < 4.2 < 4.71$.

c. The terminal point of the arc with length -5.21 lies in the first quadrant because $-6.28 < -5.21 < -4.71$.

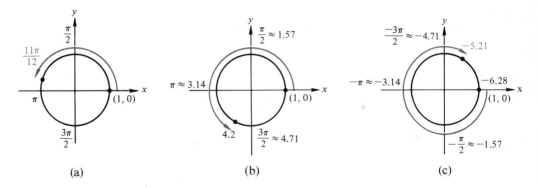

(a)   (b)   (c)

As noted in Figure 1.1, the number line can be thought of as "wrapped" about the circle. For directed lengths on the number line greater than 2π or less than -2π, the wrapping will exceed the circumference of the circle, as shown in figures (a) and (b) on page 4.

Examples

a. The terminal point of the arc with length $11\pi/4$ lies in the second quadrant because $(11\pi/4) - 2\pi = 3\pi/4$ and $\pi/2 < 3\pi/4 < \pi$.

b. The terminal point of the arc with length -7.31 lies in the fourth quadrant because $-7.31 - (-6.28) = -1.03$ and $-1.57 < -1.03 < 0$.

* The symbol $\approx$ is read "is approximately equal to."

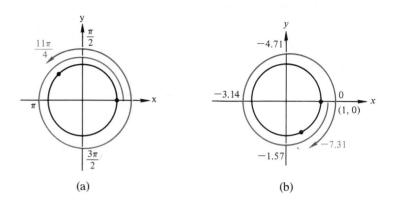

(a)   (b)

Coordinates of Points on a Unit Circle

The components of an ordered pair that is associated with the terminal point of an arc on the unit circle $x^2 + y^2 = 1$ with initial point $(1, 0)$ are given special names in terms of the arc length s.

Definition 1.1 *For each arc of length s on a unit circle, with initial point $(1, 0)$ and terminal point (x, y), $x, y \in R$,*

$$\text{cosine } s = x \quad \text{and} \quad \text{sine } s = y.$$

Cosine s is abbreviated as **cos s,** and sine s is abbreviated as **sin s.**

Example The figure illustrates Definition 1.1 for the case of an arc having its terminal point in Quadrant I.

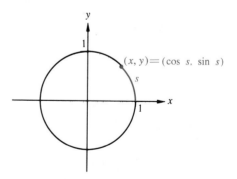

Circular Functions, Cosine and Sine

The set of pairings of each arc length s with x or cos s is called the **cosine function,** and the set of pairings of each arc length s with y or sin s

is called the **sine function.*** Thus,

$$\text{cosine} = \{(s,\ \cos s)\} \qquad \text{and} \qquad \text{sine} = \{(s,\ \sin s)\},$$

where the domain of each function is R.

The ranges of the functions are determined by the fact that $\cos s$ and $\sin s$ are the coordinates of points on the unit circle. Hence,

$$-1 \leq \cos s \leq 1 \qquad \text{or} \qquad |\cos s| \leq 1,$$

and $\qquad\qquad -1 \leq \sin s \leq 1 \qquad \text{or} \qquad |\sin s| \leq 1.$

Since $x = \cos s$ and $y = \sin s$, these ranges can also be specified by

$$-1 \leq x \leq 1 \qquad \text{and} \qquad -1 \leq y \leq 1,$$

respectively. Observe that both the cosine function and the sine function *pair real numbers with real numbers*. These functions are called **circular functions** because $\cos s$ and $\sin s$ are the coordinates of points on a circle.

Signs of $\cos s$ and $\sin s$

Notice that $\cos s$ and $\sin s$, the coordinates of a point of the unit circle, are either positive or negative depending on the quadrant in which the point lies, as shown in Figure 1.4.

These results are summarized in Table 1.1. The quadrant in each case is that in which the terminal point of the arc with length s lies.

Quadrant II
$\cos s < 0$
$\sin s > 0$

Quadrant I
$\cos s > 0$
$\sin s > 0$

Quadrant III
$\cos s < 0$
$\sin s < 0$

Quadrant IV
$\cos s > 0$
$\sin s < 0$

Figure 1.4

TABLE 1.1

quadrant	$\cos s$	$\sin s$
I	+	+
II	−	+
III	−	−
IV	+	−

Examples

a. If $s = 3\pi/4$, the terminal point of its corresponding arc is in Quadrant II. Thus, $\cos(3\pi/4)$ is negative and $\sin(3\pi/4)$ is positive.

(continued)

---

* At this time you may find it helpful to review the notion of a function introduced in Section A.3.

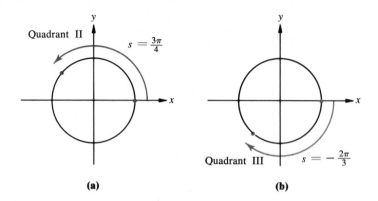

(a)   **(b)**

b. If $s = -2\pi/3$, the terminal point of its corresponding arc is in Quadrant III. Thus, $\cos(-2\pi/3)$ is negative and $\sin(-2\pi/3)$ is negative.

Relationship Between cos *s* and sin *s*

An important relationship exists between cos s and sin s. Because an equation of a unit circle is $x^2 + y^2 = 1$, $x = \cos s$ and $y = \sin s$, we have the following basic identity, which is sometimes called the **Pythagorean identity.**

Theorem 1.1   *If $s \in R$, then*

$$\cos^2 s + \sin^2 s = 1.$$

Notice that we have used the more convenient symbols $\cos^2 s$ and $\sin^2 s$ for $(\cos s)^2$ and $(\sin s)^2$, respectively. We can use this relationship to find the function values for cos s if we know the value of sin s, and to find sin s for a given value of cos s.

Example   If sin $s = -3/4$ and cos $s < 0$, we can find cos s by substituting $-3/4$ for sin s in $\cos^2 s + \sin^2 s = 1$ to obtain

$$\cos^2 s + \left(-\frac{3}{4}\right)^2 = 1 \;\leftrightarrow\; \cos^2 s + \frac{9}{16} = 1 \;\leftrightarrow\; \cos^2 s = \frac{7}{16},^*$$

from which

$$\cos s = \frac{\sqrt{7}}{4} \quad \text{or} \quad \cos s = -\frac{\sqrt{7}}{4}.$$

Since cos $s < 0$, we take the negative value, $-\sqrt{7}/4$.

* The symbol $\leftrightarrow$ is read ''is equivalent to.''

EXERCISE SET 1.1

A

Name the quadrant that contains the terminal point of each arc (of a unit circle) with the given length s and the initial point (1, 0).

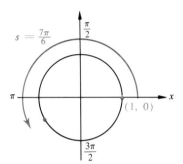

Example $\dfrac{7\pi}{6}$

Solution The terminal point of the arc lies in the third **quadrant** because $\pi < 7\pi/6 < 3\pi/2$.

1. $\dfrac{2\pi}{3}$ 2. $\dfrac{3\pi}{4}$ 3. $\dfrac{11\pi}{6}$ 4. $\dfrac{7\pi}{4}$

5. $\dfrac{13\pi}{6}$ 6. $\dfrac{10\pi}{3}$ 7. $-\dfrac{\pi}{3}$ 8. $-\dfrac{5\pi}{6}$

9. $-\dfrac{5\pi}{4}$ 10. $-\dfrac{11\pi}{6}$ 11. $-\dfrac{13\pi}{3}$ 12. $-\dfrac{9\pi}{4}$

Example 3

Solution The terminal point of the arc lies in the second quadrant because $1.57 < 3 < 3.14$.

13. 2   14. 4   15. 5   16. 6

17. 9   18. 10   19. -1 20. -2

21. -3 22. -6 23. -8 24. -9

Determine the quadrant in which the terminal point of each arc with the given length s lies.

25. $\sin s > 0$ and $\cos s > 0$ 26. $\sin s < 0$ and $\cos s < 0$

27. $\sin s < 0$ and $\cos s > 0$ 28. $\sin s > 0$ and $\cos s < 0$

Example If $\cos s = \dfrac{4}{5}$ and $\sin s < 0$, find $\sin s$.

Solution Using Theorem 1.1 and substituting 4/5 for $\cos s$ in

$$\cos^2 s + \sin^2 s = 1,$$

we obtain

$$\left(\frac{4}{5}\right)^2 + \sin^2 s = 1 \quad \leftrightarrow \quad \frac{16}{25} + \sin^2 s = 1 \quad \leftrightarrow \quad \sin^2 s = \frac{9}{25},$$

(*continued*)

from which

$$\sin s = \frac{3}{5} \quad \text{or} \quad \sin s = -\frac{3}{5}.$$

For $\sin s < 0$, we take $\sin s = -3/5$.

29. If $\sin s = \dfrac{3}{5}$ and $\cos s > 0$, find $\cos s$.

30. If $\cos s = \dfrac{8}{17}$ and $\sin s > 0$, find $\sin s$.

31. If $\cos s = \dfrac{1}{2}$ and $\sin < 0$, find $\sin s$.

32. If $\sin s = -\dfrac{5}{13}$ and $\cos s > 0$, find $\cos s$.

33. If $\sin s = \dfrac{1}{2}$ and $\cos s > 0$, find

    a. $\cos s$ **b.** $\dfrac{1}{\cos s}$ **c.** $\dfrac{1}{\sin s}$

34. If $\cos s = \dfrac{40}{41}$ and $\sin s < 0$, find

    a. $\dfrac{\sin s}{\cos s}$ **b.** $\dfrac{\cos s}{\sin s}$

1.2 Special Values for cos s and sin s

In order to use the circular functions in applications, we first have to find the function values $\cos s$ and $\sin s$ (elements in the ranges) for all real numbers s (elements in the domains). Some elementary notions of geometry can be used to find some such function values that will be useful in our work.

Function Values for s Equal to 0, $\pi/2$, π, and $3\pi/2$

Arcs with lengths $\pi/2$, π, and $3\pi/2$ are shown in Figure 1.5 with their corresponding ordered pairs $(0, 1)$, $(-1, 0)$, and $(0, -1)$. An arc with length 0 is considered to correspond to the ordered pair $(1, 0)$.

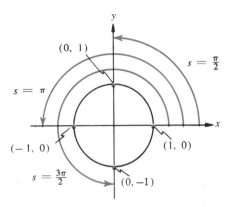

Figure 1.5

Thus,

$$\cos 0 = 1 \qquad \text{and} \qquad \sin 0 = 0,$$

$$\cos \frac{\pi}{2} = 0 \qquad \text{and} \qquad \sin \frac{\pi}{2} = 1,$$

$$\cos \pi = -1 \qquad \text{and} \qquad \sin \pi = 0,$$

$$\cos \frac{3\pi}{2} = 0 \qquad \text{and} \qquad \sin \frac{3\pi}{2} = -1.$$

Function Values for $s = \pi/4$

The terminal point of the arc with length $\pi/4$ shown in Figure 1.6 bisects the arc with length $\pi/2$, and at this point $y = x$. Substituting x for y in the equation for the unit circle $x^2 + y^2 = 1$, we obtain

$$x^2 + x^2 = 1,$$

from which, since the point is in Quadrant I,

$$x = \frac{1}{\sqrt{2}}.$$

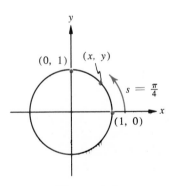

Figure 1.6

Then, since $y = x$,

$$y = \frac{1}{\sqrt{2}}.$$

Thus,

$$\cos \frac{\pi}{4} = \frac{1}{\sqrt{2}} \qquad \text{and} \qquad \sin \frac{\pi}{4} = \frac{1}{\sqrt{2}}.$$

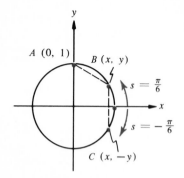

Figure 1.7

Function Values for $s = \pi/6$

In Figure 1.7, the ordered pair (x, y) corresponds to the terminal point of the arc with length $\pi/6$ and initial point $(1, 0)$ on a unit circle. Observe again that if (x, y) is a solution of the equation of the unit circle $x^2 + y^2 = 1$, then $(x, -y)$ is also a solution. Hence $(x, -y)$ corresponds to the terminal point of the arc with length $-\pi/6$.

The length of the arc from $(x, -y)$ to (x, y) equals $\pi/6 + \pi/6 = \pi/3$, and the length of the arc from (x, y) to $(0, 1)$ equals $\pi/2 - \pi/6 = \pi/3$. In a circle, arcs with equal lengths subtend chords with equal lengths, so the distance from $(x, -y)$ to (x, y) is the same as the distance from (x, y) to $(0, 1)$. Thus, from the distance formula (see Appendix A.4),

$$d^2 = (x_2 - x_1)^2 + (y_2 - y_1)^2,$$

we have

$$BC = BA$$

from which

$$(x - x)^2 + (-y - y)^2 = (x - 0)^2 + (y - 1)^2$$

or
$$4y^2 = x^2 + y^2 - 2y + 1.$$

The equation of the unit circle is $x^2 + y^2 = 1$. Hence, substituting 1 for $x^2 + y^2$ in the right-hand member, we have

$$4y^2 = 1 - 2y + 1,$$

from which

$$4y^2 + 2y - 2 = 0,$$

$$2(2y - 1)(y + 1) = 0.$$

Hence,

$$y = \frac{1}{2} \quad \text{or} \quad y = -1.$$

Because (x, y) is in Quadrant I $(x, y > 0)$, we select $1/2$ as the y-coordinate. Substituting $1/2$ for y in $x^2 + y^2 = 1$, we have

$$x^2 + \left(\frac{1}{2}\right)^2 = 1,$$

$$x = \pm \frac{\sqrt{3}}{2}.$$

Again selecting the positive value, we have

$$\cos\frac{\pi}{6} = \frac{\sqrt{3}}{2} \quad \text{and} \quad \sin\frac{\pi}{6} = \frac{1}{2}.$$

Function Values for $s = \pi/3$

In Figure 1.8, we have the ordered pair $(\sqrt{3}/2, 1/2)$ on a unit circle corresponding to the terminal point of the arc with length $\pi/6$ whose initial point is $(1, 0)$. Also, the ordered pair corresponding to the terminal point of the arc with length $\pi/3$ is shown as (x, y). An application of the distance formula, as above, enables us to find x and y. In this case,

$$(x, y) = \left(\frac{1}{2}, \frac{\sqrt{3}}{2}\right)$$

and

$$\cos\frac{\pi}{3} = \frac{1}{2} \quad \text{and} \quad \sin\frac{\pi}{3} = \frac{\sqrt{3}}{2}.$$

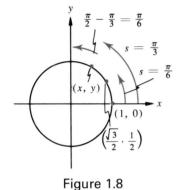

Figure 1.8

The results that we have obtained for cosine s and sine s for

$$s \in \left\{0, \frac{\pi}{6}, \frac{\pi}{4}, \frac{\pi}{3}, \frac{\pi}{2}, \pi, \frac{3\pi}{2}\right\}$$

are summarized in Table 1.2. The entries cos s and sin s are called **function values,** or **values of the function.** For example, $\sin(\pi/3)$, or $\sqrt{3}/2$, is the function value or simply the value of the sine function for $s = \pi/3$. Similarly, $\cos(\pi/4)$, or $1/\sqrt{2}$, is the function value or the value of the cosine function for $s = \pi/4$.

Note that the values $\sqrt{3}/2$ and $1/\sqrt{2}$, which involve the radicals $\sqrt{3}$ and $\sqrt{2}$, are irrational numbers and are *exact values* for $\sin(\pi/3)$ and $\cos(\pi/4)$, respectively. As we shall see, we can obtain decimal approximations for these function values and the other values in Table 1.2 that are irrational by using special tables or a calculator. However, since the exact values shown in the table arise in advanced work in mathematics, we will use these values rather than the decimal approximations when working with the domain elements $\pi/6$, $\pi/4$, and $\pi/3$.

The selected function values in Table 1.2 were obtained using geometric methods. Such methods cannot be used for all real numbers s. However, function values cos s and sin s can be obtained for all $s \in R$ by using methods that are considered in the study of the calculus. We will obtain these values using a set of tables whose entries were obtained using such methods, and also by using a hand calculator.

TABLE 1.2

s	x or cos s	y or sin s
0	1	0
$\frac{\pi}{6}$	$\frac{\sqrt{3}}{2}$	$\frac{1}{2}$
$\frac{\pi}{4}$	$\frac{1}{\sqrt{2}}$	$\frac{1}{\sqrt{2}}$
$\frac{\pi}{3}$	$\frac{1}{2}$	$\frac{\sqrt{3}}{2}$
$\frac{\pi}{2}$	0	1
π	-1	0
$\frac{3\pi}{2}$	0	-1

Approximations for cos *x* and sin *x*, 0 < *x* < π/2, Using Tables

We have been using the variable $s \in R$ to represent an element in the domain of cosine and sine functions, and we associated this variable with the length of an arc on the unit circle. Other variables can also be used; in particular, x is frequently used for this purpose. Because of this general practice, we use x in this way, even though the variable is now used in two different ways.

Table II, Appendix C, lists approximations for function values for the cosine and sine functions for elements in their domains from 0 to 1.57 at intervals of 0.01.* For example, in Table II an approximation for sin 0.91 is found in the column labeled sin x opposite 0.91 in the column labeled x. Thus, sin 0.91 ≈ 0.7895. Notice that in the table for $0 \le x \le 1.57$, the function values for sin x increase, whereas values for cos x decrease, for increasing values of x, as you would expect, since cos x (or cos s) is the x-coordinate and sin x (or sin s) is the y-coordinate of the point moving on a unit circle.

Examples   From Table II,

a. sin 0.21 ≈ 0.2085   b. cos 0.43 ≈ 0.9090

Table II consists of function values only for real number values of x at intervals of 0.01. However, values of the circular functions can also be approximated for any real number value of x within each of these intervals by a method called linear interpolation which is considered in Appendix B.

Although at this time you may not have the mathematical background to understand completely how the function values for Table II are obtained, it may interest you to become acquainted with the kinds of formulas, developed in calculus, that are used to produce this table. Two of these formulas are discussed in Exercise Set 1.2.

Approximations for cos *x* and sin *x*, 0 < *x* < π/2, Using a Calculator

Finding function values for circular functions by using a hand-held scientific calculator is a simple process. However, because the steps to be taken vary somewhat for different types of calculators, we will not consider specific procedures. The instruction booklet for your particular calculator will provide this information.

---

* Most of the values in Table II are rational approximations of irrational numbers. The entries in Table II that refer to other functions will be used in later sections.

Most calculators have a switch key that is marked in degrees (DEG) and radians (RAD). These measures will be discussed in Chapter 3. For our purpose at this time the circular function values we have defined can be obtained by using the radian setting. Calculators vary in the number of digits that are shown in the display; however, we shall round off all readings to four places so that values will be consistent with values obtained from the tables.

Example   Set Degree/Radian switch on RAD:

$$\sin 0.714 \approx 0.6548620.$$

Rounding off the result to four decimal places gives

$$\sin 0.714 \approx 0.6549.$$

Example $\cos 0.393 \approx 0.92376$

Rounding off the result to four decimal places gives

$$\cos 0.393 \approx 0.9238.$$

EXERCISE SET 1.2

A

1. Complete the entries for $(\cos s, \sin s)$ on the unit circle.

2. Complete the entries for $(\cos s, \sin s)$ on the unit circle.

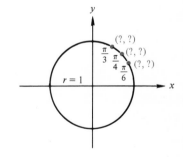

Compute each expression if the expression represents a real number. Find exact values.

Example $\sin \dfrac{\pi}{2} + \left(\cos^2 \dfrac{\pi}{6}\right)\left(\cos \dfrac{\pi}{3}\right)$

(continued)

Solution The function values can be obtained from Table 1.2, or by referring to appropriate coordinates on a unit circle:

$$\sin \frac{\pi}{2} = 1, \quad \cos \frac{\pi}{6} = \frac{\sqrt{3}}{2}, \quad \text{and} \quad \cos \frac{\pi}{3} = \frac{1}{2}.$$

Substituting these values in the given expression, we obtain

$$1 + \left(\frac{\sqrt{3}}{2}\right)^2 \left(\frac{1}{2}\right) = 1 + \frac{3}{4} \cdot \frac{1}{2}$$

$$= 1 + \frac{3}{8} = \frac{11}{8}.$$

3. $\sin^2 \dfrac{\pi}{6}$

4. $\cos^2 \dfrac{\pi}{6}$

5. $2 \left(\sin \dfrac{\pi}{2} \right) \left(\cos^2 \dfrac{\pi}{4} \right)$

6. $3(\cos \pi) \left(\sin^2 \dfrac{\pi}{3} \right)$

7. $3 \sin \dfrac{\pi}{6} - \cos^2 \dfrac{\pi}{6}$

8. $2 \cos \dfrac{\pi}{3} - \sin^2 \dfrac{\pi}{4}$

9. $\left(\cos^2 \dfrac{\pi}{2} \right) \left(\sin \dfrac{3\pi}{2} \right) (\cos 0)$

10. $\left(\sin \dfrac{\pi}{4} \right) \left(\cos \dfrac{3\pi}{2} \right) \left(\sin^2 \dfrac{\pi}{3} \right)$

11. $2(\sin^2 \pi) \left(\cos^2 \dfrac{\pi}{4} \right) + \sin \dfrac{\pi}{4}$

12. $\cos^2 \dfrac{\pi}{3} - \left(\sin \dfrac{3\pi}{2} \right) \left(\cos \dfrac{\pi}{4} \right)$

13. $\dfrac{2 \cos \dfrac{\pi}{3}}{\left(\sin \dfrac{\pi}{3} \right) (\cos^2 0)}$

14. $\dfrac{4 \left(\sin^2 \dfrac{\pi}{6} \right) (\cos \pi)}{\sin \dfrac{\pi}{2}}$

15. $\dfrac{3 \sin 0 + 2 \sin \pi}{\cos \pi}$

16. $\dfrac{2 \cos \pi - \sin 0}{\sin \pi}$

17. $\sin^2 \dfrac{\pi}{6} + \cos^2 \dfrac{\pi}{6}$

18. $\sin^2 \dfrac{\pi}{4} + \cos^2 \dfrac{\pi}{4}$

In Exercises 19–38 use Table II, Appendix C, or a calculator.

Find a decimal approximation to four places for each function value.

19. $\cos 0.08$

20. $\sin 0.15$

21. $\sin 0.35$

22. $\cos 0.57$

23. $\cos 0.72$

24. $\sin 0.96$

25. $\cos 1.21$

26. $\sin 1.45$

27. $\sin 1.53$

28. cos 0.32   **29.** cos 0.47   **30.** sin 0.51

In Exercises 31–38, if you are using tables, you will have to use linear interpolation (see Appendix B) to find the approximation that is obtained by using a calculator.

31. sin 0.255   **32.** cos 0.536   **33.** cos 1.283

34. sin 1.097   **35.** sin 0.393   **36.** cos 1.178

37. cos 0.349   **38.** sin 1.396

Find a decimal approximation to four places for each expression if the expression represents a real number.

Example $\dfrac{2(\cos 0.92)(\sin^2 1.21)}{\sin 0.32}$

Solution   Using Table II in Appendix C or a calculator, we obtain

$$\frac{2(\cos 0.92)(\sin^2 1.21)}{\sin 0.32} = \frac{2(0.6058)(0.9356)^2}{0.3146}$$

$$\approx 3.3712.^*$$

39. $\cos^2 0.70$ **40.** $\sin^2 0.20$

41. $2(\cos 0.24)(\sin^2 0.69)$ **42.** $3(\sin 0.96)(\cos^2 0.54)$

43. $3 \cos 1.15 - \sin^2 0.54$ **44.** $4 \sin 1.37 - \cos^2 0.66$

45. $(\sin 0.08)(\cos 1.28)(\sin^2 0.24)$ **46.** $(\cos^2 1.18)(\sin 0.33)(\cos 1.35)$

47. $\cos^2 0.18 - (\sin 1.17)(\cos 0.68)$

48. $(\sin^2 1.54)(\cos^2 0.72) + \sin 1.46$

49. $\dfrac{4(\sin^2 0.17)(\cos 0.52)}{\sin 1.49}$ **50.** $\dfrac{3 \cos 0.89}{(\sin 0.46)(\cos 1.38)}$

51. Verify that each value of *s* listed in Table 1.2 satisfies the relationship $\sin^2 s + \cos^2 s = 1$.

52. Using the relationship in Exercise 51, show that

$$\sin s = \pm \sqrt{1 - \cos^2 s} \quad \text{and} \quad \cos s = \pm \sqrt{1 - \sin^2 s}.$$

---

* In order that the results obtained using a calculator are consistent with the results using the tables, all function values obtained on a calculator are rounded off to four decimal places before any operations are performed.

B

In the calculus it is shown that for all $x \in R$ and $n \in N$,

$$\cos x = 1 - \frac{x^2}{2!} + \frac{x^4}{4!} + \cdots + (-1)^{n-1}\frac{x^{2n-2}}{(2n-2)!} + \cdots \qquad (1)$$

and

$$\sin x = x - \frac{x^3}{3!} + \frac{x^5}{5!} + \cdots + (-1)^{n-1}\frac{x^{2n-1}}{(2n-1)!} + \cdots , \qquad (2)$$

where $2! = 1 \cdot 2, \quad 3! = 1 \cdot 2 \cdot 3, \quad 4! = 1 \cdot 2 \cdot 3 \cdot 4, \quad$ *and so on.*

*The expression in the right member of each equation is called an **infinite power series in x.** By taking any finite number of terms in the power series to obtain an approximation for the function value, the error that exists is less than the value of the next term in the series.*

Example   Find an approximation for cos 0.3 correct to four decimal places.

Solution   Replacing x in Equation (1) by 0.3 yields

$$\cos 0.3 = 1 - \frac{(0.3)^2}{2!} + \frac{(0.3)^4}{4!} - \frac{(0.3)^6}{6!} + \cdots$$

$$= 1 - \frac{0.09}{2} + \frac{0.0081}{24} - \frac{0.000729}{720} + \cdots$$

$$= 1 - 0.045 + 0.00034 - 0.000001 + \cdots.$$

Since we wish accuracy to four decimal places, and since the error, by taking the first three terms, is less than the value of the fourth term (0.000001), then correct to at least four decimal places,

$$\cos 0.3 \approx 1 - 0.045 + 0.00034 = 0.9553.$$

Note that this is the value for cos 0.3 shown in Table II.

Use Equation (1) or (2) above to find each function value correct to four decimal places.

53. sin 0.01	**54.** cos 0.02	**55.** cos 0.50
56. sin 0.60	**57.** sin 1.00	**58.** cos 1.10

1.3 Function Values cos x and sin x for x ∈ R

In Section 1.2 we obtained values for cos x and sin x in the interval 0 to $\pi/2$. In this section we shall consider ways to find values for these functions for all $x \in R$. In order to find these values we shall use a sketch employing a *reference arc*, $\tilde{x}$.

The **reference arc** is the positive arc between the terminal point of the arc and the nearest point at which the unit circle meets the horizontal axis. See Figure 1.9 and note that $0 \le \tilde{x} < \pi/2$ in each quadrant.

Figure 1.9

Examples

a. The arc with length $3\pi/4$ terminates in Quadrant II. Hence,

$$\tilde{x} = \pi - \frac{3\pi}{4} = \frac{\pi}{4}.$$

b. The arc with length $7\pi/6$ terminates in Quadrant III. Hence,

$$\tilde{x} = \frac{7\pi}{6} - \pi = \frac{\pi}{6}.$$

c. The arc with length 5.01 terminates in Quadrant IV. Hence,

$$\tilde{x} \approx 2(3.14) - 5.01 = 1.27.$$

d. The arc with length 8.26 terminates in Quadrant II. Hence,

$$\tilde{x} \approx 3(3.14) - 8.26 = 1.16.$$

(a)

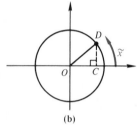

(b)

Figure 1.10

The Identities $|\cos x| = \cos \tilde{x}$ and $|\sin x| = \sin \tilde{x}$

Consider an arc of length x in a unit circle, as shown in Figure 1.10(a), having a reference arc of length $\tilde{x}$. If we construct an arc of length $\tilde{x}$ in a unit circle, as shown in Figure 1.10(b), we can show that triangles OAB and OCD are congruent, and that $OA = OC$ and $AB = CD$ (see Exercise 49, page 23). Furthermore, from the figures, we observe that

$$AO = |\cos x|, \quad AB = |\sin x|, \quad OC = \cos \tilde{x}, \quad \text{and} \quad CD = \sin \tilde{x}.$$

Now, while the arc in Figure 1.10(a) terminates in the second quadrant, the discussion above can be generalized to include an arc terminating in any quadrant, and can be used to prove the following theorem.

Theorem 1.2 *For $x \in R$,*

$$|\cos x| = \cos \tilde{x} \quad \text{and} \quad |\sin x| = \sin \tilde{x},$$

where $\tilde{x}$ is the length of the reference arc corresponding to x.

We can now find function values $\cos x$ or $\sin x$ for all $x \in R$ by simply performing the following steps:

1. Find the reference arc length $\tilde{x}$.
2. Use Theorem 1.2 and an appropriate table or a calculator to find $\cos \tilde{x}$ or $\sin \tilde{x}$.
3. Use Table 1.1 to determine the algebraic sign for $\cos x$ or $\sin x$.

Example Find $\cos \dfrac{7\pi}{6}$.

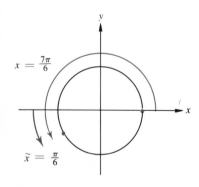

Solution Using the notion of a reference arc, we observe from the figure that $\tilde{x} = (7\pi/6) - \pi = \pi/6$. Hence, because the arc with length $7\pi/6$ terminates in Quadrant III as shown, $\cos(7\pi/6)$ is negative, and

$$\cos \frac{7\pi}{6} = -\cos \tilde{x} = -\cos \frac{\pi}{6}.$$

Using Table 1.2, we have

$$\cos \frac{7\pi}{6} = -\cos \frac{\pi}{6} = -\frac{\sqrt{3}}{2}.$$

Example Find an approximation for sin 5.84.

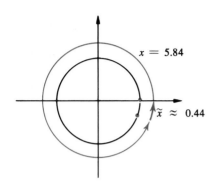

Solution We first sketch a figure showing the reference arc. Since $2\pi \approx 6.28$,

$$\tilde{x} \approx 6.28 - 5.84 = 0.44.$$

The arc of length 5.84 terminates in Quadrant IV. Hence, sin 5.84 is negative and

$$\sin 5.84 = -\sin \tilde{x} \approx -\sin 0.44.$$

Using Table II in Appendix C, we have

$$\sin 5.84 \approx -\sin 0.44 \approx -0.4259.$$

In the above examples, the elements in the domain, $7\pi/6$ and 5.84, are in the interval between 0 and 2π. The above procedure is perfectly general and is also applicable for all $x \in R$.

Examples

a. Find $\sin \dfrac{13\pi}{6}$.   b. Find $\sin \dfrac{25\pi}{6}$.

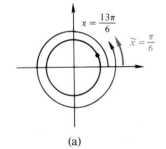

Solutions
a. In this case, $\tilde{x} = 13\pi/6 - 2\pi = \pi/6$. Hence, because the arc with length $13\pi/6$ terminates in Quadrant I,

$$\sin \frac{13\pi}{6} = \sin \frac{\pi}{6} = \frac{1}{2}.$$

b. In this case, $\tilde{x} = 25\pi/6 - 4\pi = \pi/6$. Hence,

$$\sin \frac{25\pi}{6} = \sin \frac{\pi}{6} = \frac{1}{2}.$$

(a)

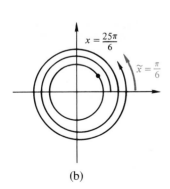

(b)

Note that in the above examples each of the elements $\pi/6$, $13\pi/6$, and $25\pi/6$ is associated with the same function value 1/2. In fact, these examples suggest that for all $x \in R$,

$$\sin(x + k \cdot 2\pi) = \sin x,$$

where k is an integer. This important periodic property of the sine function, and in fact a similar property for other circular functions that we will consider, is developed in Section 1.5 along with some applications of this property.

Values for cos x and sin x for x < 0

Arcs that are measured in a clockwise direction, which have negative directed lengths, also have reference angles. Hence, we can find the function values cos x and sin x for all $x < 0$.

Example Find $\cos\left(-\dfrac{15\pi}{4}\right)$.

Solution Observe from the figure that

$$\tilde{x} = 4\pi - \frac{15}{4}\,\pi = \frac{\pi}{4}.$$

Hence, because the arc with length x terminates in Quadrant I as shown,

$$\cos\left(-\frac{15\pi}{4}\right) = \cos \tilde{x} = \cos \frac{\pi}{4}.$$

Using Table 1.2, we have

$$\cos\left(-\frac{15\pi}{4}\right) = \cos \frac{\pi}{4} = \frac{1}{\sqrt{2}}.$$

Example Find an approximation for $\sin(-2.84)$.

Solution We first sketch a figure showing the reference arc. Since $\pi \approx 3.14$,

$$\tilde{x} \approx 3.14 - 2.84 = 0.30.$$

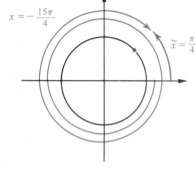

The arc of length -2.84 terminates in Quadrant III. Hence, $\sin(-2.84)$ is negative and

$$\sin(-2.84) = -\sin \tilde{x} \approx -\sin 0.30.$$

Using Table II in Appendix C, we have

$$\sin(-2.84) \approx -\sin 0.30 \approx -0.2955.$$

Using a Calculator

Calculators are programmed to give function values for values of x outside the interval $0 \le x \le \pi/2$ directly. For example,

$$\sin 5.84 \approx -0.4288192 \approx -0.4288.$$

If we first use a reference arc and then use a calculator, we would have

$$\tilde{x} \approx 6.28 - 5.84 = 0.44,$$

(see the figure for this example on page 19);

$$\sin 5.84 \approx -\sin 0.44 \approx -0.425939 \approx -0.4259.$$

Note that the value -0.4288 that we obtained without using a reduction formula differs from the value -0.4259 that we obtained by using a reduction formula. This variation occurs because we used 6.28 as the approximation for 2π when we used the reduction formula, while the calculator used a closer approximation to π for its result. In fact, if the element in the domain is a relatively large number, the difference in the values obtained by the two methods can be significant.

Because relationships between lengths of arcs and lengths of reference arcs occur in advanced courses in mathematics, we have used reference arcs with both the tables and a calculator in the examples. Furthermore, the answers to the exercises have been obtained in this way also. *If you use your calculator to find function values directly, you should expect to obtain slightly different approximations than those that are given in the text.* Admittedly, these will be more precise than the answers shown in the text.

EXERCISE SET 1.3

A

1. Complete the entries for $(\cos s, \sin s)$ on the unit circle.

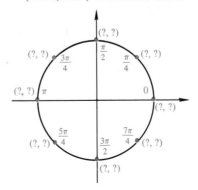

2. Complete the entries for $(\cos s, \sin s)$ on the unit circle.

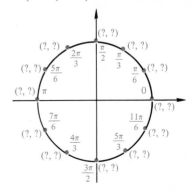

Sketch each arc with the given length, and its reference arc.

Example $\dfrac{5\pi}{6}$

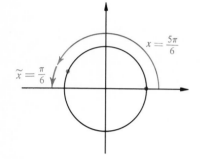

Solution   An arc with length $5\pi/6$ terminates in Quadrant II because $\pi/2 < 5\pi/6 < \pi$.

3. $\dfrac{7\pi}{6}$ 4. $\dfrac{11\pi}{6}$ 5. $-\dfrac{5\pi}{3}$ 6. $-\dfrac{5\pi}{4}$

7. $\dfrac{17\pi}{3}$ 8. $\dfrac{21\pi}{4}$ 9. $-\dfrac{19\pi}{6}$ 10. $-\dfrac{11\pi}{3}$

11. 6   12. -7 13. -4 14. 3

Find each function value (exact value).

Example $\cos \dfrac{5\pi}{4}$

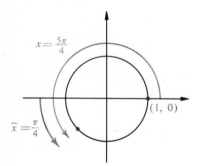

Solution   The arc with length $5\pi/4$ and the corresponding reference arc are shown in the figure. Because the arc with length $5\pi/4$ terminates in Quadrant III, $\cos(5\pi/4)$ is negative, and we have

$$\cos \frac{5\pi}{4} = -\cos \tilde{x} = -\cos \frac{\pi}{4}.$$

From Table 1.2, $\cos(\pi/4) = 1/\sqrt{2}$. Thus,

$$\cos \frac{5\pi}{4} = -\cos \frac{\pi}{4} = -\frac{1}{\sqrt{2}}.$$

15. $\cos \dfrac{2\pi}{3}$ 16. $\cos \dfrac{3\pi}{4}$ 17. $\sin \dfrac{5\pi}{6}$

18. $\sin \dfrac{7\pi}{4}$ 19. $\cos \dfrac{7\pi}{6}$ 20. $\cos \dfrac{4\pi}{3}$

21. $\sin \dfrac{11\pi}{6}$ 22. $\sin \dfrac{5\pi}{3}$ 23. $\cos \dfrac{9\pi}{4}$

24. $\cos \dfrac{7\pi}{3}$ 25. $\sin \dfrac{11\pi}{4}$ 26. $\sin \dfrac{13\pi}{6}$

27. $\cos\left(-\dfrac{3\pi}{4}\right)$ 28. $\cos\left(-\dfrac{7\pi}{6}\right)$ 29. $\sin\left(-\dfrac{4\pi}{3}\right)$

30. $\sin\left(-\dfrac{13\pi}{6}\right)$

Find approximate function values to four places for the following. Use a reference arc and π ≈ 3.14.

Examples

a. sin 5.28   b. cos(−3.74)

Solutions   From the figures below:

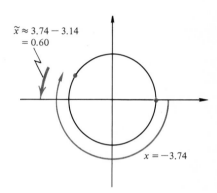

a. sin 5.28 ≈ − sin 1.00   b. cos(−3.74) ≈ − cos 0.60

  ≈ − 0.8415   ≈ − 0.8253

31. sin 1.76   **32.** cos 3.81   **33.** cos 4.91

34. sin 4.23   **35.** sin 6.06   **36.** cos 2.91

37. cos(−0.26)   **38.** sin(−1.27)   **39.** sin(−2.55)

40. cos(−3.57)   **41.** cos 10.13   **42.** sin 9.30

B

To four decimal places, find the difference between the value obtained by using a reference arc and the value obtained by using a calculator without using a reference arc.

43. sin 1.68   **44.** cos 3.04   **45.** cos 3.57

46. sin 4.62   **47.** sin 15   **48.** cos 16

49. Show that triangles *OAB* and *OCD* in Figure 1.10 are congruent.

50. Show that |cos x| = cos x̃ and |sin x| = sin x̃, where x is the length of an arc that terminates in the third quadrant.

1.4 Tangent, Secant, Cosecant, and Cotangent Functions

Four additional circular functions can be defined in terms of cos x and sin x.

Tangent Function

The ratio of the sine function value to the cosine function value is used so often that it is given a special name.

Definition 1.2   *For all* $x \in R \left(x \neq \dfrac{\pi}{2} + k\pi, \ k \in J \right)$,

$$\textbf{tangent } x = \frac{\sin x}{\cos x}.$$

Tangent x is abbreviated as **tan x.** Pairings of the form $(x, \tan x)$ make up the **tangent function.** Note that the *domain* of the tangent function contains all real numbers x such that

$$x \neq \frac{\pi}{2} + k\pi, \quad k \in J,$$

for which cos $x = 0$.

Since the elements of the range of the cosine function are between -1 and 1, including -1 and 1, and the elements of the range of the sine function are also between -1 and 1, including -1 and 1, the absolute value of the quotient

$$\frac{\sin x}{\cos x} = \tan x \quad \left(x \neq \frac{\pi}{2} + k\pi, \ k \in J \right)$$

can be made as large as we like by assigning values to x so that cos x is sufficiently close to zero. For example, as we assign values to x slightly less than $\pi/2$, sin x is nearly 1, cos x is nearly 0, and tan x is large. Furthermore, since the quotient sin x/cos x can be positive or negative, the *range* of the tangent function is the set of real numbers R.

Special Values for tan x

We can find some special values for tan x by referring to the cosine and sine function values in Table 1.2. Thus,

$$\tan 0 = \frac{\sin 0}{\cos 0} = \frac{0}{1} = 0,$$

$$\tan \pi = \frac{\sin \pi}{\cos \pi} = \frac{0}{-1} = 0;$$

$\tan(\pi/2)$ and $\tan(3\pi/2)$ are undefined since, from Definition 1.2, $\pi/2$ and $3\pi/2$ are not in the domain of the tangent function. Also,

$$\tan \frac{\pi}{6} = \frac{\sin \frac{\pi}{6}}{\cos \frac{\pi}{6}} = \frac{\frac{1}{2}}{\frac{\sqrt{3}}{2}} = \frac{1}{\sqrt{3}},$$

$$\tan \frac{\pi}{4} = \frac{\sin \frac{\pi}{4}}{\cos \frac{\pi}{4}} = \frac{\frac{1}{\sqrt{2}}}{\frac{1}{\sqrt{2}}} = 1,$$

$$\tan \frac{\pi}{3} = \frac{\sin \frac{\pi}{3}}{\cos \frac{\pi}{3}} = \frac{\frac{\sqrt{3}}{2}}{\frac{1}{2}} = \sqrt{3}.$$

TABLE 1.3

x	$\cos x$	$\sin x$	$\tan x$
0	1	0	0
$\frac{\pi}{6}$	$\frac{\sqrt{3}}{2}$	$\frac{1}{2}$	$\frac{1}{\sqrt{3}}$
$\frac{\pi}{4}$	$\frac{1}{\sqrt{2}}$	$\frac{1}{\sqrt{2}}$	1
$\frac{\pi}{3}$	$\frac{1}{2}$	$\frac{\sqrt{3}}{2}$	$\sqrt{3}$
$\frac{\pi}{2}$	0	1	undefined
π	-1	0	0
$\frac{3\pi}{2}$	0	-1	undefined

These special function values for the tangent function, together with those for the cosine and sine, are shown in Table 1.3.

By Definition 1.2,

$$\tan x = \frac{\sin x}{\cos x}.$$

Thus, $\tan x > 0$ if the arc corresponding to x terminates in Quadrant I or III, since $\sin x$ and $\cos x$ are either both positive or both negative (see Table 1.1). $\tan x < 0$ if the arc corresponding to x terminates in Quadrant II or IV, since $\sin x$ is positive and $\cos x$ is negative, or $\sin x$ is negative and $\cos x$ is positive, respectively.

These results along with the data from Table 1.1 are summarized in Table 1.4. The quadrant in each case is the quadrant in which the terminal point of the arc with length x lies.

TABLE 1.4

quadrant	$\cos x$	$\sin x$	$\tan x$
I	+	+	+
II	−	+	−
III	−	−	+
IV	+	−	−

Secant, Cosecant, and Cotangent Functions

The reciprocals of $\sin x$ and $\cos x$ and the ratio $\cos x/\sin x$ are commonly used in mathematics and are also given special names.

Definition 1.3 *For all $x \in R$,*

$$\text{I.}\quad \textbf{secant } x = \frac{1}{\cos x} \quad \left(x \neq \frac{\pi}{2} + k\pi, \, k \in J\right),$$

$$\text{II.}\quad \textbf{cosecant } x = \frac{1}{\sin x} \quad (x \neq k\pi, \, k \in J),$$

$$\text{III.}\quad \textbf{cotangent } x = \frac{\cos x}{\sin x} \quad (x \neq k\pi, \, k \in J).$$

Secant x, cosecant x, and cotangent x are abbreviated as **sec x, csc x,** and **cot x,** respectively.

Properties of Secant

Ordered pairs of the form $(x, \sec x)$ make up the **secant function.** Since sec x is the reciprocal of cos x, the domain of the secant function is the set of real numbers, except those for which $\cos x = 0$. Hence the domain contains all elements $x \in R$ such that

$$x \neq \frac{\pi}{2} + k\pi, \quad k \in J.$$

The range of the secant function is determined by $|\sec x| \geq 1$ for all x in the domain because $|\cos x| \leq 1$ for all $x \in R$.

Properties of Cosecant

Ordered pairs of the form $(x, \csc x)$ make up the **cosecant function.** Since csc x is the reciprocal of sin x, the domain of the cosecant function is the set of real numbers, except those values of x for which $\sin x = 0$. Hence the domain contains all elements $x \in R$ such that

$$x \neq k\pi, \quad k \in J.$$

Since $|\sin x| \leq 1$ for all $x \in R$, the range of the cosecant function is determined by the fact that $|\csc x| \geq 1$ for all x in the domain.

Properties of Cotangent

Ordered pairs of the form $(x, \cot x)$ make up the **contangent function.** Since $\cot x = \cos x / \sin x$, the domain of the cotangent function is the set of real numbers, except those values of x for which $\sin x = 0$.

Hence the domain contains all elements $x \in R$ such that

$$x \neq k\pi, \quad k \in J.$$

Since

$$\frac{\cos x}{\sin x} = \frac{1}{\sin x / \cos x} \quad (\sin x, \cos x \neq 0),$$

$$\cot x = \frac{1}{\tan x}, \quad x \neq k\pi, k \in J.$$

We shall view this statement as an alternate definition of cotangent x. As with the tangent function, the range of the cotangent function is R, the set of real numbers.

Special Values for sec x, csc x, and cot x

We can find function values for secant, cosecant, and cotangent for

$$x \in \left\{ 0, \frac{\pi}{6}, \frac{\pi}{4}, \frac{\pi}{3}, \frac{\pi}{2}, \pi, \frac{3\pi}{2} \right\}$$

by using Definition 1.3 and the function values for the sine, cosine, and tangent functions shown in Table 1.3.

Examples

a. $\sec 0 = \dfrac{1}{\cos 0} = \dfrac{1}{1} = 1$ b. $\csc \dfrac{\pi}{6} = \dfrac{1}{\sin \dfrac{\pi}{6}} = \dfrac{1}{\dfrac{1}{2}} = 2$

Whether particular function values of sec x, csc x, and cot x are negative or positive real numbers can be readily determined from their definitions and the data in Table 1.4 applicable to sin x, cos x, and tan x.

Using Reference Arcs

A geometric argument similar to the one used to prove Theorem 1.2 leads to the following result.

Theorem 1.3 *For $x \in R$,*

$$|\tan x| = \tan \tilde{x}, \quad |\sec x| = \sec \tilde{x},$$

$$|\csc x| = \csc \tilde{x}, \quad and \quad |\cot x| = \cot \tilde{x},$$

where $\tilde{x}$ is the length of the reference arc corresponding to x.

Some additional values for these functions can now be found directly from Definition 1.3 and Table 1.3 by using references arcs. Again note that the values in Table 1.3 are exact values.

Examples

a. $\sec \dfrac{3\pi}{4} = \dfrac{1}{\cos \dfrac{3\pi}{4}} = \dfrac{1}{-\cos \tilde{x}}$

$\quad = \dfrac{1}{-\cos \dfrac{\pi}{4}} = \dfrac{1}{-\dfrac{1}{\sqrt{2}}}$

$\quad = -\sqrt{2}.$

b. $\cot \dfrac{7\pi}{4} = \dfrac{1}{\tan \dfrac{7\pi}{4}} = \dfrac{1}{-\tan \tilde{x}}$

$\quad = \dfrac{1}{-\tan \dfrac{\pi}{4}} = \dfrac{1}{-1}$

$\quad = -1.$

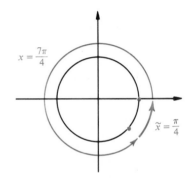

Using a Calculator

We can use a calculator to find decimal approximations for values of the functions introduced in this section in a manner similar to the way that we used a calculator to find approximations for cos x and sin x. Because scientific calculators have a TAN key, the procedure used to find values for tan x is exactly the same. We will continue to use a reference arc and round off values to four places in our examples. Furthermore, the answers to the exercises have been obtained by using a reference arc. As we noted on page 21 for cos x and sin x, if you find function values on your calculator directly (without using a reference arc), you will obtain slightly different results.

Examples Find decimal approximations to four places.

a. tan 2.48   b. tan(−2.84)

Solutions Set Degree/Radian switch on RAD.

(a)

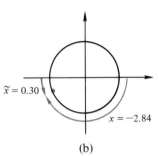

(b)

a. The sketch shows the reference angle

$$\tilde{x} \approx 3.14 - 2.48 = 0.66.$$

Since 2.48 is in Quadrant II, tan 2.48 is negative. Using a calculator and rounding off to four places,

$$\tan 2.48 \approx -\tan 0.66 \approx -0.7761$$

b. The sketch shows the reference angle

$$\tilde{x} = 3.14 - 2.84 = 0.30.$$

Since -2.84 is in Quadrant III, $\tan(-2.84)$ is positive. Using a calculator and rounding off to four places,

$$\tan(-2.84) = \tan 0.30 = 0.3093.$$

Values for sec x, csc x, and cot x can be obtained by using the reciprocal relationships specified by Definition 1.3, and the alternate definition of cot x.

Examples   Find decimal approximations to four places.

a. sec 2.14   b. cot(-1.32)

Solutions
    a. From Definition 1.3, sec $2.14 = 1/\cos 2.14$. The sketch shows the reference angle

$$\tilde{x} = 3.14 - 2.14 = 1.00.$$

Since 2.14 is in Quadrant II, sec 2.14 is negative. Thus,

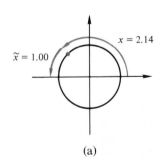

(a)

$$\sec 2.14 = \frac{1}{\cos 2.14}$$

$$\approx -\frac{1}{\cos 1.00},$$

and using a calculator,

$$-\frac{1}{\cos 1.00} \approx -\frac{1}{0.5403}$$

$$\approx -1.8508.$$

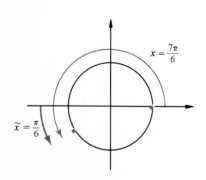

(b)

b. From the alternate definition for cot x (page 27), we have $\cot(-1.32) = 1/\tan(-1.32)$. The sketch shows the reference angle $\tilde{x} = 1.32$. Since -1.32 is in Quadrant IV, $\cot(-1.32)$ is negative. Thus,

$$\cot(-1.32) = -\frac{1}{\tan(-1.32)} = -\frac{1}{\tan 1.32},$$

and using a calculator,

$$-\frac{1}{\tan 1.32} \approx -\frac{1}{3.9034} \approx -0.2562.$$

Using Tables

Table II, Appendix C, lists function values for tan x, sec x, csc x, and cot x for values of x from 0 to 1.57. The use of reference arcs in conjunction with this table enables us to find the function values for all elements in their respective domains.

Examples From Table II,

a. $\tan 1.30 \approx 3.602$ b. $\csc 0.42 \approx 2.452$

To find approximations for function values at smaller intervals than 0.01, we can use linear interpolation as described in Appendix B.

EXERCISE SET 1.4

A

Find each function value (exact value).

Example $\tan \dfrac{7\pi}{6}$

Solution Because the arc with length $7\pi/6$ terminates in Quadrant III, $\tan(7\pi/6)$ is positive, and we have

$$\tan \frac{7\pi}{6} = \tan \tilde{x} = \tan \frac{\pi}{6}.$$

From Table 1.3, $\tan(\pi/6) = 1/\sqrt{3}$. Thus,

$$\tan \frac{7\pi}{6} = \tan \frac{\pi}{6} = \frac{1}{\sqrt{3}}.$$

1. $\tan\dfrac{5\pi}{4}$ **2.** $\tan\dfrac{5\pi}{6}$ **3.** $\tan\dfrac{7\pi}{3}$

4. $\tan\dfrac{9\pi}{4}$ **5.** $\tan\left(-\dfrac{7\pi}{6}\right)$ **6.** $\tan\left(-\dfrac{5\pi}{3}\right)$

7. $\csc\dfrac{5\pi}{6}$ **8.** $\csc\dfrac{2\pi}{3}$ **9.** $\csc\dfrac{9\pi}{4}$

10. $\csc\dfrac{13\pi}{6}$ **11.** $\csc\left(-\dfrac{9\pi}{4}\right)$ **12.** $\csc\left(-\dfrac{11\pi}{6}\right)$

13. $\sec\dfrac{5\pi}{4}$ **14.** $\sec\dfrac{7\pi}{6}$ **15.** $\sec\dfrac{7\pi}{3}$

16. $\sec\dfrac{11\pi}{4}$ **17.** $\sec\left(-\dfrac{5\pi}{3}\right)$ **18.** $\sec\left(-\dfrac{11\pi}{6}\right)$

19. $\cot\dfrac{4\pi}{3}$ **20.** $\cot\dfrac{5\pi}{4}$ **21.** $\cot\dfrac{7\pi}{3}$

22. $\cot\dfrac{9\pi}{4}$ **23.** $\cot\left(-\dfrac{13\pi}{6}\right)$ **24.** $\cot\left(-\dfrac{7\pi}{4}\right)$

Find the value of each expression.

25. $\cot\dfrac{\pi}{6}+\csc\dfrac{\pi}{4}$ **26.** $\csc\dfrac{\pi}{3}+\sec\pi$

27. $2\sec 0-3\cot\dfrac{\pi}{4}$ **28.** $3\cos\dfrac{3\pi}{2}-\cot\dfrac{\pi}{4}$

29. $\dfrac{2\csc\dfrac{\pi}{4}+\cot\dfrac{\pi}{6}}{\tan\dfrac{\pi}{3}}$ **30.** $\dfrac{\sec\dfrac{\pi}{4}+\tan\dfrac{\pi}{3}}{\cot\dfrac{\pi}{4}}$

Find an approximation for each function value. Use a calculator, or Table II, Appendix C. Use reference arcs as appropriate.

Examples

a. $\cot 1.93$ b. $\sec(-4.20)$

Solutions

   a. The sketch shows the reference arc

$$\tilde{x}\approx 3.14-1.93=1.21.$$

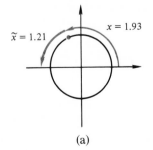

$\tilde{x}=1.21$

$x=1.93$

(a)

(continued)

Since 1.93 is in Quadrant II, cot 1.93 is negative. Hence,

$$\cot 1.93 \approx -\cot 1.21 \approx -0.3773.$$

b. The sketch shows the reference arc

$$\tilde{x} \approx |-4.20 + 3.14| = 1.06.$$

Since -4.20 is in Quadrant II, $\sec(-4.20)$ is negative. Hence,

$$\sec(-4.20) \approx -\sec 1.06 \approx -2.0455.$$

$\tilde{x} = 1.06$

$x = -4.20$

(b)

31. tan 0.48	**32.** sec 0.32	**33.** csc 0.47
34. cot 0.51	**35.** tan 4.91	**36.** sec 4.23
37. csc 6.06	**38.** cot 2.91	**39.** cot(−0.26)
40. csc(−1.27)	**41.** sec(−2.55)	**42.** tan(−3.57)

*Compute each expression.**

43. csc 0.44 + sec 0.10   **44.** cot 1.38 + csc 1.93

45. 3 csc 1.17 − cot 0.33   **46.** 3 sec 2.07 − 3 cot 1.51

47. $\dfrac{2 \csc 3.89 + \tan 0.65}{\cot 0.60}$ **48.** $\dfrac{\sec 3.84 + \cot 1.78}{\tan 1.22}$

Determine the quadrant in which the terminal point of each arc with the given length x lies.

49. sin $x > 0$ and tan $x < 0$ **50.** cos $x < 0$ and tan $x > 0$

51. tan $x > 0$ and csc $x < 0$ **52.** tan $x < 0$ and sec $x > 0$

53. cot $x < 0$ and csc $x > 0$ **54.** cot $x > 0$ and sec $x < 0$

Find each function value (exact value).

Example   If $\cos x = \dfrac{4}{5}$ and tan $x < 0$, find tan x.

Solution   Since cos $x > 0$ and tan $x < 0$, from Table 1.4, the termi-

---

* In order that the results obtained using a calculator are consistent with the results using the tables, all function values obtained on a calculator are rounded off to four decimal places before any operations are performed.

nal point of the arc x lies in Quadrant IV and $\sin x < 0$. Substituting 4/5 for $\cos x$ in $\cos^2 x + \sin^2 x = 1$, we have

$$\left(\frac{4}{5}\right)^2 + \sin^2 x = 1 \quad \leftrightarrow \quad \sin^2 x = \frac{9}{25},$$

from which

$$\sin x = \frac{3}{5} \quad \text{or} \quad \sin x = -\frac{3}{5}.$$

Because $\sin x < 0$, we take $\sin x = -3/5$. By Definition 1.2, and substituting $-3/5$ for $\sin x$ and 4/5 for $\cos x$, we have

$$\tan x = \frac{-\dfrac{3}{5}}{\dfrac{4}{5}} = -\frac{3}{4}.$$

55. If $\cos x = \dfrac{1}{\sqrt{2}}$ and $\sin x < 0$, find $\tan x$.

56. If $\sin x = \dfrac{\sqrt{3}}{2}$ and $\cos x > 0$, find $\tan x$.

57. If $\cos x = \dfrac{1}{2}$ and $\dfrac{3\pi}{2} < x < 2\pi$, find $\csc x$.

58. If $\sin x = -\dfrac{\sqrt{3}}{2}$ and $\pi < x < \dfrac{3\pi}{2}$, find $\sec x$.

59. If $\cos x = \dfrac{3}{5}$ and $\sin x < 0$, find $\cot x$.

60. If $\sin x = \dfrac{1}{\sqrt{2}}$ and $\cos x < 0$, find $\cot x$.

Use the relationships of Definitions 1.2 and 1.3 and the fact that $\sin^2 x + \cos^2 x = 1$ *for all $x \in R$ to write each expression in terms of* $\sin x$ *and/or* $\cos x$ *and simplify.*

Examples

a. $\tan x \cdot \csc x$

b. $\dfrac{\cot^2 x}{\cos x}$

Solutions

a. Since $\tan x = \sin x/\cos x$ and $\csc x = 1/\sin x$, we have that

$$\tan x \cdot \csc x = \frac{\sin x}{\cos x} \cdot \frac{1}{\sin x} = \frac{1}{\cos x}.$$

b. Since $\cot x = \cos x/\sin x$, we have that

$$\frac{\cot^2 x}{\cos x} = \frac{\left(\dfrac{\cos x}{\sin x}\right)^2}{\cos x} = \frac{\cos^2 x}{\sin^2 x} \cdot \frac{1}{\cos x} = \frac{\cos x}{\sin^2 x}.$$

61. $\tan x \cdot \csc^2 x$ **62.** $\cot^2 x \cdot \sec x$

63. $\sin^2 x \cdot \cot^2 x$ **64.** $\tan^2 x \cdot \cos^2 x$

65. $\dfrac{\cot^2 x}{\sec x}$ **66.** $\dfrac{\tan^2 x}{\csc x}$

67. $\dfrac{\tan^2 x + 1}{\sec x}$ **68.** $\dfrac{\cot^2 x + 1}{\csc x}$

69. $\dfrac{\csc^2 x - 1}{\cot x}$ **70.** $\dfrac{\sec^2 x - 1}{\tan x}$

B

71. Show that $\sin\left(\dfrac{\pi}{6} + k \cdot 2\pi\right) = \dfrac{1}{2}$ for $k \in \{-2, -1, 0, 1, 2\}$.

72. Show that $\tan\left(\dfrac{\pi}{4} + k\pi\right) = 1$ for $k \in \{-2, -1, 0, 1, 2\}$.

Circular function values can be directly associated with the lengths of certain line segments. For example, in the figure, $\overline{OA}$ and $\overline{OB}$ are radii of a unit circle, $\overline{BN}$ is perpendicular to $\overline{AT}$ and $\overline{LM}$, and $\overline{BN}$ and $\overline{AT}$ are tangents to the circle. Since the coordinates of the point P are $(\cos x, \sin x)$, the length OQ equals $\cos x$ and the length QP equals $\sin x$.

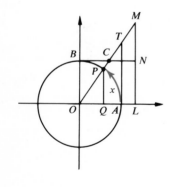

73. Show that AT equals $\tan x$.   **74.** Show that OT equals $\sec x$.

75. Show that OC equals $\csc x$.   **76.** Show that BC equals $\cot x$.

1.5 Periodic Functions; Applications

In Section 1.3 we noted that an element in the range of the sine function is paired with a number of different elements in its domain. For example,

$$\sin\frac{\pi}{6} = \frac{1}{2}, \quad \sin\left(\frac{\pi}{6} + 2\pi\right) = \frac{1}{2}, \quad \text{and} \quad \sin\left(\frac{\pi}{6} + 4\pi\right) = \frac{1}{2},$$

where 1/2 is paired with several different elements in the domain. These examples suggest that

$$x = \frac{\pi}{6} + k \cdot 2\pi, \quad k \in J,$$

are solutions of $\sin x = 1/2$. These examples further suggest a periodic property common to a variety of functions including each of the circular functions.

Definition 1.4 *If f is a function with domain a subset of the set R of real numbers, such that for all x in the domain and for some a ∈ R (a ≠ 0), x + a is in the domain and*

$$f(x + a) = f(x),$$

then f is called a **periodic function** *and a is a* **period.**

Periodic Properties

The circumference of a unit circle is 2π. Hence, the cosine and sine functions are periodic with period 2π as suggested in Figure 1.11.

Theorem 1.4 *If x ∈ R and k is an integer, then*

I. $\cos(x + k \cdot 2\pi) = \cos x,$

II. $\sin(x + k \cdot 2\pi) = \sin x.$

Using Theorem 1.4, we can readily obtain some additional function values that we previously obtained by using geometric considerations.

Figure 1.11

Examples

a. $\sin\dfrac{5\pi}{2} = \sin\left(\dfrac{\pi}{2} + 2\pi\right)$

$= \sin\dfrac{\pi}{2} = 1$

b. $\cos 5\pi = \cos(\pi + 4\pi)$

$= \cos \pi = -1$

The least positive period of a periodic function is known as the **fundamental period.** Since the terminal point of an arc on a unit circle must travel completely around the circle, a distance of 2π, before the coordinates of the point start to repeat, it seems plausible that the fundamental period of both the sine and cosine function is 2π.

It can be shown that the points with coordinates $(\cos x, \sin x)$ and $(-\cos x, -\sin x)$ are the end points of a diameter on a unit circle. Hence, the arc joining them has a length of π. Furthermore, since for each of these points,

$$\tan x = \frac{\sin x}{\cos x} = \frac{-\sin x}{-\cos x},$$

it follows that the fundamental period of the tangent function is π.

Theorem 1.5   *If $x \in R$ $(x \neq \pi/2 + k\pi)$ and k is an integer, then*

$$\tan(x + k\pi) = \tan x.$$

Examples

a. $\tan \dfrac{7\pi}{6} = \tan\left(\dfrac{\pi}{6} + \pi\right)$ b. $\tan \dfrac{13\pi}{4} = \tan\left(\dfrac{\pi}{4} + 3\pi\right)$

$\qquad\quad = \tan \dfrac{\pi}{6} = \dfrac{1}{\sqrt{3}}$ $\qquad\qquad = \tan \dfrac{\pi}{4} = 1$

Note that because $\sec x = 1/\cos x$ and $\csc x = 1/\sin x$, the secant and cosecant functions have period 2π; because $\cot x = 1/\tan x$, the cotangent function has period π.

Applications

If a point is moving so that the motion repeats itself in equal intervals of time, the motion is said to be **periodic,** or **harmonic.** Such motions occur in the vibration of a guitar string, a swinging pendulum, and sound waves, to name a few examples. Using laws of physics, it can be shown that the mathematical models determining the position of the point at any instant involve the sine and cosine functions. For *simple harmonic motion,* the models take the form

$$d = A \sin Bt \quad \text{or} \quad d = A \cos Bt,$$

where d is a measure of displacement, A and B are constants for the particular motion, and t is a measure of time.

At rest

Example A spring is displaced from its resting position as shown in the figure. The displacement d is given by the equation $d = A \cos \omega t$, where A, the initial displacement, and d are expressed in centimeters, t is expressed in seconds, and $\omega = 6\pi$. If the initial displacement is 12 centimeters, find d when $t = 2$.

Solution Since $A = 12$, $\omega = 6\pi$, and $t = 2$,

$$d = A \cos \omega t$$
$$= 12 \cos 6\pi(2) = 12 \cos 12\pi.$$

Since $\cos 12\pi = \cos(0 + 6 \cdot 2\pi) = 1$, we have

$$d = 12 \cos 0 = 12(1) = 12.$$

Hence, the displacement when $t = 2$ is 12 centimeters.

Besides mechanical systems such as the example above, certain electromagnetic systems can be analyzed using the same mathematical models.

Example The voltage e in an electrical circuit can be expressed as $e = E \sin t$, where E is the maximum voltage and t is the time in seconds. If $E = 100$, find e when $t = 2$.

Solution Since $E = 100$ and $t = 2$,

$$e = E \sin t = 100 \sin 2.$$

Since 2 is in Quadrant II, $\sin 2$ is positive. The reference arc is approximately $3.14 - 2 = 1.14$, and from Table II, $\sin 1.14 \approx 0.9086$. Thus,

$$e \approx 100 \sin 1.4$$
$$= 100(0.9086) \approx 90.9.$$

Hence, e is approximately 90.9 volts when $t = 2$.

EXERCISE SET 1.5

A

Use Theorem 1.4 and Theorem 1.5 to write each of the following expressions in the form $\cos(x + k \cdot 2\pi)$, $\sin(x + k \cdot 2\pi)$, *or* $\tan(x + k\pi)$, *where* $0 \le x \le 2\pi$, $k \in J$. *(Assume $\pi \approx 3.14$.)*

Examples

a. $\cos\dfrac{9\pi}{4} = \cos\left(\dfrac{\pi}{4} + \dfrac{8\pi}{4}\right)$ b. $\tan\dfrac{10\pi}{3} = \tan\left(\dfrac{\pi}{3} + \dfrac{9\pi}{3}\right)$

$\qquad = \cos\left(\dfrac{\pi}{4} + 2\pi\right)$ $\qquad\qquad = \tan\left(\dfrac{\pi}{3} + 3\pi\right)$

1. $\cos\dfrac{11\pi}{4}$ **2.** $\sin\dfrac{8\pi}{3}$ **3.** $\tan\dfrac{5\pi}{4}$

4. $\tan\dfrac{7\pi}{3}$ **5.** $\sin\dfrac{13\pi}{4}$ **6.** $\cos\dfrac{17\pi}{6}$

7. $\tan\dfrac{15\pi}{4}$ **8.** $\cos\dfrac{11\pi}{3}$ **9.** $\sin\dfrac{19\pi}{6}$

10. $\cos\dfrac{17\pi}{4}$ **11.** $\sin\dfrac{13\pi}{3}$ **12.** $\tan\dfrac{13\pi}{6}$

Solve Exercises 13–16 for the conditions for the spring in the example on page 37.

13. If the initial displacement is 10, find d when $t = 4$ and when $t = 4\frac{1}{2}$.

14. If the initial displacement is -10, find d when $t = 4$ and when $t = 4\frac{1}{2}$.

15. If the initial displacement is 8, find d when $t = \frac{1}{2}$ and when $t = \frac{1}{4}$.

16. If the initial displacement is -8, find d when $t = \frac{1}{2}$ and when $t = \frac{1}{4}$.

The horizontal displacement d of the bob on an oscillating pendulum is described by the equation $d = K \sin 2\pi t$, where K and d are expressed in centimeters and t is expressed in seconds.

17. Find d when $t = \frac{1}{4}$ and $K = 22$.

18. Find d when $t = \frac{1}{6}$ and $K = 20$.

19. Find K when $d = 20$ and $t = \frac{1}{6}$.

20. Find K when $d = 10$ and $t = \frac{1}{12}$.

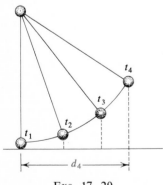

Exs. 17–20

The instantaneous voltage e in a circuit at time t is given by the equation

$$e = 1.2 \sin 997\pi t, \tag{1}$$

where e is expressed in volts and t is expressed in seconds. Find the voltage at each of the following times.

Example $t = 4.5$.

Solution   Substituting 4.5 for t in Equation (1) we obtain

$$e = 1.2 \sin 997\pi(4.5) = 1.2 \sin 4486.5\pi$$

$$= 1.2 \sin\left(\frac{1}{2} + 4486\right)\pi = 1.2 \sin\left(\frac{\pi}{2} + 2243 \cdot 2\pi\right)$$

$$= 1.2 \sin \frac{\pi}{2} = 1.2(1) = 1.2.$$

Hence, the voltage is 1.2 volts when $t = 4.5$.

21. $t = 0.5$ **22.** $t = 1.5$ **23.** $t = 2.5$

24. $t = 3.5$ **25.** $t = 6$ **26.** $t = 10$

The pressure P in a traveling sound wave is described by the equation $P = 10 \sin 200\pi[t - (x/1000)]$, where x is the distance from the source of the sound in centimeters, t is the time expressed in seconds, and P is expressed in dynes per square centimeter. Find P for each of the following conditions. Use $\pi \approx 3.14$.

27. $x = 200$ and $t = 0.06$ **28.** $x = 330$ and $t = 0.01$

29. $x = 660$ and $t = 0.02$ **30.** $x = 1650$ and $t = 0.05$

B

The instantaneous voltage e in a circuit at time t is given by the equation $e = 200 \sin 3700t$, where e is expressed in volts and t in seconds. Find the voltage at each of the following times. Use $\pi \approx 3.14$.

Example $t = 0.04$

Solution

$$e = 200 \sin 3700t$$

$$= 200 \sin 3700(0.04) = 200 \sin 148.$$

Since 148 divided by 2π yields 23 and a decimal, we first write the

(*continued*)

equation as

$$e = 200 \sin(148 - 23 \cdot 2\pi) \approx 200 \sin 3.56.$$

Since 3.56 is in Quadrant III,

$$\sin 3.56 \approx -\sin(3.56 - 3.14) = -\sin 0.42.$$

Therefore, from Table II,

$$e \approx -200 \sin 0.42$$
$$\approx -200(0.4078) \approx -81.6.$$

Hence, the voltage is approximately -81.6 volts when $t = 0.04$.

31. $t = 0.001$ **32.** $t = 0.002$ **33.** $t = 0.005$

34. $t = 0.008$ **35.** $t = 0.012$ **36.** $t = 0.020$

The instantaneous current i in an alternating system is given by the equation $i = I \sin \omega t$, where i is expressed in amperes and t is expressed in seconds. Find the current at each of the following times if $I = 0.05$ and $\omega = 377$. Use $\pi \approx 3.14$.

37. $t = 0.01$ **38.** $t = 0.03$ **39.** $t = 0.2$

40. $t = 0.4$ **41.** $t = 1.0$ **42.** $t = 3.0$

43. The displacement d of a point on a vibrating spring under certain conditions is given by $d = (1/50) \sin 50t - t \cos 50t$, where d is in feet and t is in seconds. Find the displacement when $t = 0.3$ second.

44. It is shown in calculus that an object having simple harmonic motion (described on page 36) has a velocity v given by $v = AB \cos Bt$ and an acceleration given by $a = -AB^2 \sin Bt$. The motion of a certain spring is expressed by $d = 3 \sin(\pi t/2)$, where d is a displacement in centimeters and t is in seconds.
   a. Express the velocity and the acceleration of a point on the free end of the spring in terms of t.
   b. Find the velocity and acceleration when t equals 2, 3, and 4 seconds.

Chapter Summary

1.1 Special names are given to the coordinates of a point $P(x, y)$ on a unit circle that is the terminal point of the arc with initial point corresponding to $(1, 0)$ in terms of the length s of the arc:

$$x = \text{cosine } s \quad (\cos s),$$

$$y = \text{sine } s \quad (\sin s).$$

The **cosine function**

$$\{(s, \cos s) \mid s \in R\}$$

and the **sine function**

$$\{(s, \sin s) \mid s \in R\}$$

pair the real number s with each component of $(\cos s, \sin s)$ for any point of a unit circle. For all $s \in R$ the ranges are given by $|\cos s| \leq 1$ and $|\sin s| \leq 1$.

The following important relationship follows from the definitions for the sine and cosine functions:

$$\cos^2 s + \sin^2 s = 1.$$

1.2 Function values can be obtained for the special elements 0, $\pi/2$, π, $3\pi/2$, $\pi/6$, $\pi/4$, and $\pi/3$ in the domain of the cosine and sine functions by geometric methods.

Table II, Appendix C, or a calculator can be used to find approximations for $\cos x$ and $\sin x$ for some x in the interval $0 \leq x \leq 1.57$. With Table II, function values of x at smaller intervals than 0.01 can be obtained by using linear interpolation (see Appendix B).

1.3 Values for $\cos x$ and $\sin x$ for $x > \pi/2$ and $x < 0$ can be obtained by using a reference arc, whose length is $\tilde{x}$, in conjunction with Table 1.2 or Table II in Appendix C, or a calculator.

1.4 Four additional circular functions, **tangent**, **secant**, **cosecant**, and **cotangent** are defined in terms of $\cos x$ and $\sin x$.

$$\tan x = \frac{\sin x}{\cos x}, \quad x \neq \frac{\pi}{2} + k\pi, k \in J,$$

$$\sec x = \frac{1}{\cos x}, \quad x \neq \frac{\pi}{2} + k\pi, k \in J,$$

$$\csc x = \frac{1}{\sin x}, \quad x \neq k\pi, \ k \in J,$$

$$\cot x = \frac{\cos x}{\sin x}, \quad x \neq k\pi, \ k \in J.$$

Values for $\tan x$, $\sec x$, $\csc x$, and $\cot x$ for specified values of x can be obtained by first expressing them in terms of $\cos x$ and $\sin x$.

1.5 Functions with the property that $f(x + a) = f(x)$ for all x in the domain which is a subset of R, and for some $a \in R$ ($a \neq 0$), such that $x + a$ is an element in the domain, are said to be **periodic.** The smallest positive number a for which a function is periodic is called its **fundamental period.**

The fundamental period of the sine, cosine, cosecant, and secant functions is 2π. The fundamental period of the tangent and cotangent functions is π.

The equations $d = A \sin Bt$ and $d = A \cos Bt$ are often used as mathematical models to describe periodic phenomena.

A list of the symbols introduced in this chapter is shown inside the front cover, and important properties are shown inside the back cover.

Review Exercises

1.1 *Name the quadrant in which the terminal point of each arc with the given length s lies [initial point at (1, 0)].*

1. $s = \dfrac{5\pi}{6}$ **2.** $s = \dfrac{9\pi}{4}$ **3.** $s = -\dfrac{7\pi}{3}$

4. $s = -\dfrac{19\pi}{6}$ **5.** $s = 5$ **6.** $s = -4$

Determine the quadrant in which the terminal side of each arc with length s lies [initial point at (1, 0)].

7. $\sin s < 0$ and $\cos s < 0$ **8.** $\cos s < 0$ and $\sin s > 0$

If $\sin s = -4/5$ and $\cos s < 0$, find the value of each of the following.

9. $\cos s$ **10.** $\dfrac{\sin s}{\cos s}$ **11.** $\dfrac{1}{\sin s}$ **12.** $\dfrac{1}{\cos s}$

1.2 *Compute each expression (exact value).*

13. $\dfrac{\sin^2 \dfrac{\pi}{6} - \cos \dfrac{\pi}{3}}{\cos \dfrac{\pi}{4}}$

14. $\dfrac{2\left(\sin^2 \dfrac{\pi}{3}\right) + \cos^2 \dfrac{\pi}{4}}{\sin^2 \dfrac{\pi}{2}}$

Use Table II, Appendix C, or a calculator, to find a decimal approximation to four places for each expression.

15. cos 0.96

16. sin 0.28

17. sin 1.08

18. cos 1.36

19. sin 1.32 + 3 cos 0.41

20. 2 cos 1.32 − sin 1.14

21. 2 sin 0.17 − cos² 1.44

22. $\dfrac{3(\cos^2 0.17)(\sin 0.20)}{\cos 1.46}$

1.3 *Sketch each arc with length x, and its reference arc, x̃.*

23. $\dfrac{5\pi}{6}$

24. $-\dfrac{7\pi}{4}$

25. 5

26. −3

Find each function value (exact value).

27. $\sin \dfrac{3\pi}{4}$

28. $\cos \dfrac{7\pi}{6}$

29. $\cos\left(-\dfrac{5\pi}{3}\right)$

30. $\sin\left(-\dfrac{11\pi}{4}\right)$

Find approximate function values to four places for the following. Use a reference arc and π ≈ 3.14.

31. cos 4.58

32. sin(−2.89)

1.4 *Find each function value (exact value).*

33. $\tan \dfrac{5\pi}{6}$

34. $\tan\left(-\dfrac{7\pi}{6}\right)$

35. $\csc \dfrac{5\pi}{4}$

36. $\csc\left(-\dfrac{5\pi}{3}\right)$

37. $\sec \dfrac{4\pi}{3}$

38. $\sec\left(-\dfrac{13\pi}{6}\right)$

39. $\cot \dfrac{5\pi}{4}$

40. $\cot\left(-\dfrac{7\pi}{6}\right)$

Compute each expression (exact value).

41. $3 \sec \dfrac{\pi}{4} - 2 \cos \pi$

42. $\dfrac{\cos \dfrac{\pi}{3} + \cot \dfrac{\pi}{6}}{\tan \dfrac{\pi}{4}}$

Find an approximation for each expression. Use a calculator, or Table II, Appendix C, and reference arcs.

43. $\tan 0.74$

44. $\sec 0.98$

45. $\csc(-2.21)$

46. $\cot(-3.23)$

47. $2 \cot 1.09 + \sec 3.04$

48. $\dfrac{2 \cot 1.51 - \tan 0.61}{\csc 0.57}$

Determine the quadrant in which the terminal point of each arc with the given length x lies.

49. $\cos x > 0$ and $\cot x > 0$

50. $\sec x < 0$ and $\tan x > 0$

Find each function value (exact value).

51. If $\sin x = -\dfrac{1}{2}$ and $\dfrac{3\pi}{2} < x < 2\pi$, find $\sec x$.

52. If $\cos x = \dfrac{\sqrt{3}}{2}$ and $\sin x < 0$, find $\tan x$.

Write each expression in terms of sin x and/or cos x and simplify.

53. $\csc x \cdot \tan^2 x$

54. $\dfrac{\cot^2 x}{\cos x}$

1.5 *Write each of the following expressions in the form of* $\cos(x + k \cdot 2\pi)$, $\sin(x + k \cdot 2\pi)$, *or* $\tan(x + k\pi)$, $k \in J$.

55. $\cos \dfrac{8\pi}{3}$

56. $\sin \dfrac{17\pi}{4}$

57. The displacement of a spring is given by $d = 4 \cos 8\pi t$, where d is expressed in centimeters and t is expressed in seconds. Find d when $t = 2\frac{1}{2}$ seconds.

58. The horizontal displacement d of the bob on an oscillating pendulum is given by the equation $d = 18 \sin 2\pi t$, where d is expressed in centimeters and t is expressed in seconds. Find d when $t = 2\frac{1}{2}$ seconds.

59. The instantaneous voltage e in a circuit at time t is given by the equation $e = 1.3 \sin 980\pi t$, where e is expressed in volts and t is expressed in seconds. Find the voltage when $t = 3$.

60. The instantaneous current i in an alternating current system is given by the equation $i = I \sin \omega t$, where i and I are expressed in amperes, ω in radians per second, and t in seconds. Find the current at $t = 0.002$ if $I = 0.04$ and $\omega = 352$.

2 GRAPHS; INVERSE CIRCULAR FUNCTIONS

In calculus it is shown that the circular functions are continuous over the intervals for which they are defined. This implies that, in these intervals, function values exist for every $x \in R$ and also that for small differences between two values of x there are small differences between the corresponding function values. The entries in Table II suggest the property of continuity of the circular functions.

Although Table II or a hand calculator can be used to find values for the circular functions for many values of x in order to obtain their graphs, the limited number of function values that can be obtained from Table 1.3 (page 25) is sufficient to obtain good approximations to the graphs of these functions for $0 \le x \le 2\pi$.

We have used the variable x as a real number associated with an arc length on a unit circle. In this chapter we view the variable x as a real number associated with the length of a line segment on the x-axis of a rectangular coordinate system. In Section 1.1 we thought of the number line as winding on the circumference of a unit circle (see Figure 1.1). Now line segments on the x-axis of a Cartesian coordinate system can be thought of as obtained by unwinding the arc that has the same length. Sometimes it is convenient to use rational multiples of π for scale numbers of the x-axis; sometimes it is convenient to use integers. Both of these scale numbers are shown in Figure 2.1. The y-axis is always scaled in integers.

Figure 2.1

2.1 Graphs of Sine and Cosine Functions

The Sine Graph

The graphs of the functions defined by $y = \sin x$ or $y = \cos x$ are called **sine waves** or **sinusoidal waves.** We first consider the graph of

$$y = \sin x. \tag{1}$$

In order not to distort the form of the graph of (1) and the following graphs, we shall use the same units of measurement on the x-axis and y-axis. To obtain selected ordered pairs $(x, \sin x)$, as in Figure 2.2a, we first note from Table 1.3 that

$$\sin \frac{\pi}{4} = \frac{1}{\sqrt{2}} = \frac{\sqrt{2}}{2} \approx 0.7.$$

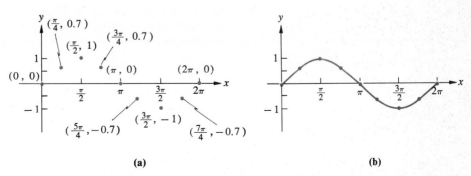

(a)   (b)

Figure 2.2

Hence,

$$\sin\frac{3\pi}{4} = \sin\frac{\pi}{4} \approx 0.7,$$

$$\sin\frac{5\pi}{4} = -\sin\frac{\pi}{4} \approx -0.7,$$

$$\sin\frac{7\pi}{4} = -\sin\frac{\pi}{4} \approx -0.7.$$

The fact that the sine function is continuous implies that its graph contains no "breaks." Furthermore, since sine function values increase as x increases from 0 to $\pi/2$ and then decrease as x increases from $\pi/2$ to $3\pi/2$, and so on, we connect the points in Figure 2.2a with a smooth curve to produce Figure 2.2b. Of course, Table II or a calculator can be used to obtain additional points to assist us in graphing the function in this interval. Now, because the sine function is periodic with period 2π,

$$\sin(x + k \cdot 2\pi) = \sin x, \quad k \in J.$$

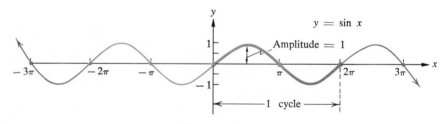

Figure 2.3

Hence we repeat the graph in Figure 2.2b in both directions and obtain Figure 2.3, which is part of the graph of $y = \sin x$ for all real numbers x. The graph over one period is called a **cycle** of the wave. The amplitude is defined formally as follows.

Definition 2.1   *The **amplitude** of a sine wave is the absolute value of half the difference of the maximum and minimum ordinates of the wave. This number is also called the amplitude of the function.*

Thus the amplitude of the wave in Figure 2.3 is

$$\left|\frac{1}{2}[1 - (-1)]\right| = 1.$$

Several important notions of the sine function are evident from the graph. Observe that the range of the function is

$$\{y \mid -1 \le y \le 1\}.$$

Also observe that the zeros of the function (see Appendix A.5), values of x for which $\sin x = 0$ and which are the coordinates of the points where the curve intersects the x-axis, are $k\pi$, $k \in J$.

The Cosine Graph

We obtain the graph of the cosine function,

$$y = \cos x,$$

in the same way that we obtained the graph of the sine function. Some ordered pairs in the function for $0 \le x \le 2\pi$ can be obtained using Table 1.3. First noting that

$$\cos \frac{\pi}{4} = \frac{1}{\sqrt{2}} = \frac{\sqrt{2}}{2} \approx 0.7,$$

we then obtain

$$\cos \frac{3\pi}{4} = -\cos \frac{\pi}{4} \approx -0.7,$$

$$\cos \frac{5\pi}{4} = -\cos \frac{\pi}{4} \approx -0.7,$$

$$\cos \frac{7\pi}{4} = \cos \frac{\pi}{4} \approx 0.7.$$

The graphs of the ordered pairs are shown in Figure 2.4a. In this case, function values decrease as x increases from zero to π and they

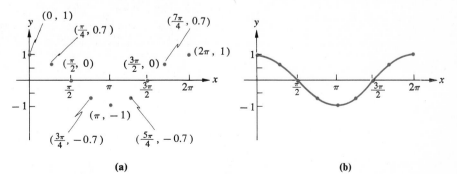

(a)   (b)

Figure 2.4

increase as x increases from π to 2π. We connect the points in Figure 2.4a with a smooth curve to produce Figure 2.4b. Again, of course, Table II or a calculator can be used to obtain additional points for graphing.

Since the cosine function is also periodic with period 2π,

$$\cos(x + k \cdot 2\pi) = \cos x, \quad k \in J.$$

Hence we repeat the pattern in Figure 2.4b and obtain Figure 2.5, which is part of the graph of $y = \cos x$ for all real numbers x. We observe that, like the sine function, the cosine function has the range

$$\{y \mid -1 \le y \le 1\},$$

and therefore the amplitude of the wave is 1. Furthermore, we observe that the zeros of the function, which are x- coordinates of the points where the curve crosses the x-axis, are $(\pi/2) + k\pi, k \in J$.

Figure 2.5

The graphs of the sine function and the cosine function are congruent; they have the same "form." For this reason both curves are called sine waves or sinusoidal waves.

In the exercises of this section we will graph functions defined by equations of the form

$$y = A \sin B(x - C) \quad \text{or} \quad y = A \cos B(x - C)$$

by first obtaining a number of ordered pairs in the function. This will give us some insight regarding the properties of these graphs.

EXERCISE SET 2.1

A

1. Graph the elements of

$$\left\{ -2\pi, \frac{-3\pi}{2}, -\pi, \frac{-\pi}{2}, 0, \frac{\pi}{2}, \pi, \frac{3\pi}{2}, 2\pi \right\}$$

on the number line below scaled in integral units. Use $\pi \approx 3.14$.

2. Graph the elements of

$$\left\{0, \frac{\pi}{4}, \frac{\pi}{2}, \frac{3\pi}{4}, \pi, \frac{5\pi}{4}, \frac{3\pi}{2}, \frac{7\pi}{4}, 2\pi\right\}$$

on a number line scaled in integral units as shown in Exercise 1. Use $\pi \approx 3.14$.

3. Graph the elements of

$$\left\{0, \frac{\pi}{4}, \frac{\pi}{2}, \frac{3\pi}{4}, \pi, \frac{5\pi}{4}, \frac{3\pi}{2}, \frac{7\pi}{4}, 2\pi\right\}$$

on the number line below scaled in multiples of π.

4. Graph the elements of

$$\left\{-2\pi, \frac{-7\pi}{4}, \frac{-3\pi}{2}, \frac{-5\pi}{4}, -\pi, \frac{-3\pi}{4}, \frac{-\pi}{2}, \frac{-\pi}{4}, 0\right\}$$

on a number line scaled in multiples of π as shown in Exercise 3.

5. Graph the elements of

$$\left\{-2\pi, \frac{-5\pi}{3}, \frac{-4\pi}{3}, -\pi, \frac{-2\pi}{3}, \frac{-\pi}{3}, 0, \frac{\pi}{3}, \frac{2\pi}{3}, \pi, \frac{4\pi}{3}, \frac{5\pi}{3}, 2\pi\right\}$$

on a number line scaled in multiples of π.

6. Graph the elements of

$$\left\{0, \frac{\pi}{6}, \frac{\pi}{3}, \frac{\pi}{2}, \frac{2\pi}{3}, \frac{5\pi}{6}, \pi, \frac{7\pi}{6}, \frac{4\pi}{3}, \frac{3\pi}{2}, \frac{5\pi}{3}, \frac{11\pi}{6}, 2\pi\right\}$$

on a number line scaled in multiples of π.

In Exercises 7–18, (a) graph the function defined by each equation by graphing one cycle and then repeating the pattern, and (b) specify the zeros and the amplitude of the function.

Example $y = 2 \sin x$

Solution

a. Some ordered pairs in the function defined by the equation are obtained in order to graph one cycle. The systematic tabulation of the data shown is helpful. The ordered pairs (x, y) are then graphed as shown, connected with a smooth curve, and the pattern of the wave duplicated. Table II or a calculator can be used to obtain additional points for graphing.

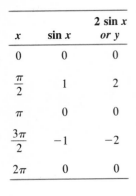

x	$\sin x$	$2 \sin x$ or y
0	0	0
$\dfrac{\pi}{2}$	1	2
π	0	0
$\dfrac{3\pi}{2}$	-1	-2
2π	0	0

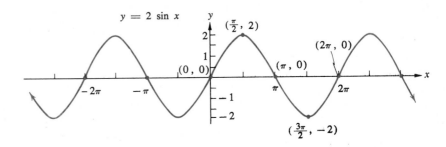

b. Zeros: $\{x \mid x = k\pi, k \in J\}$; amplitude: $\left|\dfrac{1}{2}[2 - (-2)]\right| = 2$.

7. $y = 3 \sin x$ **8.** $y = 2 \cos x$ **9.** $y = \dfrac{1}{2} \cos x$

10. $y = \dfrac{1}{3} \sin x$ **11.** $y = -\sin x$ **12.** $y = -\cos x$

Example $y = \cos 2x$

Solution

a. Some ordered pairs in the function defined by the equation are obtained in order to graph one cycle. The ordered pairs (x, y) obtained from the table are then graphed as shown, connected with a smooth curve, and the pattern of the wave duplicated.

x	$2x$	$\cos 2x$ or y
0	0	1
$\dfrac{\pi}{4}$	$\dfrac{\pi}{2}$	0
$\dfrac{\pi}{2}$	π	-1
$\dfrac{3\pi}{4}$	$\dfrac{3\pi}{2}$	0
π	2π	1

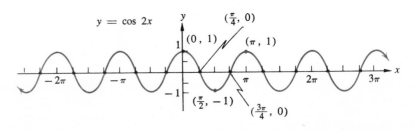

b. Zeros: $\left\{ x \mid x = \dfrac{\pi}{4} + k \cdot \dfrac{\pi}{2}, k \in J \right\};$

amplitude: $\left| \dfrac{1}{2} [1 - (-1)] \right| = 1.$

13. $y = \sin 2x$ **14.** $y = \sin \dfrac{1}{2} x$ **15.** $y = \cos \dfrac{1}{2} x$

16. $y = \cos \dfrac{1}{3} x$ **17.** $y = \sin\left(x - \dfrac{\pi}{2}\right)$ **18.** $y = \cos\left(x + \dfrac{\pi}{4}\right)$

Graph two cycles of each of the following functions.

Example $y = \cos \dfrac{\pi}{3} x$

Solution   In such cases where the coefficient of x is a multiple of π, it is helpful to label the x-axis in *rational units* 1, 2, 3, . . . , and to select *rational numbers* for x, as shown in the table. Some ordered pairs in the function defined by the equation are graphed as shown and connected with a smooth curve. Then the pattern of the wave is duplicated.

x	$\dfrac{\pi}{3} x$	$\cos \dfrac{\pi}{3} x$ or y
0	0	1
1	$\dfrac{\pi}{3}$	$\dfrac{1}{2}$
2	$\dfrac{2\pi}{3}$	$-\dfrac{1}{2}$
3	π	-1
4	$\dfrac{4\pi}{3}$	$-\dfrac{1}{2}$
5	$\dfrac{5\pi}{3}$	$\dfrac{1}{2}$
6	2π	1

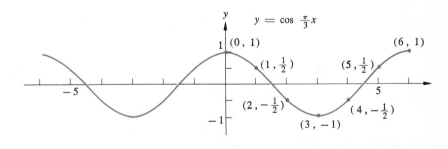

19. $y = \cos \dfrac{\pi}{2} x$ **20.** $y = \sin \dfrac{\pi}{2} x$

21. $y = \sin \pi x$ **22.** $y = \cos \pi x$

B

23. Graph $y = \dfrac{\sin x}{x}$, $-\pi < x < \pi$, and describe the graph as x approaches zero. Is the graph periodic? Why or why not?

24. Graph $y = x \sin x$, $-4\pi \le x \le 4\pi$.

25. Graph $y = \dfrac{\cos x}{x}$, $-\pi < x < \pi$, and describe the graph as x approaches zero. Is the graph periodic? Why or why not?

26. Graph $y = x \cos x$, $-4\pi \le x \le 4\pi$.

Examples of noncircular periodic functions are given below. The symbol [x] denotes the number that is the greatest integer not greater than x for each x ∈ R.

Examples

a. $[3] = 3$ b. $[5.91] = [5 + 0.91]$ c. $[-1.21] = [-2 + 0.79]$
$\hspace{6.5cm} = 5 \hspace{3.3cm} = -2$

Graph the function defined by each equation. Specify the period of the function.

27. $y = x - [x]$, $-4 \le x < 4$ 28. $y = x + [x]$, $-4 \le x < 4$

29. $y = 2x - [2x]$, $-3 \le x < 3$ 30. $y = -2x + [2x]$, $-3 \le x < 3$

2.2 General Sine Waves

Functions defined by equations of the form

$$y = A \sin B(x - C) \quad \text{or} \quad y = A \cos B(x - C), \tag{1}$$

where A, B, C, x, $y \in R$ and A, $B \ne 0$, always have sine waves for their graphs. Depending upon the values for A, B, and C, these sine waves have different amplitudes, different periods, and different horizontal positions with respect to the origin. To facilitate graphing such functions, we now consider these factors in more detail.

Amplitude

First consider how the value of A in the defining equation affects the graph of the functions in (1) above. For each value of x, each ordinate of the graph of

$$y = A \sin x$$

is A times the ordinate of the graph of $y = \sin x$. The effect of A, then, is to multiply the amplitude of the graph of $y = \sin x$ by $|A|$. The graph of $y = A \cos x$ is related to the graph of $y = \cos x$ in a similar way.

Example   Graph $y = 2 \cos x$ over the interval $-2\pi \le x \le 4\pi$.

Solution
  1. Sketch the graph of $y = \cos x$, over the interval $0 \le x \le 2\pi$, as a reference.
  2. The amplitude of the graph of $y = 2 \cos x$ is 2. Therefore, sketch the desired graph on the same coordinate system over the same interval by making each ordinate 2 times the ordinate of the graph of $y = \cos x$.
  3. Repeat the cycle over the interval $-2\pi \le x \le 4\pi$.

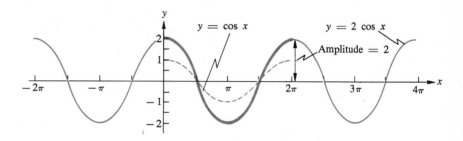

The first cycle is shown sketched with a heavier line for emphasis.

In the above example, the coefficient of cos x is a positive number. If the coefficient were a negative number, say -2, each ordinate of the graph of $y = -2 \cos x$ would be the negative of the corresponding ordinate of $y = 2 \cos x$. The graph of $y = -2 \cos x$, over the interval $-2\pi \le x \le 4\pi$, is shown in Figure 2.6.

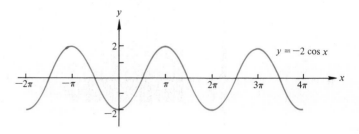

Figure 2.6

Period

Now consider how different values for B affect the graph of

$$y = \sin Bx \qquad \text{or} \qquad y = \cos Bx.$$

A complete cycle of the graph of $y = \sin x$ (or $y = \cos x$) occurs over the period 2π. Hence, a complete cycle of the graph of $y = \sin Bx$ (or $y = \cos Bx$) is obtained as Bx increases from 0 to 2π. Therefore, the period of either the sine function or the cosine function is the solution of the equation

$$Bx = 2\pi \quad \text{or} \quad x = \frac{2\pi}{B}.$$

In order to specify the period by a positive number, we use the absolute value of B. This argument establishes the following theorem.

Theorem 2.1 . *The period P of a periodic function defined by an equation of the form $y = \sin Bx$ or $y = \cos Bx$ is*

$$P = \frac{2\pi}{|B|}.$$

Example Graph $y = \sin 3x$, over the interval $0 \le x \le 2\pi$.

Solution
1. Sketch the graph of $y = \sin x$, over the interval $0 \le x \le 2\pi$, as a reference.

2. The period: $P = \dfrac{2\pi}{|B|} = \dfrac{2\pi}{3}.$

   Therefore, sketch a complete cycle of the desired graph on the same coordinate system over the interval $0 \le x \le 2\pi/3$.
3. Repeat the cycle obtained in step 2 over the interval $0 \le x \le 2\pi$.

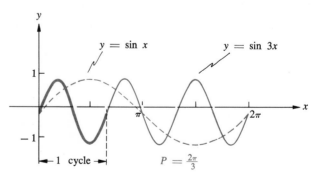

Phase Shift

Finally, consider how different values for C affect the graph of

$$y = \sin(x - C) \quad \text{or} \quad y = \cos(x - C).$$

For $x = C$,

$$sin(x - C) = sin(C - C) = sin\ 0 = 0,$$

and, for any x_1, the value of $sin(x - C)$ at $x_1 + C$ is the same as the value of $sin\ x$ at x_1. That is,

$$sin[(x_1 + C) - C] = sin\ x_1.$$

For this reason, the graph of $y = sin(x - C)$ is shifted C units to the right of the graph of $y = sin\ x$ if $C > 0$ and shifted $|C|$ units to the left of the graph of $y = sin\ x$ if $C < 0$.

Definition 2.2 *The number $|C|$ is the* **phase shift** *of the graph of periodic functions defined by equations of the form*

$$y = sin(x - C) \qquad or \qquad y = cos(x - C).$$

The number $|C|$ is also the phase shift of the corresponding function.

Example Graph $y = sin\left(x - \dfrac{\pi}{3}\right)$ over the interval $-2\pi \le x \le 4\pi$.

Solution
1. Sketch the graph of $y = sin\ x$, over the interval $0 \le x \le 2\pi$, as a reference.
2. Since $C = \pi/3$, the graph of $y = sin\ x$ is shifted $\pi/3$ units to the right to obtain the desired graph.
3. Sketch the graph over the interval $-2\pi \le x \le 4\pi$.

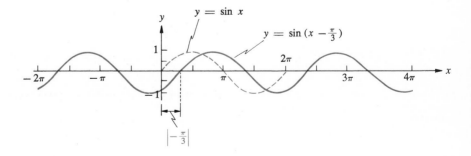

Note that in the above example the graph of $y = sin(x - \pi/3)$ was shifted $\pi/3$ *units to the right* of the graph of $y = sin\ x$ because $\pi/3$, the *value of C*, is *positive*. The graph of $y = sin(x + \pi/3)$, which is equivalent to $y = sin[x - (-\pi/3)]$, would be shifted *to the left* of the graph of $y = sin\ x$ because $-\pi/3$, the *value of C*, is *negative*.

We can now use all information about the effects of A, B, and C on the graphs of functions defined by the equation $y = A \sin B(x - C)$ or by the equation $y = A \cos B(x - C)$ to facilitate making such graphs.

If an equation were written in the form $y = A \cos(Bx - C)$, it would be necessary to first factor B from $Bx - C$ in order to make a judgment about the period and phase shift of the graph. For example, we would write

$$y = \sin\left(2x - \frac{\pi}{3}\right) = \sin 2\left(x - \frac{\pi}{6}\right)$$

from which we could observe that the period is $2\pi/2$ or π and the phase shift is $\pi/6$.

The Period P, a Positive Rational Number

If the period P of a graph is a positive rational number, instead of a multiple of π such as we encountered in the examples above, it is helpful to use selected rational values as elements of the domain and to label the x-axis in rational units to facilitate sketching the graph.

Example   Graph $y = \dfrac{1}{2} \cos \pi x$ over the interval $-5 \le x \le 5$.

Solution

1. The phase shift $|C|$ is zero. Therefore compare the equation with

$$y = A \cos Bx.$$

It is evident that the graph of $y = \frac{1}{2} \cos \pi x$ has

$$\text{amplitude: } |A| = \frac{1}{2}; \quad \text{period: } P = \frac{2\pi}{|B|} = \frac{2\pi}{\pi} = 2.$$

2. Sketch the graph, marking the x-axis in rational units.

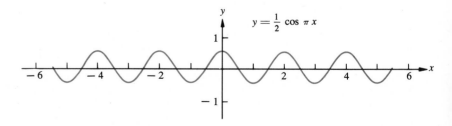

EXERCISE SET 2.2

A

Sketch the graph of each equation over the interval $-2\pi \le x \le 2\pi$.

Example $y = \dfrac{1}{2} \cos 2x$

Solution

1. Compare the equation with $y = A \cos Bx$. It is evident that the graph of $y = \frac{1}{2} \cos 2x$ has

$$\text{amplitude: } |A| = \frac{1}{2}; \quad \text{period: } P = \frac{2\pi}{|B|} = \frac{2\pi}{2} = \pi.$$

2. Sketch the graph.

1. $y = 3 \sin x$	**2.** $y = 3 \cos x$	**3.** $y = -2 \cos x$
4. $y = -5 \sin x$	**5.** $y = \dfrac{1}{2} \sin x$	**6.** $y = \dfrac{1}{3} \cos x$
7. $y = \cos 2x$	**8.** $y = \sin 3x$	**9.** $y = \sin \dfrac{1}{2} x$
10. $y = \cos \dfrac{1}{3} x$	**11.** $y = 2 \sin 2x$	**12.** $y = \dfrac{1}{3} \cos \dfrac{1}{2} x$

Example $y = 2 \cos\left(3x + \dfrac{\pi}{2}\right)$

Solution

1. Rewrite the equation by factoring 3 from the expression in parentheses and expressing $x + \pi/6$ as $x - (-\pi/6)$.

$$y = 2 \cos 3 \left(x + \frac{\pi}{6}\right) = 2 \cos 3 \left[x - \left(-\frac{\pi}{6}\right)\right].$$

(continued)

2. Compare this equation with $y = A \cos B(x - C)$. It is evident that the graph has

amplitude: $|A| = 2$;   period: $P = \dfrac{2\pi}{|B|} = \dfrac{2\pi}{3}$;

phase shift: $\pi/6$ unit to the left of the graph of $y = 2 \cos 3x$.

3. Sketch the graph.

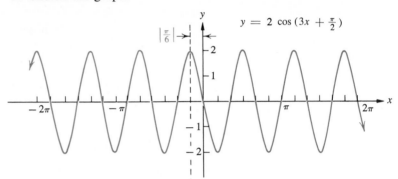

13. $y = \cos(x + \pi)$

14. $y = \sin\left(x - \dfrac{\pi}{2}\right)$

15. $y = 2 \sin\left(x - \dfrac{\pi}{4}\right)$

16. $y = \dfrac{1}{2} \cos\left(x + \dfrac{\pi}{6}\right)$

17. $y = 2 \cos\left(2x + \dfrac{\pi}{2}\right)$

18. $y = \dfrac{1}{2} \sin\left(\dfrac{1}{2} x - \dfrac{\pi}{4}\right)$

19. $y = \dfrac{1}{2} \sin\left(\dfrac{1}{2} x + \dfrac{\pi}{2}\right)$

20. $y = 2 \cos(2x - \pi)$

Graph two cycles of each of the following with positive elements in the domain.

Example $y = \sin \pi x$

Solution

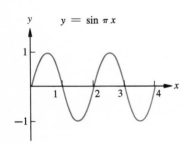

1. Compare the equation with $y = \sin Bx$. It is evident that the graph of $y = \sin \pi x$ has period

$$P = \dfrac{2\pi}{|B|} = \dfrac{2\pi}{\pi} = 2.$$

2. Sketch the graph on a coordinate system in which the x-axis is scaled in rational units.

21. $y = \cos \pi x$ **22.** $y = \sin \dfrac{\pi}{2} x$

23. $y = \dfrac{1}{2} \sin \dfrac{\pi}{3} x$ **24.** $y = 2 \cos \dfrac{\pi}{4} x$

B

Graph two cycles of each function.

25. $y = |\sin x|$ **26.** $y = |\cos x|$

27. $y = 3 |\cos 2x|$ **28.** $y = 2 \left| \sin \dfrac{1}{2} x \right|$

29. $y = |\sin \pi x|$ **30.** $y = |\cos \pi x|$

2.3 Graphical Addition

Functions defined by equations such as

$$y = 2 \sin x + \cos x \quad \text{and} \quad y = x + \cos x$$

can be graphed by methods similar to those we used in the preceding sections. We can find some elements in the range for several elements in the domain by first using available tables to find values for $\cos x$ and $\sin x$ and then performing the indicated operations. Then we can graph the set of ordered pairs obtained and complete the graph by interpolating for other elements in the range as we connect these points.

An alternative, and somewhat simpler, method involves the **graphical addition of ordinates.** Two examples illustrate this method.

Example   Graph $y = 2 \sin x + \cos x$ over the interval $0 \leq x \leq 2\pi$.

Solution   Sketch the graphs of $y_1 = 2 \sin x$ and $y_2 = \cos x$ on the same coordinate system over the given interval, as shown on page 62. The ordinate of the graph of $y = 2 \sin x + \cos x$ for each x is the algebraic sum of the ordinates of the graph of $y_1 = 2 \sin x$ and the graph of $y_2 = \cos x$. For example, for $x = \pi/3$,

$$2 \sin x = 2 \left(\frac{\sqrt{3}}{2} \right) \approx 1.7 \quad \text{and} \quad \cos x = 0.5,$$

from which

$$y = 2 \sin x + \cos x \approx 1.7 + 0.5 = 2.2.$$

(*continued*)

The ordinate 2.2 can be approximated graphically by "adding" vertical directed segments, $\overrightarrow{AC}$ and $\overrightarrow{AB}$, from the x-axis to the respective curves at $x = \pi/3$. Other ordinates can be found graphically in a similar way. The points in the graph of $y = 2 \sin x + \cos x$ for which $2 \sin x$ or $\cos x$ equals zero are particularly easy to locate. Connect the points with a smooth curve to obtain the graph shown.

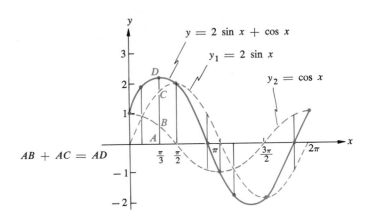

Example   Graph $y = x + \cos x$ over the interval $-\pi \le x \le 2\pi$.

Solution   Sketch the graphs of $y_1 = x$ and $y_2 = \cos x$ on the same set of axes over the given interval. Then "add" directed segments for arbitrary values of x. The points in the graph of $y = x + \cos x$ for which $\cos x = 0$ are easy to locate. Connect the points with a smooth curve to obtain the graph shown.

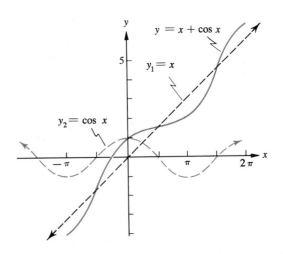

EXERCISE SET 2.3

A

Sketch the graph of each equation over the interval $-\pi \le x \le 2\pi$.

Example $y = \sin x + \cos x$

Solution
1. Graph $y_1 = \sin x$ and $y_2 = \cos x$ on the same set of axes.
2. Add the ordinates of several pairs of points for several values of x and draw a smooth curve.

1. $y = 2 \cos x + \sin x$

2. $y = \cos 2x + \dfrac{1}{2} \sin x$

3. $y = \dfrac{1}{2} \cos x + \sin \dfrac{1}{2} x$

4. $y = \cos \dfrac{1}{2} x + \dfrac{1}{3} \sin x$

5. $y = \sin 2x + \dfrac{1}{2} \cos x$

6. $y = \sin \dfrac{1}{2} x + \cos x$

7. $y = 2 \sin x + \cos \dfrac{1}{2} x$

8. $y = \sin \dfrac{1}{2} x + 2 \cos \dfrac{1}{2} x$

9. $y = 2 \sin x - \cos x$

10. $y = \cos x - \dfrac{1}{2} \sin x$

11. $y = \cos \dfrac{1}{2} x - 2 \sin x$

12. $y = 2 \cos x - \dfrac{1}{3} \sin x$

13. $y = 2 + 2 \cos x$

14. $y = 1 - 2 \sin x$

15. $y = x + \sin x$

16. $y = \dfrac{x}{2} - \cos x$

B

Sketch the graph of each equation over the specified interval.

17. $y = x - 2 + \cos x$, $0 \le x \le 2\pi$.
   Hint: First graph $y_1 = x - 2$ and $y_2 = \cos x$.

18. $y = 3 - x + \sin x$, $0 \le x \le 2\pi$.
   Hint: First graph $y_1 = 3 - x$ and $y_2 = \sin x$.

19. $y = 2 \cos x + \dfrac{x^2}{12}$, $0 \le x \le 2\pi$

20. $y = 2 \sin x + \dfrac{1}{x}$, $0 \le x \le 2\pi$

21. $y = \sin \pi x - x + 4$, $0 \le x \le 4$

22. $y = \cos \dfrac{\pi}{2} x - \dfrac{x^2}{4}$, $0 \le x \le 4$

2.4 Graphs of Other Circular Functions

We can graph the tangent, cotangent, secant, and cosecant functions on a Cartesian coordinate system in the same way that we graphed the sine and cosine functions in Sections 2.1 and 2.2. Although the graphs of these functions are not sine waves, the graphs do exhibit the periodic nature and other important features of the functions.

Tangent Function

The period of the tangent function is π. Thus, to graph $y = \tan x$ we need some values of x only in the interval 0 to π. Using Table 1.3, we obtain some ordered pairs in the function and graph these ordered pairs as shown in Figure 2.7. Observe that

$$\tan \frac{\pi}{6} = \frac{1}{\sqrt{3}} = \frac{\sqrt{3}}{3} \approx \frac{1.7}{3} \approx 0.6,$$

and

$$\tan \frac{\pi}{3} = \sqrt{3} \approx 1.7.$$

Since $\tan x = \sin x / \cos x$, the function defined by $y = \tan x$ is continuous in the domain

$$0 \le x < \frac{\pi}{2} \quad \text{and} \quad \frac{\pi}{2} < x \le \pi$$

($\cos x \neq 0$ in these intervals), and we connect the points in Figure 2.7 with a smooth curve to produce one cycle (heavy line) and then we repeat this pattern in both directions to obtain Figure 2.8. Of course,

Figure 2.7

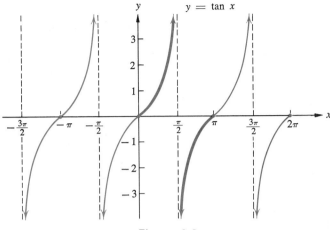

Figure 2.8

Table II or a calculator can be used to obtain additional points to assist in graphing the entire function.

Because tan x is undefined for $x = \pi/2$, there is no point in the graph of the function when $x = \pi/2$. Notice, however, that $|\tan x|$ increases indefinitely as x is taken closer and closer to $\pi/2$. The vertical dashed lines in Figures 2.7 and 2.8 are called **asymptotes.** The entire set of asymptotes to the curve is the set of lines which are the graphs of

$$x = \frac{\pi}{2} + k\pi, \quad k \in J.$$

Furthermore, observe that the zeros of the function that are associated with the points where the curve intersects the x-axis are $k\pi$, $k \in J$.

Cotangent Function

The graph of the function defined by $y = \cot x$ can also be obtained by plotting some points. However, for $x \neq k(\pi/2)$ and $x \neq k\pi$, $k \in J$,

$$\cot x = \frac{1}{\tan x}.$$

Thus, each ordinate of the graph of $y = \cot x$, where $x \neq k(\pi/2)$ and $x \neq k\pi$, is the reciprocal of the corresponding ordinate of the graph of $y = \tan x$. With this information we can quickly sketch the graph of $y = \cot x$ if we first sketch the graph of $y = \tan x$ on the same coor-

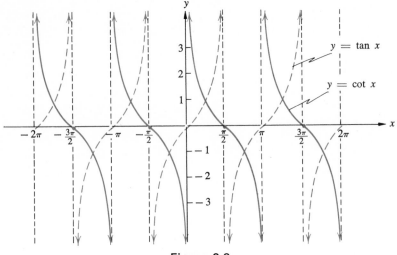

Figure 2.9

dinate system. The graphs appear in Figure 2.9. Notice that the zeros of the function defined by $y = \cot x$ are

$$\frac{\pi}{2} + k\pi, \quad k \in J,$$

and that the asymptotes to the curve are given by

$$x = k\pi, \quad k \in J.$$

Also note that the range of either the tangent or cotangent function is $\{y \mid y \in R\}$.

Secant and Cosecant Functions

The graphs of the functions defined by $y = \sec x$ and $y = \csc x$ can also be obtained by using the facts that

$$\sec x = \frac{1}{\cos x}, \quad x \neq \frac{\pi}{2} + k\pi, k \in J,$$

and

$$\csc x = \frac{1}{\sin x}, \quad x \neq k\pi, k \in J.$$

Hence, each ordinate of the graph of $y = \sec x$ is the reciprocal of the corresponding ordinate of the graph of $y = \cos x$, and each ordinate of the graph of $y = \csc x$ is the reciprocal of the corresponding ordinate of the graph of $y = \sin x$, except for the noted restrictions. Thus the graphs of

$$y = \sec x \qquad \text{and} \qquad y = \csc x$$

can be obtained directly from the graphs of

$$y = \cos x \qquad \text{and} \qquad y = \sin x,$$

respectively, as shown in Figures 2.10 and 2.11 (see exercises 7 and 8).

Figure 2.10

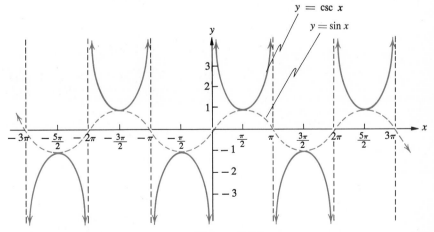

Figure 2.11

Notice that the asymptotes of the graph of $y = \sec x$ are the graphs of

$$x = \frac{\pi}{2} + k\pi, \quad k \in J;$$

the x-intercepts of the asymptotes are the zeros of the function defined by $y = \cos x$. The asymptotes of the graph of $y = \csc x$ are the graphs of

$$x = k\pi, \quad k \in J;$$

the x-intercepts of the asymptotes are the zeros of the function defined by $y = \sin x$. The range of either the secant or the cosecant function is $\{y \mid y \leq -1 \text{ or } y \geq 1\}$. Thus, there are no zeros of these functions.

Variations in the constants A, B, and C in equations such as

$$y = A \tan B(x + C) \tag{1}$$

affect their graphs in much the same way that these constants affect the graphs of $y = A \sin B(x + C)$ and $y = A \cos B(x + C)$. However, in the graphs of equations of the form of Equation (1), the coefficient A is not referred to as the amplitude.

Domains and Ranges of the Circular Functions

The domains and ranges of the six circular functions have been briefly considered in Chapter 1, and in this chapter. For convenience we summarize this data in Table 2.1.

TABLE 2.1

Function	Domain	Range
$\{(x, \sin x)\}$	$x \in R$	$-1 \leq \sin x \leq 1$
$\{(x, \cos x)\}$	$x \in R$	$-1 \leq \cos x \leq 1$
$\{(x, \tan x)\}$	$x \in R \ \left(x \neq \dfrac{\pi}{2} + k\pi\right)$	$\tan x \in R$
$\{(x, \cot x)\}$	$x \in R \ (x \neq k\pi)$	$\cot x \in R$
$\{(x, \sec x)\}$	$x \in R \ \left(x \neq \dfrac{\pi}{2} + k\pi\right)$	$\lvert \sec x \rvert \geq 1$
$\{(x, \csc x)\}$	$x \in R \ (x \neq k\pi)$	$\lvert \csc x \rvert \geq 1$

EXERCISE SET 2.4

A

Sketch the graph of each equation over the interval $0 \le x \le 2\pi$ and specify (a) the range, (b) the equations of the asymptotes, and (c) the zeros of the function (if they exist).

Example $y = \tan 2x$

Solution   Since the period of $y = \tan x$ is π, the period of $y = \tan 2x$ is $\pi/2$. The graph is sketched as shown.
   a. Range: $\{y \mid y \in R\}$

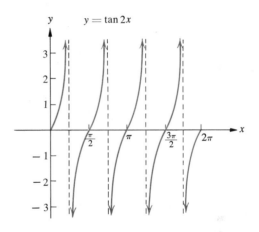

   b. Since the equations of the asymptotes of $y = \tan x$ are

$$x = \frac{\pi}{2} + k\pi, \quad k \in J,$$

the equations of the asymptotes of $y = \tan 2x$ are

$$x = \frac{1}{2}\left(\frac{\pi}{2} + k\pi\right) = \frac{\pi}{4} + k \cdot \frac{\pi}{2}, \quad k \in J.$$

   c. Zeros: $\left\{x \mid x = k \cdot \frac{\pi}{2}, k \in J\right\}$

1. $y = \tan 3x$ **2.** $y = \tan \frac{1}{2}x$ **3.** $y = \tan\left(x + \frac{\pi}{6}\right)$

4. $y = \tan\left(x - \dfrac{\pi}{4}\right)$ **5.** $y = \cot \dfrac{1}{2} x$ **6.** $y = \cot 2x$

7. Without referring to Figure 2.10, graph $y = \sec x$, by using the fact that $\sec x = \dfrac{1}{\cos x}$, $x \neq \dfrac{\pi}{2} + k\pi$, $k \in J$.

8. Without referring to Figure 2.11, graph $y = \csc x$ by using the fact that $\csc x = \dfrac{1}{\sin x}$, $x \neq k\pi$, $k \in J$.

B

9. Use the fact that $\frac{1}{2} \sec x = \dfrac{1}{2 \cos x}$ to graph $y = \frac{1}{2} \sec x$ over the interval $-\pi \leq x \leq 2\pi$.

10. Use the fact that $2 \csc x = \dfrac{1}{\frac{1}{2} \sin x}$ to graph $y = 2 \csc x$ over the interval $-\pi \leq x \leq 2\pi$.

11. Use the fact that $\csc 2x = \dfrac{1}{\sin 2x}$ to graph $y = \csc 2x$ over the interval $-\pi \leq x \leq 2\pi$.

12. Use the fact that $\sec \frac{1}{2}x = \dfrac{1}{\cos \frac{1}{2}x}$ to graph $y = \sec \frac{1}{2}x$ over the interval $-\pi \leq x \leq 2\pi$.

13. Graph $y = \sec\left(x + \dfrac{\pi}{4}\right)$ over the interval $-\pi \leq x \leq 2\pi$.

14. Graph $y = \csc\left(x - \dfrac{\pi}{6}\right)$ over the interval $-\pi \leq x \leq 2\pi$.

2.5 Graphing Systems of Equations

It is sometimes convenient to use systems of equations involving trigonometric function values to specify conditions on variables. As in algebraic equations, the solution of a system of equations is the intersection of the solution set of each equation in the system.

In this section we consider graphical methods of *approximating solutions* of such systems. In Chapter 4 we will consider algebraic methods to find such solutions.

Example   Solve the system

$$y = 2 \sin x$$

$$y = \frac{3}{2}$$

by graphical methods in the interval $0 \le x \le 2\pi$.

Solution   Graph the solution set of each equation and approximate the coordinates of the points of intersection.

An approximation to the solution set is $\{(0.8, 1.5), (2.3, 1.5)\}$.

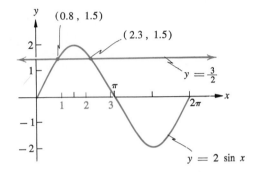

Example   Solve the system

$$y = 2 \sin x$$

$$y = \cos 2x$$

by graphical methods in the interval $0 \le x \le 2\pi$.

Solution   Graph each equation and approximate the coordinates of the points of intersection.

An approximation to the solution set is $\{(0.4, 0.7), (2.8, 0.7)\}$.

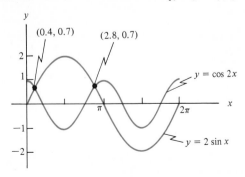

Parametric Equations

Sometimes it is convenient to define a relation (or function) in which the variable representing an element in the domain and the variable representing an element in the range are each related to a third variable, frequently a variable representing time or an angle. For example, the pair of equations

$$x = t - 3 \quad \text{and} \quad y = t + 1$$

express x in terms of t and y in terms of t. Such equations are called **parametric equations;** t is the **parameter.** To graph the relation between x and y as shown in the example below, we can choose arbitrary real number replacement values for t, and then obtain the corresponding values for x and y. Alternatively, by solving the system of equations, we can eliminate the parameter t to obtain an equation in the variables x and y. Then we can graph the equation in the usual way.

Example

a. Graph the function defined by the parametric equations

$$x = t - 3 \quad \text{and} \quad y = t + 1 \tag{1}$$

by assigning arbitrary values for t to obtain some ordered pairs (x, y) in the function

b. Eliminate t and find a Cartesian (or rectangular) equation.

Solution

a. Choosing 0, 1, 2, and 3 as replacements for t, the corresponding ordered pairs (x, y) shown in the figure can be obtained. The construction of a table is sometimes helpful to obtain these ordered pairs.

t	x	y
0	-3	1
1	-2	2
2	-1	3
3	0	4

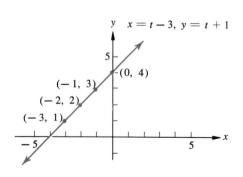

b. Equations (1) can be written equivalently as

$$t = x + 3 \quad \text{and} \quad t = y - 1,$$

from which

$$x + 3 = y - 1 \quad \leftrightarrow \quad x - y = -4,$$

the Cartesian equation of a straight line.

Example

a. Graph the function defined by the parametric equations

$$x = 3 \cos t \quad \text{and} \quad y = 4 \sin t$$

by assigning arbitrary values for t to obtain some ordered pairs (x, y) in the function.

b. Eliminate t and find the Cartesian equation.

Solution

a. Choosing selected elements of $\{t \mid 0 \leq t < 2\pi\}$ as replacements for t, we can obtain the corresponding ordered pairs (x, y) as shown in the figure. The tabulation of values is helpful.

t	x $3 \cos t$	y $4 \sin t$
0	3	0
$\dfrac{\pi}{6}$	$\dfrac{3\sqrt{3}}{2} \approx 2.6$	2
$\dfrac{\pi}{4}$	$\dfrac{3}{\sqrt{2}} \approx 2.1$	$\dfrac{4}{\sqrt{2}} \approx 2.8$
$\dfrac{\pi}{2}$	0	4
$\dfrac{5\pi}{6}$	$-\dfrac{3\sqrt{3}}{2} \approx -2.6$	2
$\vdots$	$\vdots$	$\vdots$
2π	3	0

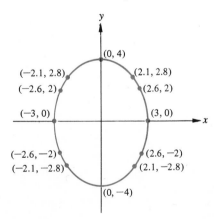

b. Motivated by the fact that $\cos^2 t + \sin^2 t = 1$, we first solve the given equations for $\cos t$ and $\sin t$.

$$x = 3 \cos t \quad \leftrightarrow \quad \cos t = \frac{x}{3};$$

$$y = 4 \sin t \quad \leftrightarrow \quad \sin t = \frac{y}{4}.$$

(*continued*)

Hence,

$$\cos^2 t + \sin^2 t = \frac{x^2}{9} + \frac{y^2}{16}.$$

Because $\cos^2 t + \sin^2 t = 1$,

$$16x^2 + 9y^2 = 144.$$

EXERCISE SET 2.5

Solve each system by graphical methods over the interval $0 \le x \le 2\pi$.

Example $y = \sin x$

$y = 2 \cos x$

Solution

An approximation to the solution set is $\{(1.1, 0.9), (4.2, -0.9)\}$.

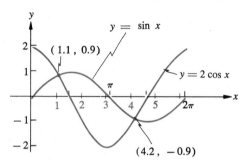

1. $y = \cos x$

   $y = 1$

2. $y = \sin 2x$

   $y = -1$

3. $y = \cos \frac{1}{2} x$

   $y = \frac{1}{2}$

4. $y = 2 \sin x$

   $y = -\frac{1}{2}$

5. $y = \tan x$

   $y = -1$

6. $y = \cot x$

   $y = \sqrt{3}$

7. $y = \sin 2x$

   $y = \frac{1}{2} \sin x$

8. $y = \cos 2x$

   $y = 2 \sin x$

9. $y = 2 \cos 2x$

   $y = \sin \frac{1}{2} x$

10. $y = \cos x$

    $y = 2 \cos \frac{1}{2} x$

In Exercises 11–18 (**a**) *graph the curve represented by the parametric equations by assigning values to t ∈ R, as specified, to obtain some ordered pairs (x, y), and* (**b**) *eliminate the parameter to find the Cartesian equation.*

Example $x = 4 \cos t$, $y = 3 \sin t$; $0 \le t \le 2\pi$.

Solution
   a. Choosing selected values as replacements for t, we obtain the corresponding ordered pairs (x, y) as shown in the figure. Tabulation of the values is also shown.

t	x $4 \cos t$	y $3 \sin t$
0	4	0
$\dfrac{\pi}{6}$	$\dfrac{4\sqrt{3}}{2} \approx 3.5$	1.5
$\dfrac{\pi}{4}$	$\dfrac{4}{\sqrt{2}} \approx 2.8$	$\dfrac{3}{\sqrt{2}} \approx 2.1$
$\dfrac{\pi}{2}$	0	3
$\dfrac{5\pi}{6}$	$-\dfrac{4\sqrt{3}}{2} \approx -3.5$	1.5
⋮	⋮	⋮
2π	4	0

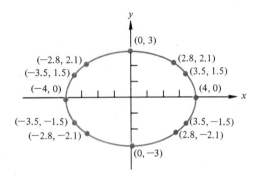

   b. Bearing in mind that $\cos^2 t + \sin^2 t = 1$ (Theorem 1.1), we first solve the given equations for $\cos t$ and $\sin t$.

$$x = 4 \cos t \qquad \text{or} \qquad \cos t = \frac{x}{4}$$

$$y = 3 \sin t \qquad \text{or} \qquad \sin t = \frac{y}{3}$$

Hence,

$$\cos^2 t + \sin^2 t = \frac{x^2}{16} + \frac{y^2}{9}.$$

Because $\cos^2 t + \sin^2 t = 1$,

$$9x^2 + 16y^2 = 144.$$

11. $x = 3t + 3$, $y = 2t - 5$; $-2 \le t \le 3$

12. $x = t - 3$, $y = t^2$; $-3 \le t \le 3$

13. $x = 2 \cos t$, $y = 2 \sin t$; $0 \le t \le 2\pi$

14. $x = 2 \cos t, \ y = 5 \sin t; \quad 0 \le t \le 2\pi$

15. $x = \cos t, \ y = \sin^2 t; \quad 0 \le t \le \pi$

16. $x = \cos^2 t, \ y = 2 \sin t; \quad -\dfrac{\pi}{2} \le t \le \dfrac{\pi}{2}$

17. $x = \sin 2t, \ y = \cos 2t; \quad 0 \le t \le \dfrac{\pi}{2}$

18. $x = \sin \dfrac{1}{2} t, \ y = \cos \dfrac{1}{2} t; \quad -\pi \le t \le \pi$

B

In Exercises 19 and 20 obtain one equation in x and y.

19. $\begin{cases} x = 2 \cot t \\ y = 2 \sin^2 t \end{cases}$
    20. $\begin{cases} x = \sin t \\ y = \cos^2 t(2 + \sin t) \end{cases}$

21. A curve called the **cycloid** is determined by the equations

$$x = a(\alpha - \sin \alpha),$$
$$y = a(1 - \cos \alpha).$$

Graph these equations in an x, y coordinate system for $a = 1$ and $0 \le \alpha \le 2\pi$.

22. Graph the equations in Exercise 21 for $a = 2$ and for $a = 3$.

2.6 Inverse Circular Functions; Notation and Graphs

In Chapter 1 we obtained function values (elements in the range) for each of the circular functions, for given elements in their respective domains. We observed that *for each element in a domain there is exactly one element in the respective range*. However, since the circular functions are periodic, *for each element in a range, there are an infinite number of elements in their respective domains*. For example, consider the graph of $y = \cos x$ in Figure 2.12, and note that the *least positive x* for which

$$\cos x = \frac{1}{\sqrt{2}}$$

Figure 2.12

(approximately equal to 0.7) is $\pi/4$. However, each value of x such that

$$x = \frac{\pi}{4} + k \cdot 2\pi, \quad k \in J,$$

is also a solution of $\cos x = 1/\sqrt{2}$ because the cosine function has a period 2π.

Similar considerations are also applicable to other circular functions. In this chapter we are interested in obtaining elements in the domains of the circular functions for given elements in their ranges. Furthermore, we will restrict the domains in such a way that there will be *one and only one* element in the domain for a given element in its range.

The mathematics involved in finding elements in the domains of functions associated with elements in their respective ranges is part of a general area of mathematics called inverse functions. Before studying the inverses of the circular functions in this chapter, it would be very helpful to review the notions relating to the inverses of algebraic functions considered in Appendix A.6.

As noted in Section A.6, the inverse of a function is the relation obtained by interchanging the components of every ordered pair in the function. Hence, the defining equation of the inverse relation of a function can be obtained by interchanging the variables in the defining equation of the original function. Furthermore, the graph of the inverse of a function is the reflection of the graph of the function with respect to the graph of the equation $y = x$.

Consider the graph of the function

$$y = \sin x,$$

with domain R and range $\{y \mid -1 \le y \le 1\}$, and its inverse

$$x = \sin y,$$

with domain $\{x \mid -1 \le x \le 1\}$ and range R, in Figure 2.13 on page 78. Notice that the graph of $x = \sin y$ is the reflection of the graph of

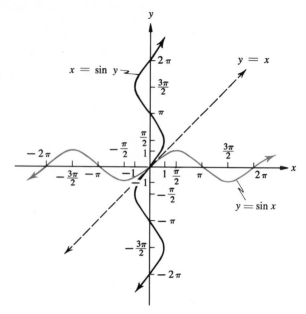

Figure 2.13

$y = \sin x$ in the graph of the equation $y = x$. Further, notice that

$$x = \sin y$$

defines a relation that is not a function because for each element x in its domain, there is an unlimited number of elements y_1, y_2, etc., in its range as shown in Figure 2.14.

Each circular function has an inverse relation. By suitably restricting the domain of the function or the range of the respective inverse relation, we can define an *inverse function* for each circular function. If we restrict the domain of the sine function to $\{x \mid -\pi/2 \le x \le \pi/2\}$, then

$$x = \sin y, \quad -\frac{\pi}{2} \le y \le \frac{\pi}{2}, \tag{1}$$

defines an inverse sine function (there is only one y for each x in the domain). Its graph is shown in color in Figure 2.14.

Inverse Notation

Generally, we wish to write the defining equation (1) in a form in which y is expressed explicitly in terms of x. This is done by using the **inverse notation**

$$y = \text{Arcsin } x,$$

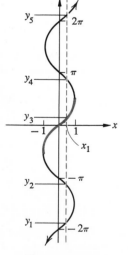

Figure 2.14

which is read "y equals arcsin x," or

$$y = \text{Sin}^{-1} x,$$

with the same meaning. It should be understood that $\text{Sin}^{-1} x$ does not mean $1/\text{Sin } x$.

Similar notation is used for the other inverse circular functions, as shown in Definition 2.3.

Notice that the ranges of the inverse functions are specified in the definition rather than following the usual procedure of stating the domain. Furthermore, the choices for the ranges are somewhat arbitrary. Those that have been chosen here involve small values of y and include values between 0 and $\pi/2$, have relatively simple graphs, and yield a one-to-one correspondence between elements in the domain and range. They are also the values that can be obtained directly with most calculators.

Definition 2.3 *The inverse notation corresponding to the six inverse circular functions is*

$$y = \text{Sin}^{-1} x \quad \leftrightarrow \quad x = \sin y, \quad -\frac{\pi}{2} \le y \le \frac{\pi}{2},$$

$$y = \text{Cos}^{-1} x \quad \leftrightarrow \quad x = \cos y, \quad 0 \le y \le \pi,$$

$$y = \text{Tan}^{-1} x \quad \leftrightarrow \quad x = \tan y, \quad -\frac{\pi}{2} < y < \frac{\pi}{2},$$

$$y = \text{Csc}^{-1} x \quad \leftrightarrow \quad x = \csc y, \quad -\frac{\pi}{2} \le y < 0 \text{ or } 0 < y \le \frac{\pi}{2},$$

$$y = \text{Sec}^{-1} x \quad \leftrightarrow \quad x = \sec y, \quad 0 \le y < \frac{\pi}{2} \text{ or } \frac{\pi}{2} < y \le \pi,$$

$$y = \text{Cot}^{-1} x \quad \leftrightarrow \quad x = \cot y, \quad -\frac{\pi}{2} \le y < 0 \text{ or } 0 < y \le \frac{\pi}{2},$$

The function values in $\text{Sin}^{-1} x$, $\text{Cos}^{-1} x$, etc., are sometimes called the **principal values** in the corresponding relation.

Graphs of the Inverse Circular Functions

The graph of the Arcsine function (shown in color in Figure 2.14) and the graphs of the other inverse circular functions, which can be obtained by graphing ordered pairs or by reflecting the graphs of the respective functions over the appropriate domain, are shown in Figure 2.15 on page 80.

Figure 2.15

Function Values

It is sometimes easier to interpret a relationship expressed in inverse notation if it is first rewritten as an equation without using such notation. For example, the equation $y = \text{Arcsin}(1/2)$ can be rewritten equivalently without inverse notation as

$$\sin y = \frac{1}{2}, \quad -\frac{\pi}{2} \le y \le \frac{\pi}{2}.$$

This equation is satisfied for $y = \pi/6$. Hence,

$$y = \text{Arcsin} \frac{1}{2} = \frac{\pi}{6}.$$

With a little practice you will be able to find an inverse function value directly from the expression involving the inverse notation.

Examples   Find the value of each of the following by using Table 1.3.

a. $\text{Arccos} \dfrac{1}{\sqrt{2}}$ b. $\text{Tan}^{-1} \dfrac{1}{\sqrt{3}}$ c. $\text{Csc}^{-1} \dfrac{2}{\sqrt{3}}$

Solutions   From Definition 2.3:

a. $\pi/4$ is the number between 0 and $\pi/2$ such that $\cos(\pi/4) = 1/\sqrt{2}$. Hence,

$$\text{Arccos } \frac{1}{\sqrt{2}} = \frac{\pi}{4}.$$

b. $\pi/6$ is the number between 0 and $\pi/2$ such that $\tan(\pi/6) = 1/\sqrt{3}$. Hence,

$$\text{Tan}^{-1} \frac{1}{\sqrt{3}} = \frac{\pi}{6}.$$

c. Because $\csc x = 1/\sin x$, we want a number x between 0 and $\pi/2$ such that $\csc x = 2/\sqrt{3}$ or $\sin x = \sqrt{3}/2$. From Table 1.3, $\pi/3$ is that number. Hence

$$\text{Csc}^{-1} \frac{2}{\sqrt{3}} = \frac{\pi}{3}.$$

Careful attention should be given to the ranges specified in Definition 2.3 when finding function values that have *negative* domains.

Examples   Find the value of each of the following using Table 1.3.

a. $\text{Arccos}\left(-\dfrac{1}{\sqrt{2}}\right)$ b. $\text{Tan}^{-1}\left(-\dfrac{1}{\sqrt{3}}\right)$ c. $\text{Csc}^{-1}\left(-\dfrac{2}{\sqrt{3}}\right)$

Solutions   From Definition 2.3:

a. Note that in the preceding example, $\text{Arccos }(1/\sqrt{2}) = \pi/4$. For $\text{Arccos}(-1/\sqrt{2})$, the number between $\pi/2$ and π is $\pi - (\pi/4)$, or $3\pi/4$, such that $\cos 3\pi/4 = -1/\sqrt{2}$. Hence,

$$\text{Arccos}\left(-\frac{1}{\sqrt{2}}\right) = \frac{3\pi}{4}.$$

b. Since $-\pi/6$ is the number between 0 and $-\pi/2$ such that $\tan(-\pi/6) = -1/\sqrt{3}$,

$$\text{Tan}^{-1}\left(-\frac{1}{\sqrt{3}}\right) = -\frac{\pi}{6}.$$

c. The number x between 0 and $-\pi/2$ such that $\csc x = -2/\sqrt{3}$ or $\sin x = -\sqrt{3}/2$ is $-\pi/3$. Hence,

$$\text{Csc}^{-1}\left(-\frac{2}{\sqrt{3}}\right) = -\frac{\pi}{3}.$$

Examples Find the value of each of the following.

a. $\mathrm{Cos}^{-1}\left(\sin\dfrac{\pi}{2}\right)$ b. $\mathrm{Tan}^{-1}(\cos 0)$ c. $\sin(\mathrm{Tan}^{-1}\sqrt{3})$

Solutions

a. $\mathrm{Cos}^{-1}\left(\sin\dfrac{\pi}{2}\right) = \mathrm{Cos}^{-1}(1) = 0$

b. $\mathrm{Tan}^{-1}(\cos 0) = \mathrm{Tan}^{-1}(1) = \dfrac{\pi}{4}$

c. Since $\mathrm{Tan}^{-1}\sqrt{3} = \pi/3$,

$$\sin(\mathrm{Tan}^{-1}\sqrt{3}) = \sin\dfrac{\pi}{3} = \dfrac{\sqrt{3}}{2}.$$

Using Tables or a Calculator

Table II or a calculator can be used to find approximations for function values of the six circular inverse functions for elements in their respective domains that are not listed in Table 1.3.

Examples Find an approximation for each of the following by using Table II or a calculator.

a. Arcsin 0.2377   b. $\mathrm{Tan}^{-1}(-0.6989)$ c. $\sin(\mathrm{Cos}^{-1} 0.8727)$

Solutions
a. Since 0.24 is the number between 0 and 1.57 such that $\sin 0.24 \approx 0.2377$,

$$\text{Arcsin } 0.2377 \approx 0.24.$$

b. Since -0.61 is the number between 0 and -1.57 such that $\tan(-0.61) \approx -0.6989$,

$$\mathrm{Tan}^{-1}(-0.6989) \approx -0.61.$$

c. Since $\mathrm{Cos}^{-1} 0.8727 = 0.51$,

$$\sin(\mathrm{Cos}^{-1} 0.8727) \approx \sin 0.51$$
$$\approx 0.4882.$$

Although values for Arcsec x, Arccsc x, and Arccot x can be found directly from Table II, these values cannot be obtained directly when using a calculator. We can obtain them by using the reciprocal relationships

$$\cos x = \frac{1}{\sec x}, \quad \sin x = \frac{1}{\csc x}, \quad \text{and} \quad \tan x = \frac{1}{\cot x}.$$

Examples   Find an approximation for each of the following by using Table II or a calculator.

a. Arcsec 1.016   b. Cot^{-1} 1.163

Solutions
   a. The reading from Table II is direct:

$$\text{Arcsec } 1.016 \approx 0.18.$$

Using a calculator, we have

$$\text{Arcsec } 1.016 = \text{Arccos } \frac{1}{1.016}$$
$$\approx 0.1777 \approx 0.18.$$

   b. The reading from Table II is direct:

$$\text{Cot}^{-1} 1.163 \approx 0.71.$$

Using a calculator, we have

$$\text{Cot}^{-1} 1.163 = \text{Tan}^{-1} \frac{1}{1.163}$$
$$\approx 0.71018 \approx 0.71.$$

   Interpolation can be used to find approximations for function values of the inverse circular functions that lie between the values given in Table II. A method of interpolation is considered in Appendix B.

Writing Equivalent Equations

   Inverse notation for the circular functions enables us to rewrite equations in one or more variables so that one of the variables can be expressed explicitly in terms of the other variables and constants.

Example Solve $4 \cos 3x = 1$ for x.

Solution We can multiply each member of

$$4 \cos 3x = 1$$

by $1/4$ to obtain

$$\cos 3x = \frac{1}{4}.$$

By Definition 2.3,

$$\cos 3x = \frac{1}{4} \quad \leftrightarrow \quad 3x = \mathrm{Cos}^{-1}\frac{1}{4}, \quad 0 \le 3x \le \pi.$$

Then, multiplying each member by $1/3$, we obtain

$$x = \frac{1}{3}\, \mathrm{Cos}^{-1}\frac{1}{4}, \quad 0 \le x \le \frac{\pi}{3}.$$

Of course, if we want to, we can now obtain a decimal approximation for x by first finding an approximation for $\mathrm{Cos}^{-1}(1/4)$.

Example Solve $y = \frac{1}{3}\tan\frac{x}{2}$ explicitly for x in terms of y.

Solution We can multiply each member of

$$y = \frac{1}{3}\tan\frac{x}{2}$$

by 3 to obtain

$$3y = \tan\frac{x}{2} \quad \leftrightarrow \quad \frac{x}{2} = \mathrm{Tan}^{-1}\,3y, \quad -\frac{\pi}{2} < \frac{x}{2} < \frac{\pi}{2}.$$

Then multiplying each member by 2, we obtain

$$x = 2\,\mathrm{Tan}^{-1}\,3y, \quad -\pi < x < \pi.$$

EXERCISE SET 2.6

A

Rewrite each expression without using inverse notation and then specify the value of y for which the statement is true.

Example $y = \text{Arccot } 1$

Solution From Definition 2.3,

$$y = \text{Arccot } 1 \quad \leftrightarrow \quad \cot y = 1, \quad 0 < y \le \frac{\pi}{2}.$$

Hence, $y = \pi/4$.

1. $y = \text{Arccos } \dfrac{\sqrt{3}}{2}$ 2. $y = \text{Arctan } 1$ 3. $y = \text{Sin}^{-1} 1$

4. $y = \text{Csc}^{-1} 2$ 5. $y = \text{Cot}^{-1} \dfrac{1}{\sqrt{3}}$ 6. $y = \text{Sec}^{-1} \sqrt{2}$

Find the exact value of each of the following by using Table 1.3.

Example $\text{Cos}^{-1}\left(-\dfrac{\sqrt{3}}{2}\right)$

Solution Let $y = \text{Cos}^{-1}(-\sqrt{3}/2)$. Then, from Definition 2.3,

$$\cos y = -\frac{\sqrt{3}}{2}, \quad 0 \le y \le \pi,$$

from which

$$y = \text{Cos}^{-1}\left(-\frac{\sqrt{3}}{2}\right)$$
$$= \frac{5\pi}{6}.$$

7. $\text{Arcsin } \dfrac{1}{\sqrt{2}}$ 8. $\text{Arccos } \dfrac{\sqrt{3}}{2}$ 9. $\text{Arctan } 1$

10. $\text{Arcsin } 0$ 11. $\text{Tan}^{-1} \sqrt{3}$ 12. $\text{Cos}^{-1} 0$

13. $\text{Cos}^{-1} 1$ 14. $\text{Tan}^{-1} 0$ 15. $\text{Sec}^{-1} \dfrac{2}{\sqrt{3}}$

16. $\text{Csc}^{-1} 1$ 17. $\text{Cot}^{-1} 1$ 18. $\text{Sec}^{-1} 1$

19. $\text{Sin}^{-1}\left(-\dfrac{1}{2}\right)$ 20. $\text{Cos}^{-1}(-1)$ 21. $\text{Tan}^{-1}(-\sqrt{3})$

22. $\text{Tan}^{-1}(-1)$ 23. $\text{Cos}^{-1}\left(-\dfrac{1}{2}\right)$ 24. $\text{Sin}^{-1}(-1)$

Find an approximation for each of the following by using Table II or a calculator.

Examples   a. $\text{Sin}^{-1}\ 0.8772$ b. Arcsec 1.238

Solution   a. Let $y = \text{Sin}^{-1}\ 0.8772$. Then from Definition 2.3,

$$\sin y = 0.8772, \quad -\frac{\pi}{2} \le y \le \frac{\pi}{2},$$

from which

$$y = \text{Sin}^{-1}\ 0.8772 = 1.07.$$

b. The reading from Table II is direct:

$$\text{Arcsec } 1.238 \approx 0.63.$$

Using a calculator, we have

$$\text{Arcsec } 1.238 = \text{Arccos } \frac{1}{1.238} \approx 0.63.$$

25. Arctan 0.5726   **26.** Arcsin 0.6442   **27.** Arccos 0.8961

28. Arctan 0.1104   **29.** $\text{Sin}^{-1}\ 0.3523$ **30.** $\text{Cos}^{-1}\ 0.6600$

31. $\text{Tan}^{-1}\ 2.912$ **32.** $\text{Sin}^{-1}\ 0.8724$ **33.** $\text{Sec}^{-1}\ 8.299$

34. $\text{Cot}^{-1}\ 0.6563$ **35.** $\text{Csc}^{-1}\ 1.077$ **36.** $\text{Sec}^{-1}\ 1.004$

37. $\text{Tan}^{-1}(-0.5463)$ **38.** $\text{Sin}^{-1}(-0.6518)$ **39.** $\text{Cos}^{-1}(-0.9759)$

40. $\text{Cos}^{-1}(-0.3153)$ **41.** $\text{Sin}^{-1}(-0.9927)$ **42.** $\text{Tan}^{-1}(-1.827)$

Rewrite each equation so that x is expressed explicitly in terms of y and/or the constants.

Example $3 \sin 2x = 1$

Solution   Multiplying each member by 1/3 yields $\sin 2x = 1/3$. By Definition 2.3,

$$\sin 2x = \frac{1}{3} \quad \leftrightarrow \quad 2x = \text{Sin}^{-1}\frac{1}{3}, \quad -\frac{\pi}{2} \le 2x \le \frac{\pi}{2}.$$

Then, multiplying each member by 1/2, we obtain

$$x = \frac{1}{2}\text{Sin}^{-1}\frac{1}{3}, \quad -\frac{\pi}{4} \le x \le \frac{\pi}{4}.$$

43. $4 \cos x = 3$ **44.** $2 \tan x = 3$ **45.** $\sin 3x = \dfrac{1}{4}$

46. $\cos 2x = \dfrac{1}{3}$ **47.** $2 \tan 2x = 5$ **48.** $3 \sin 4x = 2$

49. $2 \cos 3x = 1.24$ **50.** $5 \tan 2x = 2.25$ **51.** $y = 2 \tan 3x$

52. $y = 3 \cos 2x$ **53.** $y = 4 \sin \dfrac{x}{2}$ **54.** $y = 2 \tan \dfrac{x}{3}$

Find the exact value of each of the following.

Example $\cos\left(\text{Sin}^{-1} \dfrac{1}{2} \right)$

Solution $\text{Sin}^{-1}\left(\dfrac{1}{2}\right) = \dfrac{\pi}{6}$; therefore

$$\cos\left(\text{Sin}^{-1} \frac{1}{2} \right) = \cos \frac{\pi}{6} = \frac{\sqrt{3}}{2}.$$

55. $\cos\left(\text{Cos}^{-1} \dfrac{\sqrt{3}}{2} \right)$ **56.** $\tan(\text{Tan}^{-1} 1)$ **57.** $\tan(\text{Sin}^{-1} 0)$

58. $\cos(\text{Sin}^{-1} 1)$ **59.** $\sin[\text{Arctan}(-1)]$ **60.** $\sin\left[\text{Cos}^{-1}\left(-\dfrac{1}{2}\right) \right]$

61. $\text{Sin}^{-1}\left(\sin \dfrac{\pi}{4} \right)$ **62.** $\text{Cos}^{-1}\left(\cos \dfrac{\pi}{3} \right)$ **63.** $\text{Cos}^{-1}\left(\sin \dfrac{\pi}{3} \right)$

64. $\text{Sin}^{-1}\left(\cos \dfrac{\pi}{6} \right)$ **65.** $\text{Tan}^{-1}\left(\cos \dfrac{\pi}{2} \right)$ **66.** $\text{Csc}^{-1}(\cos \pi)$

67. $\text{Arcsec}\left(\tan \dfrac{3\pi}{4} \right)$ **68.** $\text{Arccot}\left(\sin \dfrac{3\pi}{2} \right)$

Find each of the following using the tables or a calculator.

69. $\cot(\text{Sin}^{-1} 0.8134)$ **70.** $\csc(\text{Arccot } 4.933)$

71. $\sec(\text{Cot}^{-1} 0.4475)$ **72.** $\cot[\text{Arcsec}(-1.005)]$

73. $\csc[\text{Arcsec}(-2.760)]$ **74.** $\sec(\text{Csc}^{-1} 2.452)$

Chapter Summary

2.1   Graphs of the form of the graph of the sine function are called **sine waves** or **sinusoidal waves**. The part of the graph over one period is called a **cycle** of the wave. The absolute value of half the difference of the maximum and the minimum ordinates is called the **amplitude** of the wave.

Zeros of the sine function, that is, values of x for which $\sin x = 0$, are $k\pi$, $k \in J$. Zeros of the cosine function are $(\pi/2) + k\pi$, $k \in J$. These values are associated with the points where the graphs of $y = \sin x$ and $y = \cos x$ intersect the x-axis (see Figures 2.3 and 2.5).

2.2   Functions defined by equations of the form

$$y = A \sin B(x - C) \quad \text{or} \quad y = A \cos B(x - C),$$

where A, B, C, x, $y \in R$ and A, $B \neq 0$, always have sine waves for their graphs. The **amplitude** of the wave or function is $|A|$, the **period** is $2\pi/|B|$, and the **phase shift** is $|C|$.

2.3   Functions defined by equations such as

$$y = 2 \sin x + \cos x$$

can be graphed by first graphing $y_1 = 2 \sin x$ and $y_2 = \cos x$, and then "adding" their ordinates graphically for arbitrary values of x.

2.4   The graphs of the circular functions defined by $y = \tan x$, $y = \cot x$, $y = \sec x$, and $y = \csc x$ exhibit the periodic nature of the functions (see Figures 2.8–2.11). The following table shows the zeros and/or the equations for the asymptotes of these circular functions.

Function	Zeros	Equations for Asymptotes
tangent	$k\pi, \quad k \in J$	$x = \dfrac{\pi}{2} + k\pi, \quad k \in J$
cotangent	$\dfrac{\pi}{2} + k\pi, \quad k \in J$	$x = k\pi, \quad k \in J$
secant	none	$x = \dfrac{\pi}{2} + k\pi, \quad k \in J$
cosecant	none	$x = k\pi, \quad k \in J$

2.5   Solutions of systems of equations involving circular function values can be approximated by graphical methods.

A pair of equations of the form

$$x = f(t) \quad \text{and} \quad y = g(t),$$

in which two variables, in this case x and y, are each expressed in terms of a third variable, are called **parametric equations.** The relation between x and y can be graphed by arbitrarily choosing real number replacements for the third variable, in this case t, and then obtaining the corresponding values for x and y.

2.6   The **inverse of a function** is the relation obtained by interchanging the components of every ordered pair in the function.

By suitably restricting the domains of the circular functions, or the ranges of the respective inverse relations, an inverse function is defined for each circular function (see Definition 2.3).

The function values in Arcsine, Arccosine, etc., are sometimes called the principal values of the function values in the corresponding relation.

Table II, Appendix C, or a calculator, can be used to find approximations for function values of the six inverse circular functions for elements in their respective domains. Table 1.3 can be used to find exact values for special elements in their domains.

A list of symbols introduced in this chapter is shown inside the front cover, and important properties are shown inside the back cover.

Review Exercises

2.1–2.2   *Sketch the graph of the function defined by each equation over the interval* $-2\pi \leq x \leq 2\pi$. *Specify* **(a)** *the amplitude,* **(b)** *the period, and* **(c)** *the phase shift (if applicable).*

1. $y = 4 \sin x$
2. $y = \dfrac{1}{2} \cos 2x$

3. $y = \sin\left(x + \dfrac{\pi}{2}\right)$
4. $y = 2 \cos\left(\dfrac{1}{2}x - \dfrac{\pi}{6}\right)$

Graph two cycles of each of the following.

5. $y = \cos \dfrac{\pi}{4} x$
6. $y = 2 \sin \dfrac{\pi}{3} x$

2.3   *Using the method of graphical addition of ordinates, graph the equations over the interval* $0 \leq x \leq 2\pi$.

7. $y = \sin 2x - \dfrac{1}{2} \cos x$
8. $y = \dfrac{1}{3}x - \sin x$

2.4 *Sketch the graph of the function defined by each equation over the interval $0 \leq x \leq 2\pi$. Specify **(a)** the range, **(b)** the equations of the asymptotes, and **(c)** the set of all zeros of the function (if applicable).*

9. $y = \tan\left(x - \dfrac{\pi}{3}\right)$

10. $y = \cot 3x$

11. $y = \csc \dfrac{1}{2} x$

12. $y = 2 \sec x$

2.5 *Find approximations to solutions of each system over the interval $0 \leq x \leq 2\pi$ by graphical methods.*

13. $y = \cos x$

$y = \dfrac{1}{3}$

14. $y = 2 \sin x$

$y = \dfrac{3}{4}$

15. $y = \sin 2x$

$y = \dfrac{1}{2} \cos x$

16. $y = \cos 2x$

$y = \dfrac{1}{2} \sin x$

17. Graph $x = 4t - 1$ and $y = 2t^2$ in an xy system.

18. Graph $x = 3 \cos t$ and $y = 4 \sin t$ in an xy system.

19. Eliminate the parameter in the equations in Exercise 17 to find an equation in x and y.

20. Eliminate the parameter in the equations in Exercise 18 to find an equation in x and y.

2.6 *Rewrite each expression without using inverse notation and then specify the value of y for which the statement is true.*

21. $y = \text{Arccos} \dfrac{1}{\sqrt{2}}$

22. $y = \text{Arccot}(-1)$

23. $y = \text{Csc}^{-1}(-2)$

24. $y = \text{Sec}^{-1} \dfrac{2}{\sqrt{3}}$

Find the exact value of each expression.

25. Arcsin 1

26. $\text{Arccot}(-\sqrt{3})$

27. $\text{Cos}^{-1}\left(-\dfrac{1}{\sqrt{2}}\right)$

28. $\text{Tan}^{-1} \dfrac{1}{\sqrt{3}}$

Find an approximation for each of the following by using Table II or with a calculator.

29. Arccos 0.1205

30. Arctan 1.398

31. $\text{Sin}^{-1}\ 0.4529$

32. $\text{Cot}^{-1}(-0.6142)$

Rewrite each equation so that x is expressed explicitly in terms of y and/or the constants.

33. $5 \cos x = 3$

34. $\sin 2x = \dfrac{1}{5}$

35. $y = 3 \tan 2x$

36. $y = 2 \cos \dfrac{x}{2}$

Find the exact value of each of the following.

37. $\tan\left(\text{Cos}^{-1} \dfrac{1}{2} \right)$

38. $\cos(\text{Arccot}\ \sqrt{3})$

39. $\text{Sin}^{-1}\left(\tan \dfrac{\pi}{4} \right)$

40. $\text{Tan}^{-1}(\cos 0)$

3 TRIGONOMETRIC FUNCTIONS; SOLUTION OF TRIANGLES

The circular functions that we considered in Chapters 1 and 2 are pairings in which the domain and range are sets of real numbers. In this chapter we discuss functions in which the domain is a set of *angles* and the range is a set of real numbers. As you will see, a very close relationship exists between these functions and the circular functions.

3.1 Angles and Their Measures

In geometry an angle is defined as the union of two rays having a common endpoint (see Appendix A.7). In trigonometry we also consider the rotation associated with an angle. For example, consider ∠*AOB* as shown in Figure 3.1a and visualize the angle as being formed by rotating ray $\overrightarrow{OA}$, with *O* as the pivotal point, to the ray $\overrightarrow{OB}$. Viewed in this manner, ray $\overrightarrow{OA}$ is called the **initial side,** and ray $\overrightarrow{OB}$ is called the **terminal side** of the angle. Angles for which rotation is considered are called **directed angles.**

Standard Position of an Angle

Each angle in the plane can be made to coincide with (or is congruent to) an angle that has one of its sides along the positive half of the *x*-axis and its vertex at the origin, as shown in Figure 3.1b. Such an angle is said to be in **standard position.** The terminal side of an angle in standard position may lie in any quadrant or on any axis. The angle is said to be

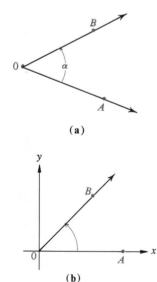

(a)

(b)

Figure 3.1

92

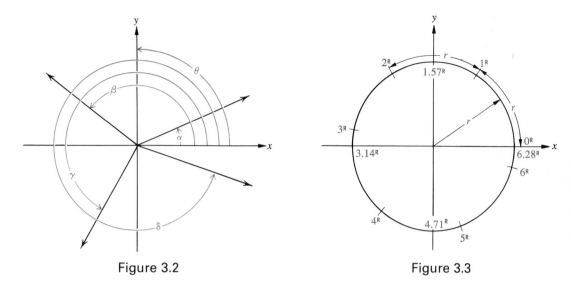

Figure 3.2   Figure 3.3

in that quadrant in which the terminal side lies. If the terminal side lies on an axis, the angle is called a **quadrantal angle.** For example, in Figure 3.2, α is in Quadrant I, β (beta) is in Quadrant II, γ (gamma) is in Quadrant III, δ (delta) is in Quadrant IV, and θ (theta) is a quadrantal angle.

Measure of an Angle

Just as different real numbers can be specified as the length of a particular line segment, say 36, 3, or 1, depending on whether the unit of length is an inch, a foot, or a yard, different real numbers can be specified as the measure of a particular angle depending on the unit of measure. Two kinds of angle measure most commonly used are called **degree measure** and **radian measure.** Such measures can be assigned to an angle by using a circle whose center is at the vertex of the angle.

If the circle is divided into 360 arcs of equal length, the number of such unit arcs intercepted by a central angle, α, is called the measure of the angle in *degree units* (see Appendix A.7) and is designated by $m°(\alpha)$.

In radian measure, the circle is divided into unit arcs, each having a length equal to the length of the circle's radius, as shown in Figure 3.3. The circumference of a circle whose radius has length r is $2\pi r$; hence the circle will include $2\pi r/r$ or 2π (approximately 6.28) of these arcs. The number of such arcs intercepted by a central angle is called the measure of the angle in *radian units* and is designated by $m^R(\alpha)$.

Positive numbers are assigned for the measures of angles in which

Figure 3.4

Figure 3.5

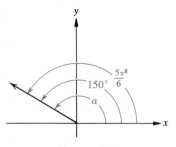

Figure 3.6

the rotation from the initial to the terminal side is in a counterclockwise direction, and negative numbers are assigned for the measure if the rotation is in a clockwise direction. In Figure 3.4, a circle is scaled in degree units and radian units for positive measures that are often used. In Figure 3.5, a circle is scaled for similar negative units. The correspondence between degree units and radian units is verified by elementary algebraic operations. If $2\pi^R$ and 360° are the measures of the same angle, then so are π^R and 180°, $(\pi/2)^R$ and 90°, etc.

We shall use the usual conventions concerning symbolism for angles and their measures. For example, we shall express the measures of the angle in Figure 3.6 as

$$m°(\alpha) = 150 \qquad \text{or} \qquad m^R(\alpha) = \frac{5\pi}{6},$$

or alternatively as

$$m°(\alpha) = 150° \qquad \text{or} \qquad m^R(\alpha) = \frac{5\pi}{6}^R,$$

where the use of the degree or radian symbol in the right-hand member of the equations should be interpreted as a redundancy for emphasis. We shall also simply write

$$\alpha = 150° \qquad \text{and} \qquad \alpha = \frac{5\pi^R}{6}.$$

Furthermore, we shall also refer to a "least positive angle" as meaning the angle of a set of angles that has the least positive measure, a "negative angle" as meaning an angle with a negative measure, etc.

Notice that for a given angle the number of units in one measure generally does not equal the number in another measure. For example, $150 \neq 5\pi/6$. However, an angle whose measure in degree units is 150 is congruent to (has the same amount of rotation as) an angle whose measure in radian units is $5\pi/6$. Symbolically, this is written as

$$150° = \frac{5\pi^{\text{R}}}{6},$$

where 150 and $5\pi/6$ are simply measures in degree units and radian units, respectively, for the same or congruent angles.

Degree-Radian Conversion Formulas

The relations between the radian and degree measures of some angles are shown in Figures 3.4 and 3.5. The measure of any angle in radians can be related to the measure of the angle in degrees. Since the ratio of the measure of a given central angle to the measure of the central angle intercepting the entire circle is the same for any unit of measurement, we have the following relationship between degree measure and radian measure.

Theorem 3.1 *For all angles α,*

$$\frac{m°(\alpha)}{360} = \frac{m^{\text{R}}(\alpha)}{2\pi}.$$

The equation in this theorem is sometimes written in either of the following equivalent forms:

$$m°(\alpha) = \frac{180}{\pi} m^{\text{R}}(\alpha), \tag{1}$$

$$m^{\text{R}}(\alpha) = \frac{\pi}{180} m°(\alpha). \tag{2}$$

Examples   Find the degree measure (to the nearest tenth of a degree) of each angle α with the given radian measure.

a. $\alpha = \dfrac{3\pi^{\text{R}}}{5}$ b. $\alpha = 0.81^{\text{R}}$

(continued)

Solutions

a. $m°(\alpha) = \left(\dfrac{180}{\pi} \cdot \dfrac{3\pi}{5}\right)°$

$\qquad = 108.0°$

b. $m°(\alpha) = \left(\dfrac{180}{\pi} \cdot 0.81\right)°$

$\qquad \approx 46.4°$

In Example b above, we used a calculator approximation for π equal to 3.1415926 to obtain the approximation shown. Slightly different values may be expected for different approximations.

Examples Find the radian measure (to the nearest hundredth of a radian) of each angle α with the given degree measure.

a. $\alpha = 60°$

b. $\alpha = 330°$

Solutions

a. $m^R(\alpha) = \left(\dfrac{\pi}{180} \cdot 60\right)^R$

$\qquad = \dfrac{\pi^R}{3} \approx 1.05^R$

b. $m^R(\alpha) = \left(\dfrac{\pi}{180} \cdot 330\right)^R$

$\qquad = \dfrac{11\pi^R}{6} \approx 5.76^R$

From conversion formulas (1) and (2) on page 95, we see that the measure in degrees of an angle α with a measure of 1^R is given by

$$m°(\alpha) = \left(\dfrac{180}{\pi} \cdot 1\right)° \approx 57.30°$$

and that the measure in radians of an angle α with a measure of $1°$ is

$$m^R(\alpha) = \left(\dfrac{\pi}{180} \cdot 1\right)^R \approx 0.01745^R.$$

These results can also be used to make conversions from radian units to degree units and from degree units to radian units, respectively.

Examples
   a. The degree measure of an angle $\alpha = 0.37^R$ is given by

$$m°(\alpha) \approx (57.30 \cdot 0.37)° \approx 21.2°.$$

   b. The radian measure of an angle $\alpha = 200°$ is given by

$$m^R(\alpha) \approx (0.01745 \cdot 200)^R = 3.49^R.$$

Coterminal Angles

If an angle is viewed as being formed by rotation of the terminal side from the initial side to its final position, then the terminal side may be rotated through more than 360°. Thus, as indicated in the figure, there are several conditions under which angles may have the same initial side and the same terminal side but have different measures.

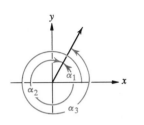

Figure 3.7

Definition 3.1   Coterminal angles *are two or more angles that have the same initial side and the same terminal side.*

In Figure 3.7, α_1, α_2, and α_3 are coterminal.

Examples   Find the least positive angle that is coterminal with each of the following.

a. 6.59^R b. 520°

Solutions

a. Sketch the angle, showing its initial and terminal sides. Since the angle generated in one revolution is $2\pi^R \approx 6.28^R$, the least positive angle having the same sides is approximately $(6.59 - 6.28)^R = 0.31^R$.

b. Sketch the angle. In this case, the least positive angle having the same initial and terminal sides is $(520 - 360)° = 160°$.

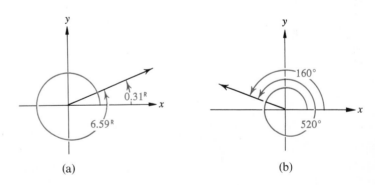

(a)   (b)

Sketches can also be helpful in determining the measures of angles coterminal with angles having negative measures.

Examples   Find the least positive angle that is coterminal with each of the following.

a. $-\dfrac{3\pi^R}{4}$ b. $-210°$

(continued)

Solutions

a. Sketch the angle, showing the initial and terminal sides. The least positive angle is $\left(2\pi - \dfrac{3\pi}{4}\right)^R = \dfrac{5\pi^R}{4}$.

b. Sketch the angle. The least positive angle having the same initial and terminal sides is $(360 - 210)° = 150°$.

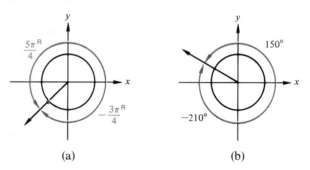

(a)   (b)

One method of specifying the measures of the infinite number of angles coterminal with a given angle is shown in the following example.

Example   Write an expression for all angles coterminal with 45°.

Solution   Since one revolution from a terminal side of any angle brings us back to that terminal side, then all angles coterminal with an angle of 45°, or $(\pi/4)^R$, are given by

$$(45 + k \cdot 360)°, \quad k \in J \qquad \text{or} \qquad \left(\frac{\pi}{4} + k \cdot 2\pi\right)^R, \quad k \in J.$$

Note that

$$\text{for } k = 0, \qquad \alpha_1 = (45 + 0)° = 45° \quad \text{or} \quad \left(\frac{\pi}{4} + 0\right)^R = \frac{\pi^R}{4};$$

$$\text{for } k = 1, \qquad \alpha_2 = (45 + 360)° = 405° \quad \text{or} \quad \left(\frac{\pi}{4} + 2\pi\right)^R = \frac{9\pi^R}{4};$$

$$\text{for } k = -1, \quad \alpha_3 = (45 - 360)° = -315° \quad \text{or} \quad \left(\frac{\pi}{4} - 2\pi\right)^R = -\frac{7\pi^R}{4}.$$

EXERCISE SET 3.1

A

1. State the conversion formulas relating the degree measure and the radian measure of an angle α.

2. Complete the degree-radian conversion wheels for special angles without referring to Figures 3.4 and 3.5. (These wheels are a handy reference.)

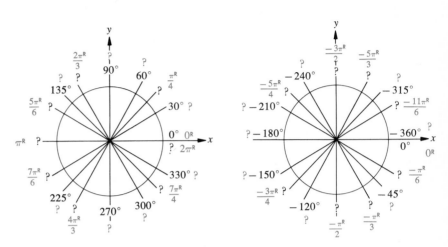

Find the degree measure to the nearest tenth of a degree of an angle α with the given radian measure.

Examples

a. $\alpha = \dfrac{6\pi^R}{5}$

b. $\alpha = -1.24^R$

Solutions

a. $m^\circ(\alpha) = \left(\dfrac{180}{\pi} \cdot \dfrac{6\pi}{5}\right)^\circ$

$= 216.0°$

b. $m^\circ(\alpha) \approx \left[\left(\dfrac{180}{\pi}\right)(-1.24)\right]^\circ$

$\approx -71.0°$

3. $\dfrac{\pi^R}{3}$ 4. $\dfrac{2\pi^R}{3}$ 5. $\dfrac{4\pi^R}{3}$ 6. $\dfrac{5\pi^R}{4}$

7. $\dfrac{8\pi^R}{5}$ 8. $\dfrac{11\pi^R}{8}$ 9. $\dfrac{-13\pi^R}{8}$ 10. $\dfrac{-\pi^R}{5}$

11. 0.18^R 12. 0.94^R 13. -1.54^R 14. -4.55^R

Find the radian measure to the nearest hundredth of a radian of an angle α with the given degree measure.

Examples

a. $118°$ b. $-140°$ *(continued)*

Solutions

a. $m^R(\alpha) = \left(\dfrac{\pi}{180} \cdot 118\right)^R$

$\approx 2.06^R$

b. $m^R(\alpha) = \left[\dfrac{\pi}{180} \cdot (-140)\right]^R$

$\approx -2.44^R$

15. $30°$ **16.** $45°$ **17.** $75°$ **18.** $125°$

19. $43°$ **20.** $137°$ **21.** $-202°$ **22.** $-342°$

23. $1'$ [One minute $(1') = \frac{1}{60}$ of a degree.]

24. $1''$ [One second $(1'') = \frac{1}{60}$ of a minute.]

Find the least positive angle which is coterminal with each of the following. Sketch each angle.

Examples

a. 6.65^R b. $-242°$

Solutions

a. Sketch the angle, showing its initial and terminal sides. The angle generated in one revolution is $2\pi^R \approx 6.28^R$. Hence the angle of least positive measure having the same initial and terminal sides is approximately equal to

$$(6.65 - 6.28)^R = 0.37^R.$$

b. Sketch the angle. The angle of least positive measure having the same initial and terminal sides is

$$(360 - 242)° = 118°.$$

25. 6.72^R **26.** 8.91^R **27.** $379°$ **28.** $423°$

29. 11.11^R **30.** 13.48^R **31.** $-792°$ **32.** $-863°$

Write a general expression for all angles coterminal with an angle having the given measure. Give each expression in terms of the least positive measure.

Examples

a. $60°$ b. $-\dfrac{2\pi^R}{3}$

(a)

(b)

Solutions

   a. One revolution from a terminal side of any angle brings us back to that terminal side. Therefore all angles coterminal with an angle 60° are given by

$$(60 + k \cdot 360)°, \quad k \in J.$$

   b. All angles coterminal with an angle $(-2\pi/3)^R$ are given by

$$\left(-\frac{2\pi}{3} + k \cdot 2\pi\right)^R, \quad k \in J.$$

33. 21°   **34.** 128°   **35.** $-\dfrac{5\pi^R}{6}$

36. $\dfrac{5\pi^R}{3}$ **37.** 242°   **38.** −310°

B

If a wheel is rotating at the given number of revolutions per minute (rpm), find the exact radian measure and degree measure of the angle through which a spoke rotates in the given time.

39. 3 rpm, 1 min.   **40.** 4 rpm, 2 min.

41. 12 rpm, 30 sec.   **42.** 60 rpm, 2 sec.

43. 6000 rpm, 0.1 sec.   **44.** 12,000 rpm, 0.01 sec.

3.2 Uniform Circular Motion

   In this section we will consider a point moving along a circle at a constant (uniform) speed. First, however, we discuss a relationship between the measure of a central angle of a circle, the length of the intercepted arc, and the length of the radius.

Arc Length

   The measure of an angle in radians, $m^R(\alpha)$, indicates how many times the length r of the radius of the circle is used as a unit length along the intercepted arc of length s (see Figure 3.8). We have the following theorem as a direct consequence.

Figure 3.8

Theorem 3.2   *If r is the length of the radius of a circle, then the length s of the arc intercepted by a central angle α is*

$$s = r \cdot m^R(\alpha). \tag{1}$$

Notice that the length s is a directed length; it is a positive or a negative real number as $m^R(\alpha)$ is a positive or a negative real number. Also notice that the central angle α in (1) is measured in radians. Thus, the measure of an angle that is given in degrees must first be changed to radians before Equation (1) can be used.

Examples On each circle with the given radius, find the length of the arc intercepted by the given angle.

a. $r = 10$ centimeters; $\alpha = 2^R$ b. $r = 2$ meters; $\alpha = -150°$

Solutions
 a. From Theorem 3.2,

$$s = r \cdot m^R(\alpha) = 10 \cdot 2 = 20.$$

Therefore the arc is 20 centimeters in length.

 b. From Theorem 3.1, the radian measure of α is given by

$$m^R(\alpha) = \left[\frac{\pi}{180} (-150) \right]^R = -\frac{5\pi}{6}^R.$$

From Theorem 3.2,

$$s = 2\left(-\frac{5\pi}{6} \right) = -\frac{5}{3}\pi \approx -5.24.$$

Therefore the arc length (directed) is approximately -5.24 meters.

Linear and Angular Velocity

Now consider a point moving along a circle at a constant speed. If the point moves from P_1 to P_2 in time t, the distance traveled equals the length of the arc shown in Figure 3.8.

Definition 3.2 *The **linear velocity** v of a point moving along an arc of a circle at a constant speed is*

$$v = \frac{length\ of\ the\ arc}{time} = \frac{r \cdot m^R(\alpha)}{t}. \qquad (2)$$

Definition 3.3 *The **angular velocity** ω (omega) of a point moving along an arc of a circle at a constant speed is*

$$\omega = \frac{measure\ of\ the\ angle\ of\ rotation}{time}.$$

If the measure of the angle is in radians,

$$\omega = \frac{m^R(\alpha)}{t}, \tag{3}$$

where ω is in radians per unit time.

Notice that the linear velocity and angular velocity are both positive if the motion is in a counterclockwise direction because the length of the arc and the measure of the angle of rotation are both positive. The linear velocity and angular velocity are both negative if the motion is in a clockwise direction.

Example   In the figure, point *B* revolves in a circular path about *A* making 10 complete revolutions in 4 seconds. Find the linear and the angular velocities of point *B* if the radius is 2 centimeters.

Solution   One revolution corresponds to an angle of rotation of 2π radians. From Definition 3.2, with $r = 2$,

$$v = \frac{2 \cdot 10(2\pi)}{4} = 10\pi$$

$$\approx 31.4.$$

Hence the linear velocity is approximately 31.4 centimeters per second. From Definition 3.3,

$$\omega = \frac{10 \cdot 2\pi}{4} = 5\pi$$

$$\approx 15.7.$$

Therefore, the angular velocity is approximately 15.7 radians per second.

Substituting ω, the left-hand member of Equation (3), for $m^R(\alpha)/t$ in the right-hand member of Equation (2) leads to the following theorem.

Theorem 3.3   *The linear velocity v of a point moving along the arc of a circle at a constant speed is*

$$v = r\omega, \tag{4}$$

where r is the length of the radius of the circle and ω is the angular velocity of the moving point in radians per unit time.

Example   A turbine with a radius of length 0.74 meter turns at the rate of 10,000 revolutions per minute. What is the linear velocity of a point on the rim of the turbine?

Solution   One revolution corresponds to 2π radians. Therefore, 10,000 revolutions per minute corresponds to an angular velocity of $20,000\pi$ radians per minute. From Theorem 3.3, with $r = 0.74$, we have

$$v = r\omega = 0.74 \cdot 20,000\pi$$

$$\approx 46,496.$$

Hence, the linear velocity is approximately 46,496 meters per minute.

EXERCISE SET 3.2

A

On each circle with the given radius, find the length of the arc (to the nearest tenth of a unit) intercepted by each angle with given measure.

Example $r = 9$ centimeters; 240°

Solution   From Theorem 3.1, the related radian measure of 240° is

$$m^R(\alpha) = \left(\frac{\pi}{180} \cdot 240\right)^R = \frac{4\pi^R}{3}.$$

Thus,

$$s = r \cdot m^R(\alpha) = 9 \cdot \frac{4\pi}{3}$$

$$= 12\pi \approx 37.7,$$

and the length of the intercepted arc is approximately 37.7 centimeters.

1. $r = 2$ meters; 3.1^R
2. $r = 30$ centimeters; 1.5^R
3. $r = \pi$ decimeters; 150°
4. $r = 2\pi$ meters; 210°
5. $r = 3$ feet; $-135°$
6. $r = 20$ inches; $-240°$

Find the measure (to the nearest tenth of a degree) of the central angle that intercepts each arc on a circle with given radius.

Example $s = 15$ centimeters; $r = 5$ centimeters

Solution   Substituting 5 for r and 15 for s in $s = r \cdot m^R(\alpha)$ yields

$$15 = 5 \cdot m^R(\alpha).$$

Thus

$$m^R(\alpha) = \frac{15^R}{5} = 3^R.$$

From Theorem 3.1,

$$m°(\alpha) = \left(\frac{180}{\pi} \cdot 3\right)° \approx 171.9°.$$

7. $s = 31$ decimeters; $r = 14$ decimeters

8. $s = 2.5$ meters; $r = 2.5$ meters

9. $s = 4.9$ centimeters; $r = 1$ centimeter

10. $s = 14.20$ inches; $r = 1.27$ inches

In Exercises 11–18, consider a flywheel with uniform circular motion, where v is the linear velocity of a point on the rim and ω is the angular velocity. Find v, r, or ω to the nearest tenth of a unit.

Example   Find ω in degrees per hour if $v = 0.5$ meter per minute and $r = 0.63$ meter.

Solution   0.5 meter per minute is 60(0.5) or 30 meters per hour. From Theorem 3.3, we have that

$$30 = 0.63\omega,$$

from which ω equals approximately 47.62 radians per hour. Therefore, in degrees per hour,

$$\omega = 47.62 \left(\frac{180}{\pi}\right) \approx 2728.4.$$

11. Find v if $r = 0.3$ meter and $\omega = 12$ radians per second.

12. Find r if $v = 10$ centimeters per second and $\omega = 10$ radians per second.

13. Find ω in radians per minute if $v = 3$ meters per second and $r = 6$ centimeters.

14. Find ω in degrees per minute if $v = 4$ meters per second and $r = 0.2$ meter.

15. Find v if $r = 9$ decimeters and $\omega = -3$ revolutions per second.

16. Find v if $r = 4$ decimeters and $\omega = -120$ degrees per second.

17. Find ω in degrees per second if $r = 2.5$ feet and $v = -10$ feet per minute.

18. Find r in inches if $\omega = 1/12$ revolution per second and $v = 8.2$ feet per minute.

19. The center line of a freeway curve is laid out as an arc of a circle of radius 300 meters. What is the length of the center line of the curve if it subtends an angle of 20° at the center of the circle?

20. A pendulum 24 decimeters long oscillates 4.2° on each side of its vertical position. Find the length of arc through which the end of the pendulum swings.

21. Two points on the earth's surface (assuming the earth to be a perfect sphere) are located so that the radii from the center of the earth to each point form an angle of 25°. Assuming the earth's radius to be 4000 miles, find the distance between the points measured along the earth's surface.

22. A wheel 10 inches in diameter is turning at a rate of 200 revolutions per minute. If it is rolling on the ground without slipping, how far *in feet* will it travel in 5 minutes?

23. A belt moving at a rate of 100 centimeters per minute is turning a pulley at an angular velocity of 8 revolutions per minute. Find the pulley diameter.

24. The rear gear of a bicycle has a radius of 10 centimeters and the front gear has a radius of 25 centimeters. Through what angle (in radians) does the front gear turn if the back gear turns through 5 radians?

25. A propeller, 2 meters from tip to tip, is rotating at a rate of 800 revolutions per minute. Find the linear velocity of a tip of the propeller in meters per minute.

26. Find the linear velocity, in centimeters per minute, of the tip of an hour hand of a clock, if the hand has a length of 1.5 decimeters.

27. A racing driver moves around a curved track at a speed of 160 miles per hour. If the radius of the circle, of which the driver's path is an arc, is 1500 feet, what is the driver's angular speed in radians per minute around the curve?

28. Using 8000 miles for the diameter of the earth, find the linear velocity, in miles per hour, of a point on the equator.

29. Assuming that the earth's orbit about the sun is circular, what is the angular velocity of the earth in radians per hour (assuming 365 days per year and 24 hours per day)?

30. Using the information in Exercise 29, what is the linear velocity in miles per hour of the earth in its orbit around the sun if the circular path of the earth has a radius of 9.3×10^7 miles?

31. Assuming that the moon's orbit about the earth is circular with a radius of 2.4×10^5 miles and that it takes 28 days for one orbit, what is the linear velocity of the moon in miles per hour?

32. The planet Mars moves around the sun in 686 earth-days. If the radius of Mars' orbit (assumed to be circular) around the sun is approximately 227,000,000 kilometers, find the linear velocity of Mars in its orbit in kilometers per hour. Assume 1 earth-day equals 24 hours.

Ex. 33

Ex. 35

B

33. Show that the area $\mathscr{A}$ of the sector of a circle (see figure) with central angle θ is given by $\mathscr{A} = \frac{1}{2}r^2\,\theta^R$.

34. Use the formula in Exercise 33 to find the area of a sector of a circle whose radius has a length of 1 meter, where the sector has a central angle with measure of 148°.

35. A unit of distance used in astronomy is the **parsec.** It is the distance r shown in the drawing. Assuming point C is the center of a circle through the sun and the earth on which the indicated arc is 93,000,000 miles long, find r, or 1 parsec, in miles. Give the answer to three significant figures.

36. Assuming that the earth travels in a circular orbit about the sun as in the figure, what would be the measure of θ during one week's travel? If the earth is 93,000,000 miles from the sun, how far does it travel in its orbit in one week?

37. If a bicycle wheel has a diameter of 27 inches, find the radian measure of the angle through which the wheel turns as the bicycle travels a distance of 1 mile.

38. If a pulley has a diameter of 20 centimeters, find the radian measure of the angle through which it turns as 4 meters of pulley belt is pulled over it. Assume the belt does not slip on the pulley.

Ex. 36

3.3 Trigonometric Ratios and Functions

Consider the three real numbers x, y, and $r = \sqrt{x^2 + y^2}$ that can be associated with any point on the terminal side of an angle in standard position, as shown in Figure 3.9. The components of the ordered pair (x, y) are the coordinates of the point and r is the length of the line segment from the origin to the point. For each angle α, there are six possible ratios that may be formed using these three numbers.

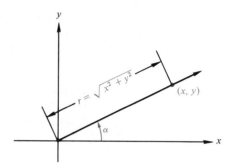

Figure 3.9

Trigonometric Ratios

The names given to the ratios formed by the three numbers x, y, and r are the same as the ones that are used to name elements in the ranges of the circular functions because, as we shall see, they are closely related. These ratios are defined as follows.

Definition 3.4 *For all angles α in standard position, if x and y (not both 0) are the coordinates of any point in the terminal side of α and $r = \sqrt{x^2 + y^2}$, then*

$$\textbf{cosine } \alpha = \frac{x}{r}, \qquad\qquad \textbf{secant } \alpha = \frac{r}{x} \quad (x \neq 0),$$

$$\textbf{sine } \alpha = \frac{y}{r}, \qquad\qquad \textbf{cosecant } \alpha = \frac{r}{y} \quad (y \neq 0),$$

$$\textbf{tangent } \alpha = \frac{y}{x} \quad (x \neq 0), \qquad \textbf{cotangent } \alpha = \frac{x}{y} \quad (y \neq 0).$$

These ratios are sometimes called **trigonometric ratios**. Cosine, sine, etc., are abbreviated in the same way as they were for the circular

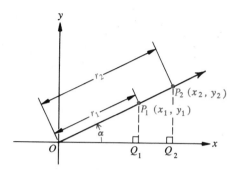

Figure 3.10

functions. Note that in each ratio where r occurs, only the positive square root of $x^2 + y^2$ is used.

In Figure 3.10, P_1 and P_2 are two points on the terminal side of angle α. Hence, triangles OQ_1P_1 and OQ_2P_2 are similar. From this it follows that

$$\frac{x_1}{r_1} = \frac{x_2}{r_2}, \quad \frac{y_1}{r_1} = \frac{y_2}{r_2}, \quad \frac{y_1}{x_1} = \frac{y_2}{x_2},$$

$$\frac{r_1}{x_1} = \frac{r_2}{x_2}, \quad \frac{r_1}{y_1} = \frac{r_2}{y_2}, \quad \text{and} \quad \frac{x_1}{y_1} = \frac{x_2}{y_2}.$$

Thus, we have the following theorem.

Theorem 3.4 *The six trigonometric ratios of an angle in standard position are determined only by the position of the terminal side of the angle.*

Example Consider P_1 (4, 3) and P_2 (8, 6), both points being in the terminal side of angle α. Using P_1 (4, 3), where $r_1 = \sqrt{4^2 + 3^2} = 5$, we have

$$\cos \alpha = \frac{4}{5}.$$

Using P_2 (8, 6), where $r_2 = \sqrt{8^2 + 6^2} = 10$,

$$\cos \alpha = \frac{8}{10} = \frac{4}{5}.$$

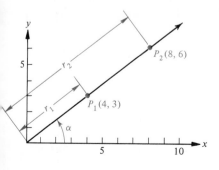

Trigonometric Functions

Theorem 3.4 implies that each angle α in standard position can be paired with a unique real number for each of the six trigonometric ratios. Hence, the equations in Definition 3.4 determine six functions. Each of these **trigonometric functions** is named by the name of the trigonometric ratio in its range. The domains of these functions are determined by their definitions. For $A = \{\text{all angles}\}$, the domains are as follows:

cosine and sine: $\quad\quad\quad\quad \{\alpha \mid \alpha \in A\};$

tangent and secant: $\quad\quad\quad \left\{\alpha \mid \alpha \in A, \quad \alpha \neq \left(\frac{\pi}{2} + k\pi\right)^{R}, k \in J\right\};$

cotangent and cosecant: $\quad \{\alpha \mid \alpha \in A, \quad \alpha \neq k\pi^{R}, k \in J\}.$

Because r, equal to $\sqrt{x^2 + y^2}$, is nonnegative for all (x, y), whether a trigonometric ratio is less than zero, equal to zero, or greater than zero depends on the values of x and y, which in turn depend on the quadrant in which the angle lies. Therefore, Table 1.4 (page 25), which pertains to circular function values, is also applicable to trigonometric function values.

Examples   Determine the quadrant in which α lies.

a. $\cos \alpha > 0$ and $\cot \alpha < 0$.   b. $\cos \alpha < 0$ and $\tan \alpha > 0$.

Solutions
   a. For $\cos \alpha > 0$, the terminal side of α lies in either Quadrant I or IV and for $\cot \alpha < 0$, the terminal side of α lies in either Quadrant II or IV. Thus, α must lie in Quadrant IV, the intersection of {I, IV} and {II, IV}.

   b. For $\cos \alpha < 0$, the terminal side of α lies in either Quadrant II or III and for $\tan \alpha > 0$, the terminal side of α lies in either Quadrant I or III. Thus, α must lie in Quadrant III, the intersection of {II, III} and {I, III}.

EXERCISE SET 3.3

A

Find the value of each of the six trigonometric functions of α, if the terminal side of α (in standard position) contains the given point. Sketch each angle.

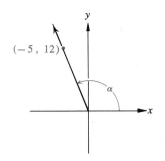

Example $(-5, 12)$

Solution $r = \sqrt{x^2 + y^2} = \sqrt{(-5)^2 + 12^2} = 13$. Hence,

$$\cos \alpha = \frac{x}{r} = \frac{-5}{13}, \qquad \sec \alpha = \frac{r}{x} = \frac{13}{-5},$$

$$\sin \alpha = \frac{y}{r} = \frac{12}{13}, \qquad \csc \alpha = \frac{r}{y} = \frac{13}{12},$$

$$\tan \alpha = \frac{y}{x} = \frac{12}{-5}, \qquad \cot \alpha = \frac{x}{y} = \frac{-5}{12}.$$

1. $(3, 4)$ 　　　　　 2. $(-15, 8)$ 　　　　　 3. $(-12, -5)$

4. $(1, -1)$ 　　　　　 5. $(2, 3)$ 　　　　　 6. $(-3, 5)$

7. $(-\sqrt{3}, -1)$ 　　　 8. $(1, -\sqrt{3})$ 　　　 9. $(3\sqrt{3}, 3)$

10. $(-5, -5)$ 　　　　 11. $(3, 0)$ 　　　　 12. $(0, -4)$

Specify the measures of angles for which the given function is (**a**) *not defined and* (**b**) *equal to* 0.

13. Tangent 　　　　　　 14. Cotangent

15. Secant 　　　　　　 16. Cosecant

Determine the quadrant in which each angle lies.

Examples

a. $\sin \alpha < 0$ and $\tan \alpha > 0$ 　　　 b. $\sin \alpha > 0$ and $\cos \alpha < 0$

Solutions

　　a. For $\sin \alpha < 0$, the terminal side of α lies in either Quadrant III or IV and for $\tan \alpha > 0$, the terminal side of α lies in Quadrant I or III. Thus, α must lie in Quadrant III, the intersection of {III, IV} and {I, III}.

　　b. For $\sin \alpha > 0$, the terminal side of α lies in either Quadrant I or II, and for $\cos \alpha < 0$, the terminal side of α lies in Quadrant II or III. Thus, α must lie in Quadrant II, the intersection of {I, II} and {II, III}.

17. $\sin \alpha < 0$ and $\cos \alpha < 0$ 　　　 18. $\sin \alpha < 0$ and $\tan \alpha < 0$

19. $\sin \alpha > 0$ and $\sec \alpha > 0$ 　　　 20. $\sin \alpha > 0$ and $\cot \alpha < 0$

21. $\cos \alpha < 0$ and $\tan \alpha > 0$ 　　　 22. $\cos \alpha < 0$ and $\csc \alpha > 0$

23. $\cos \alpha > 0$ and $\cot \alpha > 0$ 　　　 24. $\tan \alpha < 0$ and $\csc \alpha < 0$

B

Express each of the six trigonometric functions of α *in terms of the given variable, if the terminal side of* α *contains the point with the given coordinates.*

25. $(x, \sqrt{4 - x^2})$, $0 < x < 2$ **26.** $(x, \sqrt{9 - x^2})$, $0 < x < 3$

27. $(\sqrt{16 - y^2}, y)$, $0 < y < 4$ **28.** $(\sqrt{25 - y^2}, y)$, $0 < y < 5$

29. $(x, \sqrt{x^2 - 4})$, $x > 2$ **30.** $(x, \sqrt{x^2 - 9})$, $x > 3$

3.4 Function Values

The circular functions were defined in Chapter 1 by making use of a unit circle. Since the unit circle can also be used to assign measures to angles, we can relate the circular and trigonometric functions.

Basic Relationship

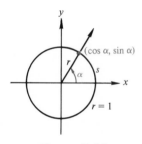

Figure 3.11

The trigonometric functions are defined in terms of the coordinates of any point, except $(0, 0)$, on the terminal side of an angle in standard position. If a point is taken such that $r = 1$ (see Figure 3.11), then, since the arc length $s = r \cdot m^R(\alpha)$, it follows that $s = m^R(\alpha)$. Thus, if an element in the range of any one of the six trigonometric functions is denoted by $\text{Trig}(\alpha^R)$ or $\text{Trig}(\alpha°)$, and $\text{Circ}(s)$ is an element in the range of the analogous circular function, then

$$\text{Circ}(s) = \text{Trig}(\alpha^R) = \text{Trig}(\alpha°), \qquad (1)$$

where s is the length of the arc intercepted by α on the unit circle. The elements in the domain of the circular functions are *real numbers,* while the elements in the domain of trigonometric functions are *angles.* The elements in the ranges of both circular and trigonometric functions are real numbers. For example,

$$\sin \frac{\pi^R}{4} = \sin \frac{\pi}{4} \quad \text{and} \quad \sin 45° = \sin \frac{\pi}{4},$$

where the left-hand member in each equation is an element in the range of the trigonometric function and the right-hand member is an element in the range of the corresponding circular function.

As a consequence of Equation (1), we can find trigonometric function values from the tables used for circular functions. We can use

Table 1.3 or Table II (for angles in radian measure) and Table III* (for angles in degree measure) in Appendix C for angles α, $0^R < \alpha < (\pi/2)^R$ and $0° < \alpha < 90°$. Alternatively we can use a calculator.

In general, we shall use the relationships in Table 1.3 to obtain exact function values when we work with the angles whose measures are 0°, 30°, 45°, 60°, 90°, 180°, and 270°, or integral multiples thereof. We shall use Table II or III, or a calculator, and use decimal approximations for function values when we work with other angles.

Since the relationships given in Table 1.3 are often employed when working with trigonometric functions, the entries in this table are shown again in Table 3.1 for convenient reference. In this table, however, the entries are shown in relation to elements (angles) in the domain of the trigonometric functions.

TABLE 3.1

$m^R(\alpha)$	$m°(\alpha)$	$\cos \alpha$	$\sin \alpha$	$\tan \alpha$
0	0	1	0	0
$\dfrac{\pi}{6}$	30	$\dfrac{\sqrt{3}}{2}$	$\dfrac{1}{2}$	$\dfrac{1}{\sqrt{3}}$
$\dfrac{\pi}{4}$	45	$\dfrac{1}{\sqrt{2}}$	$\dfrac{1}{\sqrt{2}}$	1
$\dfrac{\pi}{3}$	60	$\dfrac{1}{2}$	$\dfrac{\sqrt{3}}{2}$	$\sqrt{3}$
$\dfrac{\pi}{2}$	90	0	1	undef.
π	180	-1	0	0
$\dfrac{3\pi}{2}$	270	0	-1	undef.

Examples

a. From Table 3.1,

$$\sin \frac{\pi^R}{3} = \frac{\sqrt{3}}{2}.$$

b. From Definition 1.3 and Table 3.1,

$$\cot \frac{\pi^R}{6} = \frac{1}{\tan(\pi/6)^R} = \frac{1}{1/\sqrt{3}} = \sqrt{3}.$$

When using a calculator to find function values, you must remember to use the appropriate setting on the DEG/RAD switch.

We will continue our practice of rounding off calculator readings of function values (circular or trigonometric functions) to be consistent with the readings in the table.

Examples

a. From Table III, or by using a calculator (with the DEG/RAD switch on DEG),

$$\cos 28° \; 12' = \cos 28.2° \approx 0.8813.$$

b. From Table III,

$$\sec 14° \; 18' \approx 1.0320;$$

using a calculator,

$$\sec 14° \; 18' = \frac{1}{\cos 14.3°} \approx 1.0320.$$

* Table III is graduated in intervals of tenths of a degree and in intervals of six minutes (6').

Function values for angles whose measures are between those listed in Tables II and III can be approximated by using linear interpolation in the same way that we interpolate for circular function values. See Appendix B.

Using Angles to Obtain Function Values

It is sometimes preferable to obtain a function value directly from a sketch of the angle rather than by using Table 3.1. Trigonometric function values for the quadrantal angles 0°, 90°, 180°, and 270° can be obtained directly by using the coordinates of a point on the unit circle, just as we found the corresponding values for the circular functions in Chapter 1. See Figure 3.12.

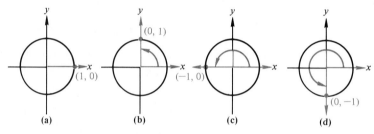

Figure 3.12

Trigonometric function values for 30°, 45°, and 60° can also be obtained by sketching angles in a unit circle as shown in Figure 3.13.

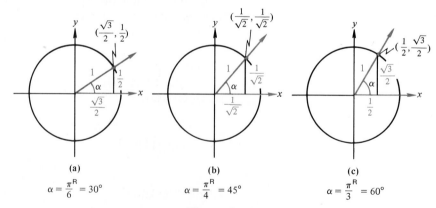

$$\alpha = \frac{\pi^{R}}{6} = 30° \qquad \alpha = \frac{\pi^{R}}{4} = 45° \qquad \alpha = \frac{\pi^{R}}{3} = 60°$$

Figure 3.13

However, it is often convenient to select a point on the terminal side of the angle whose coordinates are not fractions. Observe from Figure 3.14 that right triangles ABC and $AB'C'$ are similar. Hence, the lengths of their sides are proportional (see Appendix A.9) and the coordinates

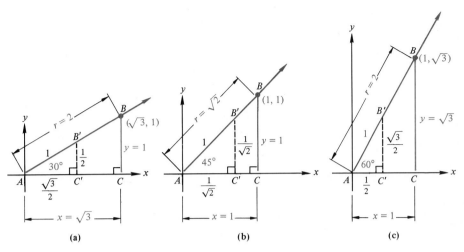

Figure 3.14

at B with the corresponding value for r can now be used to obtain the trigonometric ratios of 30°, 45°, and 60°. Thus,

$$\sin 30° = \frac{y}{r} = \frac{1}{2}, \qquad \csc 30° = \frac{r}{y} = 2,$$

$$\cos 30° = \frac{x}{r} = \frac{\sqrt{3}}{2}, \qquad \sec 30° = \frac{r}{x} = \frac{2}{\sqrt{3}},$$

$$\tan 30° = \frac{y}{x} = \frac{1}{\sqrt{3}}, \qquad \cot 30° = \frac{x}{y} = \sqrt{3},$$

and

$$\sin 45° = \frac{y}{r} = \frac{1}{\sqrt{2}}, \qquad \csc 45° = \frac{r}{y} = \sqrt{2},$$

$$\cos 45° = \frac{x}{r} = \frac{1}{\sqrt{2}}, \qquad \sec 45° = \frac{r}{x} = \sqrt{2},$$

$$\tan 45° = \frac{y}{x} = 1, \qquad \cot 45° = \frac{x}{y} = 1,$$

and

$$\sin 60° = \frac{y}{r} = \frac{\sqrt{3}}{2}, \qquad \csc 60° = \frac{r}{y} = \frac{2}{\sqrt{3}},$$

$$\cos 60° = \frac{x}{r} = \frac{1}{2}, \qquad \sec 60° = \frac{r}{x} = 2,$$

$$\tan 60° = \frac{y}{x} = \sqrt{3}, \qquad \cot 60° = \frac{x}{y} = \frac{1}{\sqrt{3}}.$$

Use of Reference Angles

A reference angle $\tilde{\alpha}$ can be used in the same way that a reference arc $\tilde{x}$ is used to find function values of angles with measure greater than 90° or less than 0°.

Example $\cos 135° = -\cos \tilde{\alpha} = -\cos 45°$
From Table 3.1, we have that $\cos 45° = 1/\sqrt{2}$. Hence,

$$\cos 135° = -\cos 45° = -\frac{1}{\sqrt{2}}.$$

Example $\sin 3.74^R = -\sin \tilde{\alpha} \approx -\sin 0.60^R$
From Table II, or by using a calculator, $\sin 0.60^R \approx 0.5646$. Hence,

$$\sin 3.74^R \approx -\sin 0.60^R \approx -0.5646.$$

Example $\cos 123° \ 48' = -\cos \tilde{\alpha}$

$$= -\cos 56° \ 12' = -\cos 56.2°$$

From Table III, or by using a calculator, $\cos 56.2° \approx 0.5563$. Hence,

$$\cos 123° \ 48' = -\cos 56° \ 12'$$

$$= -\cos 56.2° \approx -0.5563.$$

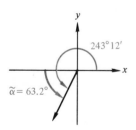

Example $\cot 243° \ 12' = \cot \tilde{\alpha} = \cot 63.2°$
From Table III, or by using a calculator, $\cot 63.2° \approx 0.5051$. Hence,

$$\cot 243° \ 12' = \cot 63.2°$$

$$= \frac{1}{\tan 63.2°} \approx 0.5051.$$

Periodic Properties

The tangent and cotangent trigonometric functions are periodic with period π^R or 180°. Hence, for these functions

$$\text{Trig}(\alpha) = \text{Trig}(\alpha + k\pi)^R = \text{Trig}(\alpha + k \cdot 180)°, \quad k \in J.$$

The trigonometric functions cosine, sine, secant, and cosecant are periodic with period $2\pi^R$ or $360°$. Hence, for these functions

$$\text{Trig}(\alpha) = \text{Trig}(\alpha + k \cdot 2\pi)^R = \text{Trig}(\alpha + k \cdot 360)°, \quad k \in J.$$

Thus, function values of angles with measures greater than $360°$ or less than $-360°$ can also be obtained by using Table 3.1, or Table II or Table III, or a calculator.

Examples
a. From Table 3.1, we have

$$\cos\frac{7\pi^R}{3} = \cos\left(\frac{\pi}{3} + 2\pi\right)^R$$

$$= \cos\frac{\pi^R}{3} = \frac{1}{2}.$$

$$\tan 840° = \tan(120 + 4 \cdot 180)°$$

$$= \tan 120° = -\tan 60°$$

$$= -\sqrt{3}.$$

b. From Table III or a calculator, we have

$$\tan 755° = \tan(35 + 4 \cdot 180)°$$

$$= \tan 35°$$

$$\approx 0.7002.$$

c. From Table III or a calculator and Definition 1.3, we have

$$\cot(-385°) = \cot(-25°) = -\cot 25°$$

$$= -\frac{1}{\tan 25°}$$

$$\approx -2.1445.$$

As we discussed in Section 1.3 regarding the use of reference arcs, the approximations that are obtained for function values using Table II and a reference angle may be different from the values that are obtained by using a calculator directly. In our examples, we will use reference angles with $\pi = 3.14$, as we did in Section 1.3, before we use a calculator. Furthermore, the answers for the problems in the exercises were also obtained using reference arcs with this approximation for π.

Examples   From Table II or a calculator:

a. $\sin 7.49^R = \sin(1.21 + 6.28)^R$ b. $\csc 11.38^R \approx \csc 5.10^R$

$\qquad\qquad \approx \sin 1.21^R$ $\qquad\qquad\qquad \approx -\csc 1.18^R$

$\qquad\qquad \approx 0.9356$ $\qquad\qquad\qquad = \dfrac{-1}{\sin 1.18^R}$

$\qquad\qquad\qquad\qquad\qquad\qquad\qquad \approx -1.0815$

Inverse Trigonometric Functions

The inverse circular functions were defined in Section 2.6. The analogous inverse trigonometric functions are defined in a similar way. Thus an equation such as

$$\sin \alpha = \frac{1}{2}, \quad -90° \le \alpha \le 90°,$$

can be written using inverse notation as

$$\alpha = \text{Arcsin}\,\frac{1}{2} \quad \text{or} \quad \alpha = \text{Sin}^{-1}\frac{1}{2}.$$

You can interpret the right-hand member of each equation as another name (symbol) for the angle α.

Examples

a. $\alpha = \text{Arccos}\,\dfrac{\sqrt{3}}{2}$ b. $\alpha = \text{Arctan}\,1.2002$

Solutions
    a. α is the angle such that $\cos \alpha = \sqrt{3}/2$ and $0° \leq \alpha \leq 180°$. From Table 3.1, $\alpha = 30°$.

    b. α is the angle such that $\tan \alpha = 1.2002$ and $-90° < \alpha < 90°$. From Table III or by using a calculator,

$$\alpha \approx 50.2° = 50° \ 12'.$$

EXERCISE SET 3.4
Find each of the following (exact value).

Examples

a. $\sin 900°$
                                          b. $\cot \dfrac{13\pi^R}{6}$

Solutions   Using the periodic property of the trigonometric functions and Table 3.1, we have

a. $\sin 900° = \sin(180 + 2 \cdot 360)°$ b. $\cot \dfrac{13\pi^R}{6} = \cot\left(\dfrac{\pi}{6} + 2\pi\right)^R$

             $= \sin 180°$

                   $= 0$ $= \cot \dfrac{\pi^R}{6}$

                                          $= \dfrac{1}{\tan(\pi/6)^R} = \sqrt{3}$

1. $\sin 390°$ **2.** $\cos 405°$ **3.** $\tan \dfrac{7\pi^R}{3}$ **4.** $\sec \dfrac{5\pi^R}{2}$

5. $\csc 780°$ **6.** $\tan 3\pi^R$ **7.** $\cot 7 \ \pi^R$ **8.** $\cos \dfrac{15\pi^R}{2}$

9. $\sec 900°$ **10.** $\tan 1110°$ **11.** $\csc 990°$ **12.** $\sin 1350°$

Example $\sin(-150°)$

Solution   Using the reference angle $\tilde{\alpha}$ in the figure, we have that

$$\sin(-150°) = -\sin 30°.$$

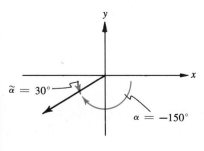

From Table 3.1,

$$\sin(-150°) = -\sin 30° = -\frac{1}{2}.$$

13. $\cos 120°$ **14.** $\sin 135°$ **15.** $\tan \dfrac{7\pi^R}{6}$

16. $\tan \dfrac{4\pi^R}{3}$ **17.** $\csc \dfrac{7\pi^R}{4}$ **18.** $\sec \dfrac{5\pi^R}{6}$

19. $\sin(-30°)$ **20.** $\sec(-90°)$ **21.** $\cos(-240°)$

22. $\cos(-150°)$ **23.** $\cos 480°$ **24.** $\tan 855°$

Find an approximation for each of the following. Use Table II or a calculator; use a reference angle as necessary.

Example $\cos 2.35^R$

Solution   Using the reference angle $\tilde{\alpha}$ in the figure, we have that

$$\cos 2.35^R \approx -\cos 0.79^R.$$

From Table II, or by using a calculator, $\cos 0.79^R \approx 0.7038$. Hence

$$\cos 2.35^R \approx -0.7038.$$

$\tilde{\alpha} = 3.14^R - 2.35^R$
$= 0.79^R$

25. $\sin 0.83^R$ **26.** $\tan(-1.24^R)$ **27.** $\cos(-0.16^R)$

28. $\csc 1.34^R$ **29.** $\cot 7.19^R$ **30.** $\sec 13.67^R$

Find an approximation for each of the following. Use Table III or a calculator; use a reference angle as necessary.

Example $\tan 624° \ 36'$

Solution   Using the reference angle $\tilde{\alpha}$ in the figure, we have that

$$\tan 624° \ 36' = \tan 84° \ 36' = \tan 84.6°$$

From Table III, or by using a calculator,

$$\tan 84.6° \approx 10.579.$$

Hence,

$$\tan 624° \ 36' \approx 10.579.$$

$\tilde{\alpha} = 624°36' - (360 + 180)° = 84°36'$

31. $\cos 9.7°$ **32.** $\sin 2.3°$ **33.** $\tan 46.6°$

34. $\sin 76.2°$ **35.** $\tan 422.8°$ **36.** $\cos 738.5°$

37. tan 435° 12'   **38.** cos 339° 54'   **39.** cot 549° 24'

40. sec 986° 6'   **41.** cos(−83° 30')   **42.** sin(−23° 12')

Find the measure of α in degrees (exact value).

Examples

a. $\alpha = \text{Arcsin } \dfrac{\sqrt{3}}{2}$ b. $\alpha = \text{Arcsin}\left(-\dfrac{\sqrt{3}}{2}\right)$

Solutions

 a. α is the angle such that sin α = $\sqrt{3}/2$ and $-90 \le \alpha \le 90°$. From Table 3.1, α = 60°.

 b. α is the angle such that sin α = $-\sqrt{3}/2$ and $-90° \le \alpha \le 90°$. Thus, α = −60°.

43. α = Arctan 1   **44.** $\alpha = \text{Arccos } \dfrac{1}{2}$ **45.** α = Arccsc 2

46. $\alpha = \text{Arccot } \sqrt{3}$ **47.** $\alpha = \text{Arcsin}\left(-\dfrac{1}{2}\right)$ **48.** α = Arctan(−1)

Use Table III or a calculator to find an approximation in degrees for each α.

Examples

a. α = Arcsin 0.4633   b. α = Arccos(−0.4337)

Solutions

 a. α is the angle such that sin α = 0.4633, $-90° \le \alpha \le 90°$. From Table III, or by using a calculator,

$$\alpha \approx 27.6° = 27° \ 36'.$$

 b. In this case, cos α = −0.4337, where $0° \le \alpha \le 180°$. Hence, cos $\tilde{\alpha}$ = 0.4337 and from Table III, or by using a calculator,

$$\tilde{\alpha} \approx 64.3° = 64° \ 18'.$$

Thus,

$$\alpha \approx 180° - 64.3° = 115.7° = 115° \ 42'.$$

49. α = Arccos 0.2773   **50.** α = Arcsin 0.9367

51. $\alpha = \text{Arctan } 0.5938$ **52.** $\alpha = \text{Arccos } 0.1305$

53. $\alpha = \text{Arcsin}(-0.7934)$ **54.** $\alpha = \text{Arctan}(-2.4383)$

B

Write each of the following as a numerical, or an algebraic, expression without using inverse notation. Assume values for x for which each function value exists.

Example $\sin\left(\text{Arccos } \dfrac{3}{5}\right)$

Solution   Because the value of Arccos 3/5 is not evident by inspection, we let $\beta = \text{Arccos } 3/5$, from which $\cos \beta = 3/5$. The sketch shows a right triangle in which $\cos \beta = 3/5$. From the Pythagorean theorem, we have

$$y^2 + 3^2 = 5^2$$

$$y = 4.$$

Hence,

$$\sin\left(\text{Arccos } \frac{3}{5}\right) = \sin \beta = \frac{y}{5} = \frac{4}{5}.$$

55. $\cos\left(\text{Arcsin } \dfrac{3}{5}\right)$ **56.** $\sin\left(\text{Arccos } \dfrac{5}{13}\right)$ **57.** $\sin\left(\text{Arcsin } \dfrac{2}{5}\right)$

58. $\cos\left(\text{Arccos } \dfrac{1}{3}\right)$ **59.** $\tan\left(\text{Arccos } \dfrac{4}{5}\right)$ **60.** $\tan\left(\text{Arcsin } \dfrac{5}{13}\right)$

61. $\cos\left(\text{Arcsin } \dfrac{x}{3}\right)$ **62.** $\tan\left(\text{Arccos } \dfrac{x}{4}\right)$ **63.** $\sin(\text{Arccos } x)$

64. $\sin(\text{Arctan } x)$

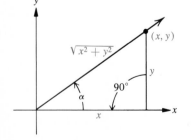

Figure 3.15

3.5 Right Triangles

When we use given information about the lengths of one, two, or three sides of a triangle and the measure of one or two angles to find the remaining, or unknown, lengths and measures, we are said to be *solving a triangle.* You may want to review some pertinent topics of geometry in Appendix A (Secs. A.7–A.9) before you begin this section.

Right triangles can be solved by using the trigonometric ratios of the acute angles of the triangle. Figure 3.15 shows that, in the first quadrant, any point (x, y) on the terminal side of an angle α in standard position determines a right triangle with sides of length x and y and with hypotenuse of length $\sqrt{x^2 + y^2}$. Therefore, in the special case where α is an acute angle in a right triangle,

$$\sin \alpha = \frac{\text{length of side opposite } \alpha}{\text{length of hypotenuse}}, \qquad \csc \alpha = \frac{\text{length of hypotenuse}}{\text{length of side opposite } \alpha},$$

$$\cos \alpha = \frac{\text{length of side adjacent to } \alpha}{\text{length of hypotenuse}}, \qquad \sec \alpha = \frac{\text{length of hypotenuse}}{\text{length of side adjacent to } \alpha},$$

$$\tan \alpha = \frac{\text{length of side opposite } \alpha}{\text{length of side adjacent to } \alpha}, \qquad \cot \alpha = \frac{\text{length of side adjacent to } \alpha}{\text{length of side opposite } \alpha}.$$

It is not necessary that α be in standard position. The above relations involving the ratios of the lengths of the sides of a right triangle are equally applicable to a right triangle in any position. For example, in Figure 3.16a, the six trigonometric ratios of the angle α are

$$\sin \alpha = \frac{a}{c}, \qquad \csc \alpha = \frac{c}{a},$$

$$\cos \alpha = \frac{b}{c}, \qquad \sec \alpha = \frac{c}{b},$$

$$\tan \alpha = \frac{a}{b}, \qquad \cot \alpha = \frac{b}{a}.$$

(a)

In Figure 3.16b, the trigonometric ratios of the angle β are

$$\sin \beta = \frac{b}{c}, \qquad \csc \beta = \frac{c}{b},$$

$$\cos \beta = \frac{a}{c}, \qquad \sec \beta = \frac{c}{a},$$

$$\tan \beta = \frac{b}{a}, \qquad \cot \beta = \frac{a}{b}.$$

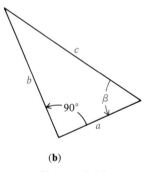

(b)

Figure 3.16

Generally, the sides of a triangle are labeled with their lengths, a, b, and c, and the angles opposite a, b, and c are labeled α, β, and γ, or A, B, and C, respectively, where γ or C names the right angle in a right triangle. The measures of angles in triangles are usually given in degree units.

Cofunctions

Two functions f and g are called **cofunctions** if

$$f(x) = g(y) \qquad \text{and} \qquad x + y = 90°.$$

In the trigonometric ratios above, observe that $\sin \alpha = \cos \beta$ and $\cos \alpha = \sin \beta$, where $\alpha + \beta = 90°$. Hence, the sine and cosine are cofunctions. Furthermore, for the same reason, the secant and cosecant are cofunctions, as are the tangent and cotangent. Note that these relationships are used in the construction of Table III. For example,

$$\tan 32° = 0.6249 \quad \text{and} \quad \cot(90° - 32°) = \cot 58° = 0.6249.$$

Solution of Triangles

Right triangles can be solved by using the trigonometric ratios on page 123 and the fact that *the sum of the measures of the angles of any triangle equals* 180°.

Example If one angle of a right triangle measures 34° and the side opposite this angle has a length of 12 inches, solve the triangle and find its area.

Solution Sketch the right triangle, showing the given information. First, from the fact that $\alpha + \beta + \gamma = 180°$ and $\gamma = 90°$,

$$\beta = 90° - \alpha = 90° - 34° = 56°.$$

By definition,

$$\cot 34° = \frac{b}{a} = \frac{b}{12} \qquad \text{or} \qquad b = 12 \cot 34°,$$

and

$$\csc 34° = \frac{c}{a} = \frac{c}{12} \qquad \text{or} \qquad c = 12 \csc 34°.$$

From Table III or by using a calculator, we have $\cot 34° \approx 1.4826$ and $\csc 34° \approx 1.7883$. Thus,

$$b \approx 12(1.4826) \approx 17.8,$$

$$c \approx 12(1.7883) \approx 21.5.^*$$

---

* In order that the results obtained using a calculator are consistent with the results using the tables, all function values obtained on a calculator are rounded off to four decimal places before any operations are performed.

The area $\mathcal{A}$ of a triangle equals one-half the product of the length of the altitude and the length of the base. Thus,

$$\mathcal{A} \approx \frac{1}{2}(12)(17.8) \approx 107.$$

Note that the ratio selected in each case in the above example for cot 34° and csc 34° was one in which the desired length, b or c, appeared in the numerator of the ratio. With these choices, b and c were found by multiplication. If the ratios

$$\tan 34° = \frac{12}{b} \quad \text{and} \quad \sin 34° = \frac{12}{c}$$

had been used, then, equivalently,

$$b = \frac{12}{\tan 34°} \quad \text{and} \quad c = \frac{12}{\sin 34°},$$

and the operation of division would have to be performed to find b and c. If a calculator is used, there would be no advantage in using a ratio that leads to a multiplication operation over a ratio that leads to a division operation.

In the foregoing example the lengths b and c and the area $\mathcal{A}$ were expressed by an approximation using *three significant digits.** Unless otherwise stated, we shall continue to specify lengths of line segments and areas of triangles to this degree of accuracy when solutions are given in decimal notation, and we shall specify measures of angles to the *nearest tenth of a degree or nearest six minutes.* Furthermore, we shall assume that all data have similar accuracy. Thus, $a = 12$ implies that $a = 12.0$ and $\alpha = 34°$ implies that $\alpha = 34.0° = 34° 00'$.

Certain angles are given special names in the fields of surveying and navigation. For example, the angle formed by a horizontal ray and an observer's "line of sight" to any object above the horizontal is called an **angle of elevation** (Figure 3.17a). The angle formed by a horizontal ray and an observer's "line of sight" to any object below the horizontal is called an **angle of depression** (Figure 3.17b)

(a)

(b)

Figure 3.17

Example On level ground at point A the measure of the angle of elevation of the top of a tower is 57° 24'. The distance from A to the base of the tower is 50 meters. How high is the tower?

(continued)

* Significant digits are the digits required for specifying n when a number is written in scientific notation as $n \cdot 10^k$, $k \in J$; $1 \leq n < 10$. For example, since $0.030552 = 3.0552 \times 10^{-2}$, an approximation for 0.030552 to *three* significant digits is 0.0306, where the third significant digit was arbitrarily changed from 5 to 6 because the following digit was 5.

Solution By definition,

$$\tan 57° 24' = \frac{h}{50},$$

where h represents the height of the tower. Equivalently,

$$h = 50 \tan 57° 24' = 50 \tan 57.4°$$
$$\approx 50(1.5637) \approx 78.2.$$

Thus, the height of the tower is approximately 78.2 meters.

EXERCISE SET 3.5

A

Express each of the following in terms of a function value of an angle between 0° and 45°.

Examples

a. sin 83.6°

b. sec 63° 24′

Solutions

a. $\sin 83.6° = \cos(90° - 83.6°)$
    $= \cos 6.4°$

b. $\sec 63° 24' = \csc(90° - 63° 24')$
    $= \csc 26° 36'$

1. $\cos 62°$ **2.** $\sec 51°$ **3.** $\tan 79.3°$

4. $\sin 59.6°$ **5.** $\csc 88° 12'$ **6.** $\cot 48° 48'$

Solve each right triangle. In each case, $\gamma = 90°$.

7. $a = 2$ and $b = 3$ **8.** $c = 41$ and $b = 9$

9. $c = 17$ and $a = 15$ **10.** $c = 14$ and $\alpha = 17°$

11. $c = 23.5$ and $\beta = 51°$ **12.** $a = 6.1$ and $\alpha = 73°$

13. $a = 11$ and $\beta = 22° 12'$ **14.** $b = 5$ and $\alpha = 64° 42'$

15. $b = 15$ and $\alpha = 50° 18'$ **16.** $c = 20$ and $\beta = 27° 30'$

17. $b = 30$ and $\beta = 41° 36'$ **18.** $a = 32$ and $\beta = 75° 6'$

Find the area of the indicated triangle.

19. The triangle in Exercise 9.   **20.** The triangle in Exercise 10.

21. The triangle in Exercise 13.   **22.** The triangle in Exercise 14.

Ex. 31

Ex. 32

Ex. 33

Ex. 34

Ex. 35

23. The measure of an angle of elevation from a surveyor's position (ignoring the surveyor's height) to the top of a hill is 37° 24′. The top of the hill is 275 meters above a level line through the surveyor's position. How far is the surveyor from a point directly below the top of the hill?

24. From the top of a vertical cliff, 80 meters above the surface of the ocean, the measure of the angle of depression to a marker on the surface of the ocean is 18° 12′. How far is the marker from the foot of the cliff?

25. A 40-foot ladder is used to reach the top of a 24-foot wall. If the ladder extends 10 feet past the top of the wall, find the measure of the angle that the ladder forms with the horizontal ground.

26. The lengths of the sides of an isosceles triangle are 17, 17, and 30 centimeters. Find the measures of the angles in the triangle. *Hint:* Use the altitude of the triangle.

27. A ladder 30 decimeters long is leaning against the side of a building. If the ladder makes an angle of 25° 18′ with the side of the building, how far up from the ground does the ladder touch the building?

28. A tower 120 feet high casts a shadow 60 feet long. Find the angle of elevation of the sun.

29. A railroad track makes an angle of 4° 48′ with the horizontal. How far must a train go up the track to gain 20 meters in altitude?

30. A rectangle is 20 centimeters long and 14 centimeters wide. Find the angles that a diagonal makes with the sides.

31. A parachutist is descending vertically. How far does the parachutist fall as the angle of elevation from A changes from 50° to 20°?

32. A surveyor measures AC as 35.3 meters and α as 57.2°. How wide is the river?

33. An observer at P notes that the angle of elevation to the top of a mountain is 16.5°. If the mountain is 3500 feet high, how far is P from the top of the mountain?

34. In the figure, the angle of depression from the top of one tower to the top of the other is 20°. If the height of the taller tower is 150 feet, how high is the shorter?

B

35. A regular pentagon is inscribed in a circle of radius 5 centimeters. Find the length of a side of the pentagon.

Ex. 36

36. The angle of elevation of the top of the tower is 62.3° from A and 37.1° from B. If AB is 60 feet, find the height of the tower.

37. If $\alpha = 30°$, $\beta = 60°$, and $BC = 2$, find AD.

38. Show that (see drawing for Exercise 37)

$$\cos \beta = \frac{BC \cot x}{AD}$$

Exs. 37, 38

39. Prove that when a simple pendulum of length l is inclined at an angle α with the vertical, the bob is at a height h above its lowest position, where $h = l(1 - \cos \alpha)$.

40. Show that the length h of the perpendicular from C to the side c of any triangle ABC can be found by

$$h = \frac{c}{\cot \alpha + \cot \beta}.$$

Hint: $AD = h \cot \alpha$.

Ex. 39

3.6 The Law of Sines

In Section 3.5 we solved right triangles using trigonometric ratios expressed in terms of the lengths of the sides of the triangle. In this section and in the next, special formulas will be derived to enable us to solve any triangle, right, acute, or obtuse.

Consider $\triangle ABC$ in Figure 3.18 (β may be either acute or obtuse), and introduce the altitude $\overline{CD}$. Thus, $\triangle ADC$ and $\triangle BDC$ are right triangles. In either figure, in $\triangle ADC$,

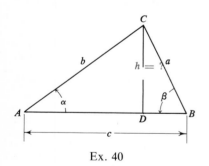

Ex. 40

$$\sin \alpha = \frac{h}{b}, \quad \text{from which} \quad h = b \sin \alpha.$$

In $\triangle BDC$ in Figure 3.18a,

$$\sin \beta = \frac{h}{a}, \quad \text{from which} \quad h = a \sin \beta.$$

In $\triangle BDC$ in Figure 3.18b, $\angle CBD$ is equal to the reference angle for β; therefore,

$$\sin \beta = \sin \angle CBD = \frac{h}{a},$$

$$h = a \sin \beta.$$

(a)

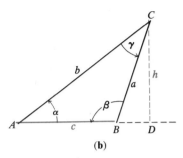

(b)

Figure 3.18

Hence, we have in each case

$$h = b \sin \alpha = a \sin \beta.$$

Dividing each member of $b \sin \alpha = a \sin \beta$ by ab, we have

$$\frac{\sin \alpha}{a} = \frac{\sin \beta}{b}. \qquad (1)$$

If in Figure 3.18 we use the altitude from vertex A and a similar argument, we will have

$$\frac{\sin \beta}{b} = \frac{\sin \gamma}{c}. \qquad (2)$$

Comparing Equations (1) and (2), we observe that we have proved the following theorem.

Theorem 3.5 *If α, β, and γ are the angles of any triangle, and if a, b, and c are the lengths of the sides opposite α, β, and γ, respectively, then*

$$\frac{\sin \alpha}{a} = \frac{\sin \beta}{b} = \frac{\sin \gamma}{c}.$$

In many applications this relationship, called the **Law of Sines,** is conveniently used in the form

$$\frac{a}{\sin \alpha} = \frac{b}{\sin \beta} = \frac{c}{\sin \gamma}.$$

Two Angles and a Side

The Law of Sines can be used to solve triangles when several kinds of data are given. We consider first the case in which the measures of two angles and the length of one side of a triangle are given.

Example   Solve the triangle for which $\alpha = 30°$, $\beta = 45°$, and $a = 20$.

Solution   A sketch of the triangle showing the given information is helpful. First, from the fact that $\alpha + \beta + \gamma = 180°$, it follows that

$$\gamma = 180° - \alpha - \beta$$

$$= 180° - 30° - 45° = 105°.$$

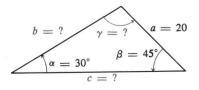

(continued)

From the Law of Sines,

$$\frac{20}{\sin 30°} = \frac{b}{\sin 45°},$$

or, equivalently,

$$b = \frac{20 \sin 45°}{\sin 30°} \approx \frac{20(0.7071)}{0.5000} \approx 28.3.$$

Then, again from the Law of Sines,

$$\frac{20}{\sin 30°} = \frac{c}{\sin 105°},$$

or, equivalently,

$$c = \frac{20 \sin 105°}{\sin 30°} = \frac{20 \sin 75°}{\sin 30°} \approx \frac{20(0.9659)}{0.5000}$$

$$\approx 38.6.$$

Hence,

$$b \approx 28.3, \quad c \approx 38.6, \quad \text{and} \quad \gamma = 105°.$$

Two Sides and an Opposite Angle

A second case in which the Law of Sines is used is one in which the lengths of two sides of a triangle, say a and b, and the measure of an angle opposite one of them, say, α, are given. Ambiguity may arise here, depending on a in relation to b and the measure of α. Figure 3.19, in which α is an *acute angle* and h is the length of a perpendicular segment, illustrates the following possibilities that may occur.

1. If $a < h$, the side with length a cannot intersect the side opposite C and no triangle is possible, as shown in Figure 3.19a. In this case, since $h = b \sin \alpha$, we have $a < b \sin \alpha$.
2. If $a = h = b \sin \alpha$, the side with length a intersects the side opposite C at D. In this case exactly one right triangle is possible, as shown in Figure 3.19b.
3. If $a > h$ (or $b \sin \alpha$) and $a < b$, or $b \sin \alpha < a < b$, two triangles are possible, as shown in Figure 3.19c.
4. If $a \geq b$, the triangle $AB'C$, shown in Figure 3.19d, does not contain the given angle α and therefore does not lead to a solution. Hence, in this case, only one triangle is possible. In particular, if $a = b$, the triangle is isosceles.

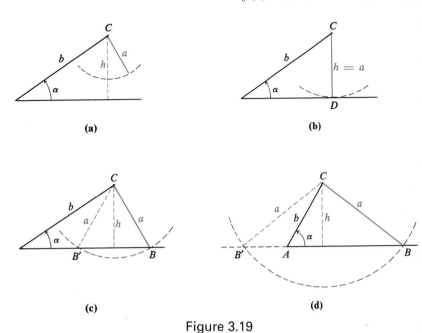

(a)   (b)

(c)   (d)

Figure 3.19

(a)

(b)

Figure 3.20

Figure 3.20, in which α is an *obtuse angle,* illustrates the following two possibilities.

1. If $a > b$, then one triangle is possible, as shown in Figure 3.20a.
2. If $a \leq b$, then no triangle is possible as shown in Figure 3.20b.

While we have concerned ourselves only with the variables a, b, and α in the above discussion, similar results are valid when other variables are involved in the given information. A sketch of the triangle using the given information will help to indicate the possibilities that exist. In particular, sketches of triangles like those shown in Figures 3.19 and 3.20, in which the given angle is drawn on the left, are usually the most helpful in deciding which possibility exists for given data.

Example   Solve the triangle(s) for which $a = 7$, $b = 5$, and $\beta = 30°$.

Solution   Sketch the triangle(s) using the given information. Since the lengths of two sides and the measure of an angle β, opposite the side with measure b, are given, a check must be made to see how many triangles are possible. Since

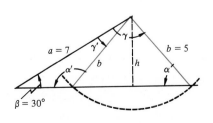

$$h = a \sin \beta = 7 \sin 30°$$

$$= 7(0.5000) = 3.5,$$

(continued)

it follows that $h < b < a$ and that two triangles are possible, as indicated in the figure. From the Law of Sines,

$$\frac{\sin \alpha}{7} = \frac{\sin 30°}{5}$$

$$\sin \alpha = \frac{7 \sin 30°}{5} = \frac{7(0.5000)}{5} = 0.7000.$$

Since $\sin \alpha > 0$ in Quadrants I and II, to the nearest tenth,

$$\alpha \approx 44.4° \quad \text{or} \quad \alpha' \approx 180° - 44.4° = 135.6°.$$

For $\alpha \approx 44.4°$, the solution of one of the two possible triangles is completed as follows. Since the sum of the measures of the angles of a triangle equals 180°,

$$\gamma = 180° - \alpha - \beta$$
$$\approx 180° - 44.4° - 30° = 105.6°.$$

From the Law of Sines and the fact that $\sin 105.6° = \sin 74.4°$,

$$\frac{5}{\sin 30°} = \frac{c}{\sin 105.6°};$$

$$c = \frac{5 \sin 74.4°}{\sin 30°} \approx \frac{5(0.9632)}{0.5000} \approx 9.63.$$

For $\alpha' \approx 135.6°$, the solution of the second possible triangle can be completed. Since

$$\gamma' \approx 180° - 135.6° - 30° = 14.4°,$$

then by the Law of Sines

$$\frac{5}{\sin 30°} = \frac{c'}{\sin 14.4°};$$

$$c' \approx \frac{5(0.2487)}{0.5000} \approx 2.49.$$

Thus, the two solutions are

$$\alpha \approx 44.4°, \quad \gamma \approx 105.6°, \quad \text{and} \quad c \approx 9.63;$$
$$\alpha' \approx 135.6°, \quad \gamma' \approx 14.4°, \quad \text{and} \quad c' \approx 2.49.$$

EXERCISE SET 3.6

A

Solve each triangle.

   1. $a = 5$, $\alpha = 20°$, and $\beta = 75°$

   2. $a = 32$, $\alpha = 26.3°$, and $\gamma = 81.8°$

   3. $a = 58.4$, $\beta = 37.2°$, and $\gamma = 100°$

   4. $b = 1.9$, $\alpha = 111.7°$, and $\beta = 5.1°$

   5. $b = 0.42$, $\alpha = 35° \, 36'$, and $\gamma = 91° \, 30'$

   6. $b = 0.88$, $\beta = 63° \, 54'$, and $\gamma = 34° \, 12'$

   7. $c = 13.6$, $\alpha = 30° \, 24'$, and $\beta = 72° \, 6'$

   8. $c = 1.4$, $\alpha = 135° \, 12'$, and $\gamma = 34° \, 48'$

Determine the number of triangles that satisfy each set of conditions and solve each triangle.

   9. $a = 7$, $b = 5$, and $\alpha = 30°$

   10. $a = 10$, $b = 9$, and $\beta = 60°$

   11. $a = 4.2$, $c = 6.1$, and $\alpha = 32.2°$

   12. $a = 38$, $c = 45$, and $\gamma = 35.6°$

   13. $b = 16$, $c = 32$, and $\beta = 30°$

   14. $b = 0.3$, $c = 0.4$, and $\gamma = 62°$

   15. $b = 3.9$, $a = 5$, and $\beta = 42° \, 42'$

   16. $b = 37$, $a = 51$, and $\alpha = 135° \, 30'$

Find the area of each triangle.

   17. $a = 3.4$, $\beta = 13°$, and $\alpha = 50°$

   18. $c = 3.8$, $\beta = 15° \, 6'$, and $\gamma = 50°$

Ex. 19

   19. To find the distance from an observer's point A on one side of a river (see figure) to a point P on the other side, a line AP' measuring 2540 feet was laid out on one side and the angles $P'AP$ and $AP'P$ were measured and found to be $47° \, 18'$ and $78° \, 6'$, respectively. Find the distance from A to P to the nearest foot.

Ex. 23

Ex. 24

Ex. 25

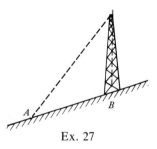

Ex. 26

20. Two men, 400 feet apart, observe a balloon between them that is in a vertical plane with them. The respective angles of elevation of the balloon are observed by the men to be 75° 24′ and 49° 30′. Find the height of the balloon above the ground.

21. One diagonal of a parallelogram is 20 centimeters long and at one end forms angles of 20° and 40° with the sides of the parallelogram. Find the lengths of the sides.

22. A ship at sea is sighted from two points, A and B, on the shore. A and B are 5 kilometers apart, and the line of sight from A to the ship forms an angle of 30° 18′ with $\overline{AB}$, while the line of sight from B to the ship forms an angle of 41° 12′ with $\overline{AB}$. How far is the ship from point A?

23. A tower is built vertically on a hillside that slants upward 10° from the horizontal. From a point 200 meters uphill from the foot of the tower, the angle of elevation of the top of the tower is 12° 30′ (see figure). How high is the tower?

24. From a window 75 meters above the ground, the measure of the angle of elevation to the top of a nearby building is 29° 42′ (see figure). From a point on the ground directly below the window, the measure of the angle of elevation of the top of the same building is 52° 24′. Find the height of the building.

25. The angle of elevation of the building is 48° from A, and 61° from B. If AB is 20 feet, find the height of the building.

26. The pole is tilted toward the sun at an angle of 8° from the vertical. When the angle of elevation of the sun is 54°, the shadow of the pole is 12 feet long. How long is the pole?

27. A hill makes an angle of 10° with the horizontal. From a point 50 meters downhill from a vertical tower, the angle of elevation of the tower is 56°. Find the height of the tower.

28. From two points on shore, the angles α and β to a light at C are 16.4° and 58.6°, respectively. If AB is 1500 feet, find the distance, d, of the light from the shore.

B

29. Using the figure, show that

$$c = \frac{a \sin \beta \tan \gamma}{\sin(\alpha + \beta)}$$

Ex. 27

Ex. 28

Ex. 29

30. Using the figure for Exercise 29, if $\alpha = 40°$, $\beta = 60°$, $\gamma = 30°$, and $a = 100$ feet, find c.

Show that, in any triangle ABC, each of the following statements is true. Hint: In Exercises 31 and 32 start with the Law of Sines.

31. $\dfrac{a + b}{b} = \dfrac{\sin \alpha + \sin \beta}{\sin \beta}$ **32.** $\dfrac{a - b}{b} = \dfrac{\sin \alpha - \sin \beta}{\sin \beta}$

33. $\dfrac{a - b}{a + b} = \dfrac{\sin \alpha - \sin \beta}{\sin \alpha + \sin \beta}$

34. $\dfrac{a + b + c}{b} = \dfrac{\sin \alpha + \sin \beta + \sin \gamma}{\sin \beta}$

3.7 The Law of Cosines

The Law of Sines considered in Section 3.6 cannot be used directly to solve triangles in which the lengths of two sides and the measure of the angle formed by their respective rays are specified or in which only the lengths of the three sides are specified.

Consider a triangle ABC in which the lengths a and b and the measure of angle γ are known. Orienting triangle ABC with γ at the origin, as shown in Figure 3.21, we find that

$$\cos \gamma = \frac{x}{b} \quad \text{and} \quad \sin \gamma = \frac{y}{b},$$

from which the coordinates of A are

$$x = b \cos \gamma \quad \text{and} \quad y = b \sin \gamma.$$

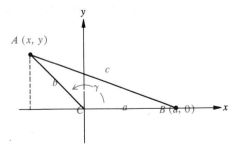

Figure 3.21

From the distance formula (see Appendix A.4),

$$c^2 = (y - 0)^2 + (x - a)^2$$
$$= (b \sin \gamma - 0)^2 + (b \cos \gamma - a)^2$$
$$= b^2 \sin^2 \gamma + b^2 \cos^2 \gamma - 2ab \cos \gamma + a^2$$
$$= b^2(\sin^2 \gamma + \cos^2 \gamma) - 2ab \cos \gamma + a^2.$$

Since $\sin^2 \gamma + \cos^2 \gamma = 1$, we have

$$c^2 = a^2 + b^2 - 2ab \cos \gamma.$$

The discussion above is a proof of one of the parts of the following theorem, known as the Law of Cosines. By placing vertex A or vertex B at the origin, the proofs of the other parts can be completed in a similar way.

Theorem 3.6 *If α, β, and γ are the angles of any triangle, and a, b, and c are the lengths of the sides opposite α, β, and γ, respectively, then*

$$c^2 = a^2 + b^2 - 2ab \cos \gamma,$$
$$b^2 = a^2 + c^2 - 2ac \cos \beta,$$
$$a^2 = b^2 + c^2 - 2bc \cos \alpha.$$

Notice that if $\gamma = 90°$, then $\cos \gamma = \cos 90° = 0$ and the Law of Cosines reduces to

$$c^2 = a^2 + b^2 - 2ab(0),$$
$$c^2 = a^2 + b^2,$$

the familiar formula applicable to right triangles (the Pythagorean theorem).

Two Sides and the Included Angle

Now consider how the Law of Cosines can be used to solve a triangle when the measure of an angle and the lengths of the adjacent sides are known.

Example Given the measures $\beta = 75°$, $a = 7$, and $c = 5$ of an oblique triangle, find the length b.

Solution   Sketch a triangle showing the given information. The length *b* can be obtained by using the Law of Cosines expressed in the form $b^2 = a^2 + c^2 - 2ac \cos \beta$. Substituting the known values gives

$$b^2 = 7^2 + 5^2 - 2(7)(5) \cos 75°$$

$$\approx 49 + 25 - 70(0.2588) \approx 55.9;$$

$$b \approx \sqrt{55.9}.$$

Using a calculator,

$$b \approx \sqrt{55.9} \approx 7.48.$$

Alternatively, from Table I, Appendix C, we have $\sqrt{55} \approx 7.416$ and $\sqrt{56} \approx 7.483$. The difference $7.483 - 7.416 = 0.067$. Hence, using linear interpolation,

$$b \approx 7.416 + 0.9(0.067) \approx 7.48.$$

Three Sides

The Law of Sines could be used to complete the solution of the triangle in the above example since the length *b*, opposite the given angle β, is known. However, we shall use the Law of Cosines in the following example in order to show how it can be used to determine the measure of an angle if the lengths of three sides of a triangle are known.

Example   To find the measure of α in the foregoing example,

$$a^2 = b^2 + c^2 - 2bc \cos \alpha$$

is first written in the form

$$\cos \alpha = \frac{b^2 + c^2 - a^2}{2bc}.$$

From the previous calculations, $b^2 \approx 55.9$ and $b \approx 7.48$. Thus,

$$\cos \alpha \approx \frac{55.9 + 25 - 49}{2(7.48)(5)} \approx 0.4265.$$

Because α, an angle in a triangle, must have a measure less than 180°, and $\cos \alpha > 0$, then

$$\alpha \approx 64.8°.$$

(*continued*)

Because $\alpha + \beta + \gamma = 180°$,

$$\gamma \approx 180° - 64.8° - 75° = 40.2°.$$

Thus, the solution to the triangle is

$$b \approx 7.48, \quad \alpha \approx 64.8°, \quad \text{and} \quad \gamma \approx 40.2°.$$

If, after first finding the length of the third side, $b \approx 7.48$ in the above example, the Law of Sines is used to find the measure of a second angle, the angle selected should be the smaller of the two remaining angles (the one opposite the shorter of the two given sides) and hence *an acute angle*. Thus, if the Law of Sines had been used to find the second angle in the above example, we would have found $\sin \gamma$ rather than $\sin \alpha$ because, of the two given sides, $c < a$ and γ is opposite c.

EXERCISE SET 3.7

A

Solve each triangle.

1. $b = 4$, $c = 3.5$, and $\alpha = 71°$

2. $c = 0.3$, $a = 0.1$, and $\beta = 70°$

3. $a = 3.2$, $b = 2.2$, and $\gamma = 75.3°$

4. $b = 6.0$, $a = 5.1$, and $\gamma = 83.5°$

5. $a = 0.7$, $c = 0.8$, and $\beta = 141° \ 30'$

6. $b = 3.4$, $a = 2.1$, and $\gamma = 122° \ 12'$

7. $b = 1.6$, $c = 3.2$, and $\alpha = 100° \ 24'$

8. $c = 2.1$, $b = 4.3$, and $\alpha = 130° \ 36'$

Solve the triangles for which the lengths of the three sides are given.

Example $a = 3.4$, $b = 2.7$, and $c = 1.3$

Solution   Draw a sketch showing the given information. From the Law of Cosines,

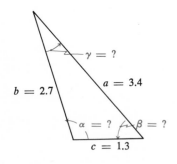

$$\cos \alpha = \frac{b^2 + c^2 - a^2}{2bc} = \frac{(2.7)^2 + (1.3)^2 - (3.4)^2}{2(2.7)(1.3)}$$

$$\approx -0.3675.$$

Hence, $\tilde{\alpha} \approx 68.4°$. Then, because $\cos \alpha < 0$, α is an angle such that $90° < \alpha < 180°$. Thus,

$$\alpha \approx 180° - 68.4° = 111.6°.$$

From the Law of Sines,

$$\frac{\sin \alpha}{a} = \frac{\sin \beta}{b},$$

$$\frac{\sin 111.6°}{3.4} = \frac{\sin \beta}{2.7},$$

from which

$$\sin \beta = \frac{2.7(\sin 111.6°)}{3.4} \approx \frac{2.7(0.9298)}{3.4} \approx 0.7384.$$

Thus,

$$\beta \approx 47.6°.$$

From the fact that $\gamma = 180° - \alpha - \beta,$

$$\gamma \approx 180° - 111.6° - 47.6°$$

$$\approx 20.8°.$$

9. $a = 9$, $b = 7$, and $c = 5$ **10.** $a = 2.7$, $b = 5.1$, and $c = 4.4$

11. $a = 1.2$, $b = 9$, and $c = 10$ **12.** $a = 4.5$, $b = 7.5$, and $c = 5.8$

13. $a = 6$, $b = 8$, and $c = 12$ **14.** $a = 6$, $b = 12$, and $c = 13$

15. $a = 4$, $b = 5$, and $c = 6$ **16.** $a = 5$, $b = 7$, and $c = 8$

17. Find the measure of the smallest angle of the triangle whose sides have lengths 4.3, 5.1, and 6.3.

18. Find the measure of the smallest angle of the triangle whose sides have lengths 3.0, 4.2, and 3.8.

19. Find the measure of the largest angle of the triangle whose sides have lengths 2.9, 3.3, and 4.1.

20. Find the measure of the largest angle of the triangle whose sides have lengths 6.0, 8.2, and 9.4.

21. Find the area of the triangle in Exercise 17.

Ex. 27

Ex. 28

Ex. 29

Ex. 30

22. Find the area of the triangle in Exercise 18.

23. A ship is supposed to travel directly from port A to port B, a distance of 10 kilometers. After traveling a distance of 5 kilometers, the captain discovers he has been traveling 15° off course. At this point, how far is the ship from port B?

24. Two ships leave the same port on courses that form an angle of 37° 12′. When one ship has traveled 12 kilometers, the other has traveled 18 kilometers. How far apart are the ships at that time?

25. Two sides of a parallelogram that is 6 centimeters by 8 centimeters include an angle of 67°. Find the length of the longer diagonal.

26. A tower 40 meters high is on top of a hill. A cable 50 meters long runs from the top of the tower to a point 20 meters down the hill. Find the angle the hillside forms with a horizontal line.

27. A crane at the edge of a dock is supported by a cable 11 meters long, attached to the dock 7 meters from the base of the crane (see figure). If the crane arm is 5 meters long, find the acute angle that the crane arm forms with the horizontal.

28. Three circles with radii 1, 3, and 4 centimeters are tangent to each other (see figure). To the nearest 6′, find the three angles formed by the lines joining their centers.

29. Points P and Q are on opposite ends of a lake. If point R is 1200 feet from P and 1600 feet from Q, and the angle at R is 50°, how long is the lake?

30. A vertical tower 30 feet high is on a hill that forms an angle of 15° with the horizontal. How long is a guy wire that runs from the top of the tower to a point 20 feet downhill from the base of the tower?

31. Two airplanes leave a field at the same time. One flies with a bearing of 30° at 250 kilometers per hour; the other with a bearing of 135° at 300 kilometers per hour. How far apart are they at the end of 2 hours?

32. A pilot is flying from Salt Lake City to Denver, a distance of about 500 miles. When she is 300 miles from Salt Lake City, she discovers she has been flying 16° off course. How far is she from Denver at that time?

B

The formulas in Exercises 33–36 where $s = \frac{1}{2}(a + b + c)$, are sometimes used in the solution of triangles. Show that each statement is true for all $\alpha \in A$.   *Hint: Use the fact that* $\cos \alpha = \dfrac{b^2 + c^2 - a^2}{2bc}$.

Ex. 31

Ex. 40

Ex. 41

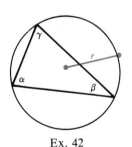

Ex. 42

33. $1 + \cos \alpha = \dfrac{(b + c + a)(b + c - a)}{2bc}$

34. $1 - \cos \alpha = \dfrac{(a - b + c)(a + b - c)}{2bc}$

35. $\dfrac{1 + \cos \alpha}{2} = \dfrac{s(s - a)}{bc}.$

36. $\dfrac{1 - \cos \alpha}{2} = \dfrac{(s - b)(s - c)}{bc}.$

37. Use the results of Exercises 35 and 36 to prove Hero's (or Heron's) formula, $\mathscr{A} = \sqrt{s(s - a)(s - b)(s - c)}$, which can be used to find the area of any triangle directly from the lengths of its three sides.

38. Use Hero's formula to find the area of the triangle in Exercise 9 above.

39. use Hero's formula to find the area of the triangle in Exercise 11 above.

40. Two sides of a parallelogram are of lengths 6.8 and 8.3 inches, and one of the diagonals is of length 4.2 inches (see figure). Find the area of the parallelogram.

41. Show that the radius r of an inscribed circle of a triangle (see figure) is given by

$$r = \sqrt{\dfrac{(s - a)(s - b)(s - c)}{s}}$$

where $s = \frac{1}{2}(a + b + c)$.

42. Show that the radius r of a circumscribed circle of a triangle (see figure) is given by

$$r = \dfrac{a}{2 \sin \alpha} = \dfrac{b}{2 \sin \beta} = \dfrac{c}{2 \sin \gamma}.$$

Chapter Summary

3.1   An angle that has its initial side along the positive x-axis and its vertex at the origin is said to be in **standard position.** Such an angle is said to be in that quadrant in which its terminal side lies.

Two kinds of angle measure most commonly used are **degree measure** and **radian measure.**

The measure of an angle in radians is related to the measure of the angle in degrees by the equation

$$\frac{m°(\alpha)}{360} = \frac{m^R(\alpha)}{2\pi}$$

or by the equations

$$m°(\alpha) = \frac{180}{\pi} m^R(\alpha) \qquad \text{and} \qquad m^R(\alpha) = \frac{\pi}{180} m°(\alpha).$$

Angles having the same initial side and the same terminal side are called **coterminal angles.**

3.2 The arc length s of an arc of a circle of radius of length r intercepted by an angle α whose vertex is at the center of the circle is given by

$$s = r \cdot m^R(\alpha).$$

The **linear velocity** v of a point moving along a circle at a constant speed is given by

$$v = \frac{s}{t} = \frac{r \cdot m^R(\alpha)}{t},$$

where t is the time required to move a distance $s = r \cdot m^R(\alpha)$. The **angular velocity** ω of the moving point is given by

$$\omega = \frac{m^R(\alpha)}{t},$$

where ω is given in radians per unit time.

The linear velocity v and the angular velocity ω in reference to the same circle of radius with length r are related by the equation

$$v = r \cdot \omega,$$

where ω is given in radians per unit time.

3.3 If α is an angle in standard position, x and y (not both 0) are the coordinates of any point on the terminal side of α, and $r = \sqrt{x^2 + y^2}$, then

$$\text{cosine } \alpha = \frac{x}{r}, \qquad\qquad\qquad \text{secant } \alpha = \frac{r}{x} \ (x \neq 0),$$

$$\text{sine } \alpha = \frac{y}{r}, \qquad\qquad\qquad \text{cosecant } \alpha = \frac{r}{y} \ (y \neq 0),$$

$$\text{tangent } \alpha = \frac{y}{x} \ (x \neq 0), \qquad \text{cotangent } \alpha = \frac{x}{y} \ (y \neq 0).$$

These six ratios, called **trigonometric ratios,** are determined only by the position of the terminal side of an angle in standard position and not by the point selected on the terminal side. Each of these ratios determines a **trigonometric function** of the same name.

3.4 The elements in the ranges of the trigonometric functions are equal to the corresponding elements in the ranges of the analogous circular functions. That is,

$$\text{Circ}(s) = \text{Trig}(\alpha°) = \text{Trig}(\alpha^R),$$

where a central angle α intercepts an arc with length s on a unit circle.

Many properties of circular functions are, with appropriate rewording, also valid for trigonometric functions.

Inverse trigonometric functions are defined in a manner similar to the definitions for the inverse circular fnctions.

3.5 The six trigonometrc function values of an acute angle of a right triangle can be expressed as ratios of the sides of the triangle.

$$\sin \alpha = \frac{a}{c}, \qquad \csc \alpha = \frac{c}{a},$$

$$\cos \alpha = \frac{b}{c}, \qquad \sec \alpha = \frac{c}{b},$$

$$\tan \alpha = \frac{a}{b}, \qquad \cot \alpha = \frac{b}{a}.$$

3.6 The **Law of Sines:**

If α, β, and γ are the angles of any triangle, and if a, b, and c are the lengths of the sides opposite α, β, and γ, respectively, then

$$\frac{\sin \alpha}{a} = \frac{\sin \beta}{b} = \frac{\sin \gamma}{c}.$$

This law is used if the measures of two angles and the length of any side, or if the lengths of two sides and the measure of an angle opposite one of these sides, are given. In the latter case, certain ambiguities may arise. Two, one, or no triangles may exist.

3.7 The **Law of Cosines:**

If α, β, and γ are the angles of any triangle, and a, b, and c are the lengths of the sides opposite α, β, and γ, respectively, then

$$c^2 = a^2 + b^2 - 2ab \cos \gamma,$$

$$b^2 = a^2 + c^2 - 2ac \cos \beta,$$

$$a^2 = b^2 + c^2 - 2bc \cos \alpha.$$

This law is used if the lengths of two sides and the measure of the included angle, or if the lengths of three sides, are given.

A list of symbols introduced in this chapter is shown on the inside front covers and important properties are shown on the inside back covers.

Review Exercises

3.1 *Find the degree measure of α to the nearest tenth of a degree.*

1. $\alpha = \dfrac{2\pi^{R}}{5}$

2. $\alpha = 2.41^{R}$

Find the radian measure of α to the nearest hundredth of a radian.

3. $\alpha = 75°$

4. $\alpha = 257°$

Find the least positive angle coterminal with each angle α.

5. $\alpha = 938°$

6. $\alpha = 7.23^{R}$

Write a general expression for all angles coterminal with α.

7. $\alpha = 131°$

8. $\alpha = \dfrac{7\pi^{R}}{4}$

3.2   **9.** Find the length of the arc intercepted on a circle by a central angle α with measure 2.2^{R} if the radius of the circle is 1.3 meters in length.

10. Find the measure of the central angle that intercepts an arc with length 60.2 centimeters on a circle whose radius is 3.1 meters in length.

11. Find the linear velocity v of a point on a circle moving with constant speed if $r = 2$ decimeters and $\omega = 6$ radians per minute.

12. Find the angular velocity ω of a point on a circle moving with constant speed if $r = 0.5$ meter and $v = 19.7$ centimeters per second.

3.3 *Find the value of each of the six trigonometric functons of α, if the terminal side of α (in standard position) contains the point corresponding to the given ordered pair.*

13. (4, 3)   **14.** (5, 12)

15. $(-2\sqrt{3}, 2)$ **16.** $(-2, 5)$

Determine the quadrant in which each angle α lies.

17. $\sin \alpha < 0$ and $\cos \alpha > 0$ **18.** $\cos \alpha > 0$ and $\tan \alpha < 0$

19. $\tan \alpha > 0$ and $\sec \alpha < 0$ **20.** $\csc \alpha < 0$ and $\cot \alpha < 0$

3.4 *Find each of the following (exact value).*

21. $\sin 405°$ **22.** $\cot 1110°$ **23.** $\tan 5\pi^R$

24. $\sin \dfrac{15\pi^R}{2}$ **25.** $\cos(-120°)$ **26.** $\csc\left(-\dfrac{7\pi^R}{4}\right)$

Find an approximation for each of the following. Use Table II or a calculator. Use a reference angle as necessary.

27. $\cos 0.61$ **28.** $\tan(-1.07)$

Find an approximation for each of the following. Use Table III or a calculator. Use a reference angle as necessary.

29. $\sin 4.9°$ **30.** $\sec 183.3°$

31. $\cot 480.9°$ **32.** $\csc(-74° \; 36')$

Find each measure of α in degrees.

33. $\text{Arcsin} \dfrac{1}{2}$ **34.** $\text{Arccos} \dfrac{1}{\sqrt{2}}$

35. $\text{Arctan } 2.3332$ **36.** $\text{Arccos}(-0.5344)$

3.5 *Solve each right triangle. In each case, $\gamma = 90°$.*

37. $c = 14, \beta = 51°$ **38.** $c = 6.7, a = 5.4$

39. $a = 12.9, \alpha = 32° \; 36'$ **40.** $b = 9.72, \alpha = 71° \; 18'$

3.6 *Solve each triangle.*

41. $c = 13.6, \alpha = 30.3°, \beta = 72.2°$

42. $c = 1.4, \alpha = 135° \; 6', \gamma = 34° \; 54'$

Determine the number of triangles that satisfy the conditions in each exercise and solve each triangle.

43. $b = 3.9$, $a = 5$, $\beta = 42.7°$ **44.** $b = 37$, $a = 51$, $\alpha = 135° \, 30'$

3.7 *Solve each triangle.*

45. $a = 1.9$, $b = 2.3$, $\gamma = 58° \, 12'$ **46.** $b = 2.3$, $c = 5.7$, $\alpha = 23.1°$

47. $a = 3.6$, $b = 4.2$, $c = 6.1$ **48.** $a = 2.1$, $b = 3.4$, $c = 4.1$

4 IDENTITIES AND CONDITIONAL EQUATIONS

Equations such as

$$a \cdot 1 = a, \quad a + b = b + a, \quad \text{and} \quad a(b + c) = ab + ac,$$

which are true for all real numbers a, b, and c, are called **identities;** *the left-hand member and the right-hand member of each equation are equivalent expressions.** In algebra, we have used such identities to simplify algebraic expressions whenever we substituted one expression for an equivalent expression.

In this chapter we will review some basic identities that involve trigonometric (or circular) function values that have been introduced in previous chapters and we will introduce additional ones that will be useful in our work. We will then use these identities to rewrite expressions that involve trigonometric function values as equivalent expressions.

In our work with identities we shall not explicitly specify the replacement set of the variable in each case. The variables α, β, γ, and θ will represent elements of the set of all angles, and the variables x and y will be considered as representing elements either of the set of all angles or of the set of real numbers. Furthermore, it should be understood that

an equation that is specified to be an identity without noting the restrictions is in fact an identity only for all replacements of the variables for which both members of the equation are defined.

* Also see Appendix A.3.

4.1 Basic Trigonometric Identities

The trigonometric identities

$$\csc \alpha = \frac{1}{\sin \alpha}, \quad \sec \alpha = \frac{1}{\cos \alpha}, \quad \cot \alpha = \frac{1}{\tan \alpha},$$

$$\tan \alpha = \frac{\sin \alpha}{\cos \alpha}, \quad \cot \alpha = \frac{\cos \alpha}{\sin \alpha}, \quad \text{and} \quad \sin^2 \alpha + \cos^2 \alpha = 1,$$

stated in Chapter 1, have been shown to be consequences of the definition of the trigonometric ratios.

Two other identities follow from the equation $\sin^2 \alpha + \cos^2 \alpha = 1$. For any α for which $\cos \alpha \neq 0$, we multiply each member by $1/\cos^2 \alpha$ to obtain the equivalent equations

$$\frac{\sin^2 \alpha}{\cos^2 \alpha} + \frac{\cos^2 \alpha}{\cos^2 \alpha} = \frac{1}{\cos^2 \alpha},$$

$$\tan^2 \alpha + 1 = \sec^2 \alpha.$$

Multiplying each member of $\sin^2 \alpha + \cos^2 \alpha = 1$ by $1/\sin^2 \alpha$ for $\sin \alpha \neq 0$, we obtain

$$\frac{\sin^2 \alpha}{\sin^2 \alpha} + \frac{\cos^2 \alpha}{\sin^2 \alpha} = \frac{1}{\sin^2 \alpha},$$

$$1 + \cot^2 \alpha = \csc^2 \alpha.$$

The basic identities that we have stated above should be recognized in equivalent forms. For example, using the symbol $\leftrightarrow$ to mean "is equivalent to," we have

$$\sec \alpha = \frac{1}{\cos \alpha} \quad \leftrightarrow \quad (\cos \alpha)(\sec \alpha) = 1 \quad \leftrightarrow \quad \cos \alpha = \frac{1}{\sec \alpha};$$

$$\csc \alpha = \frac{1}{\sin \alpha} \quad \leftrightarrow \quad (\sin \alpha)(\csc \alpha) = 1 \quad \leftrightarrow \quad \sin \alpha = \frac{1}{\csc \alpha};$$

$$\cot \alpha = \frac{1}{\tan \alpha} \quad \leftrightarrow \quad (\tan \alpha)(\cot \alpha) = 1 \quad \leftrightarrow \quad \tan \alpha = \frac{1}{\cot \alpha};$$

$$\sin^2 \alpha + \cos^2 \alpha = 1 \quad \leftrightarrow \quad \sin^2 \alpha = 1 - \cos^2 \alpha \quad \leftrightarrow \quad \cos^2 \alpha = 1 - \sin^2 \alpha;$$

$$\tan^2 \alpha + 1 = \sec^2 \alpha \quad \leftrightarrow \quad \tan^2 \alpha = \sec^2 \alpha - 1;$$

$$\cot^2 \alpha + 1 = \csc^2 \alpha \quad \leftrightarrow \quad \cot^2 \alpha = \csc^2 \alpha - 1.$$

There is no general method for proving identities. Following is a list of suggestions that may help in determining the best method to use to prove an identity.

1. If one member of an equation appears to be the more complicated, it should be transformed so that it reduces to the simpler member of the equation.
2. It is frequently helpful to change all the terms to expressions involving only sines and/or cosines, and then to simplify both members.
3. In each step of a proof, look for any possible application of algebraic procedures, including factoring and simplifying fractions.

Example   Show that

$$\frac{\cos \alpha - \sin \alpha}{\cos \alpha} = 1 - \tan \alpha$$

is an identity.

Solution   We shall rewrite the right-hand member in terms of sines and cosines. Substituting $\sin \alpha / \cos \alpha$ for tan α into the right-hand member,

$$\frac{\cos \alpha - \sin \alpha}{\cos \alpha} = 1 - \frac{\sin \alpha}{\cos \alpha}.$$

Writing the right-hand member as a single term yields

$$\frac{\cos \alpha - \sin \alpha}{\cos \alpha} = \frac{\cos \alpha - \sin \alpha}{\cos \alpha},$$

which is clearly an identity.

Sometimes it is helpful to express *both* members of an identity in terms of sines and cosines.

Example   Show that the equation

$$\cot \alpha + \tan \alpha = \csc \alpha \sec \alpha$$

is an identity.

Solution   Substituting $\cos \alpha / \sin \alpha$ for cot α and $\sin \alpha / \cos \alpha$ for tan α

(continued)

in the left-hand member,

$$\frac{\cos \alpha}{\sin \alpha} + \frac{\sin \alpha}{\cos \alpha} = \csc \alpha \sec \alpha,$$

$$\frac{\cos^2 \alpha + \sin^2 \alpha}{\sin \alpha \cos \alpha} = \csc \alpha \sec \alpha,$$

$$\frac{1}{\sin \alpha \cos \alpha} = \csc \alpha \sec \alpha,$$

Substituting $1/\sin \alpha$ for csc α and $1/\cos \alpha$ for sec α in the right-hand member,

$$\frac{1}{\sin \alpha \cos \alpha} = \frac{1}{\sin \alpha} \cdot \frac{1}{\cos \alpha},$$

$$\frac{1}{\sin \alpha \cos \alpha} = \frac{1}{\sin \alpha \cos \alpha}.$$

The two members are identical, and the original equation is an identity.

In the next example, we use the fundamental principle of fractions to rewrite one member of the identity.

Example   Show that the equation

$$\frac{\cos x}{1 + \sin x} = \frac{1 - \sin x}{\cos x}$$

is an identity.

Solution   Multiplying the left-hand member by $\dfrac{1 - \sin x}{1 - \sin x}$,

$$\frac{\cos x(1 - \sin x)}{(1 + \sin x)(1 - \sin x)} = \frac{1 - \sin x}{\cos x},$$

from which

$$\frac{\cos x(1 - \sin x)}{1 - \sin^2 x} = \frac{1 - \sin x}{\cos x}.$$

Substituting $\cos^2 x$ for $1 - \sin^2 x$ in the left-hand member yields

$$\frac{\cos x(1 - \sin x)}{\cos^2 x} = \frac{1 - \sin x}{\cos x}.$$

Then, dividing the numerator and denominator of the left-hand member by cos x,

$$\frac{1 - \sin x}{\cos x} = \frac{1 - \sin x}{\cos x},$$

which is clearly an identity.

Identities for sin(−α), cos(−α), and tan(−α)

Several other useful trigonometric relationships can be obtained from geometric considerations. In Figure 4.1a,

$$\angle AOB = \angle COB, \quad OB = OB, \quad \text{and} \quad \angle OBA = \angle OBC.$$

Hence (see Appendix A.9),

$$\triangle AOB \cong \triangle COB,$$

from which we have that each pair of corresponding sides are congruent and the absolute values of the respective components of the ordered pairs corresponding to points A and C are equal. Because

$$\sin(-\alpha) = \frac{-y}{r} \quad \text{and} \quad \sin \alpha = \frac{y}{r},$$

$$\sin(-\alpha) = -\sin \alpha. \tag{1}$$

Also, $\cos(-\alpha) = x/r$ and $\cos \alpha = x/r$, from which

$$\cos(-\alpha) = \cos \alpha, \tag{2}$$

and $\tan(-\alpha) = -y/x$ and $\tan \alpha = y/x$, from which

$$\tan(-\alpha) = -\tan \alpha. \tag{3}$$

A similar argument for angles α and $-\alpha$ that are in Quadrants II and III, as shown in Figure 4.1b, leads to the results stated by Equations (1), (2), and (3).

(a)

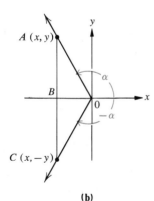

(b)

Figure 4.1

Example Show that

$$\sin(-\alpha) = \cos(-\alpha) \tan(-\alpha) \tag{4}$$

Solution From Equations (2) and (3), we substitute cos α for cos(−α)

(continued)

and $-\tan \alpha$ for $\tan(-\alpha)$ in the right-hand member to obtain

$$\sin(-\alpha) = \cos \alpha(-\tan \alpha)$$

$$= \cos \alpha\left(-\frac{\sin \alpha}{\cos \alpha}\right)$$

$$= -\sin \alpha$$

$$= \sin(-\alpha).$$

Hence, Equation (4) is an identity.

In general, it is a relatively simple matter to show that an equation is not an identity, if such is the case, by finding a *counterexample*. For example, substituting 0 for α in the equation

$$\sin \alpha = \cos \alpha$$

yields

$$\sin 0 = \cos 0,$$

$$0 = 1,$$

which is a false statement. Thus, the equation $\sin \alpha = \cos \alpha$ is not an identity.

Of course, in demonstrating a counterexample, we should select a replacement for the variable so that each member of the equation is defined.

EXERCISE SET 4.1

A

Express each of the following in terms of the function values $\sin \alpha$ *and/or* $\cos \alpha$ *and simplify the expression.*

Example $(\sin \alpha)(\cot^2 \alpha)(\sec^2 \alpha)$

Solution   Substituting $\cos \alpha/\sin \alpha$ for $\cot \alpha$ and $1/\cos \alpha$ for $\sec \alpha$ yields

$$(\sin \alpha)(\cot^2 \alpha)(\sec^2 \alpha) = (\sin \alpha)\left(\frac{\cos^2 \alpha}{\sin^2 \alpha}\right)\left(\frac{1}{\cos^2 \alpha}\right)$$

$$= \frac{1}{\sin \alpha}.$$

1. $(\sec \alpha)(\cot \alpha)$ **2.** $(\tan^2 \alpha)(\csc^2 \alpha)$ **3.** $1 + \tan^2 \alpha$

4. $1 + \cot^2 \alpha$ **5.** $(\sec^2 \alpha - 1)(\cos^2 \alpha)$ **6.** $(\csc^2 \alpha)(\tan \alpha)$

7. $\dfrac{\sec \alpha}{\tan \alpha}$ **8.** $\dfrac{\cot^2 \alpha}{\csc^2 \alpha}$ **9.** $\cos \alpha + \dfrac{\sin^2 \alpha}{\cos \alpha}$

10. $\dfrac{\cos^2 \alpha}{\sin \alpha} + \sin \alpha$ **11.** $\tan \alpha + \cot \alpha$ **12.** $\sec^2 \alpha + \csc^2 \alpha$

Show that each expression on the left is equivalent to the expression on the right for all values of the variable for which both expressions are defined.

Example $(1 - \cos^2 \beta)(1 + \cot^2 \beta); \ 1$

Solution   Substituting $\sin^2 \beta$ for $1 - \cos^2 \beta$ and $\csc^2 \beta$ for $1 + \cot^2 \beta$ yields

$$(1 - \cos^2 \beta)(1 + \cot^2 \beta) = (\sin^2 \beta)(\csc^2 \beta).$$

Since $\csc^2 \beta = 1/\sin^2 \beta$,

$$(1 - \cos^2 \beta)(1 + \cot^2 \beta) = (\sin^2 \beta) \left(\frac{1}{\sin^2 \beta} \right) = 1.$$

13. $\sec \alpha \sin \alpha; \ \tan \alpha$ **14.** $\tan \alpha \cos \alpha; \ \sin \alpha$

15. $\sin \beta \cot \beta; \ \cos \beta$ **16.** $\csc \beta \tan \beta; \ \sec \beta$

17. $\dfrac{\sin \gamma}{\tan \gamma}; \ \cos(-\gamma)$ **18.** $\dfrac{\sin(-\gamma) \sec \gamma}{\tan(-\gamma)}; \ 1$

19. $\cot^2 \gamma \sin^2 \gamma; \ \cos^2 \gamma$ **20.** $\tan^2 \alpha \cos^2 \alpha; \ \sin^2 \alpha$

21. $\cos^2 \alpha(1 + \tan^2 \alpha); \ 1$ **22.** $(\csc^2 \beta - 1)(\sin^2 \beta); \ \cos^2 \beta$

23. $\dfrac{(1 + \sin \beta)(1 - \sin \beta)}{\cos \beta}; \ \cos \beta$ **24.** $\dfrac{(1 + \cos \gamma)(1 - \cos \gamma)}{\sin \gamma}; \ \sin \gamma$

25. $\dfrac{\cos^2 \gamma}{\cot^2 \gamma}; \ \sin^2 \gamma$ **26.** $\dfrac{1 + \tan^2 \gamma}{\csc^2 \gamma}; \ \tan^2 \gamma$

27. $\dfrac{\sin^2 \alpha}{\tan^2 \alpha - \sin^2 \alpha}; \ \cot^2 \alpha$ **28.** $\dfrac{\cos^2 \alpha}{\cot^2 \alpha - \cos^2 \alpha}; \ \tan^2 \alpha$

29. $\dfrac{1}{\tan \alpha + \cot \alpha}; \ \dfrac{\cos \alpha}{\csc \alpha}$ **30.** $\dfrac{1}{\csc \alpha - \sin \alpha}; \ \dfrac{\tan \alpha}{\cos \alpha}$

Verify that each equation is an identity.

Example $\dfrac{\sin^2 x}{1 + \cos x} = \dfrac{\tan x - \sin x}{\tan x}$

Solution   In this case we will simplify both members' by appropriate substitutions. Expressing the right hand member in terms of sines and cosines,

$$\frac{\sin^2 x}{1 + \cos x} = \frac{\tan x - \sin x}{\tan x}$$

$$= \frac{\tan x}{\tan x} - \frac{\sin x}{\tan x}$$

$$= 1 - \frac{\sin x}{\dfrac{\sin x}{\cos x}}$$

$$= 1 - \cos x$$

Rewriting the left-hand member by substituting $1 - \cos^2 x$ for $\sin^2 x$,

$$\frac{1 - \cos^2 x}{1 + \cos x} = 1 - \cos x$$

$$\frac{(1 - \cos x)(1 + \cos x)}{1 + \cos x} = 1 - \cos x$$

$$1 - \cos x = 1 - \cos x.$$

Hence, the equation is an identity.

31. $\cos x \tan x \csc x = 1$

32. $\csc x = \cot x \sec x$

33. $\sec y - \cos y = \tan y \sin y$

34. $\cos y = \sec y - \tan y \sin y$

35. $\cos^2 x - \sin^2 x = 2 \cos^2 x - 1$

36. $(\sec^2 y - 1)(\csc^2 y - 1) = 1$

37. $\tan^2 y + \sec^2 y = \dfrac{2}{\cos^2 y} - 1$

38. $(\tan x + \cot x)\dfrac{\sin x}{\sec x} = 1$

39. $\dfrac{\cos x + \sin x}{\sin x} = 1 + \cot x$

40. $\dfrac{1 - \tan^2 y}{\tan y} = \cot y - \tan y$

41. $\tan^2 y - \sin^2 y = \tan^2 y \sin^2 y$

42. $\dfrac{1}{1 + \sin x} + \dfrac{1}{1 - \sin x} = \dfrac{2}{\cos^2 y}$

43. $\tan y + \cot y = \sec y \csc y$

44. $\dfrac{1 + \tan^2 y}{\tan^2 y} = \csc^2 y$

45. $\cos^4 x - \sin^4 x = \cos^2 x - \sin^2 x$ *Hint:* Factor left-hand member.

46. $\dfrac{1 + \sec x}{\sec x} = \dfrac{\sin^2 x}{1 - \cos x}$ *Hint:* $\sin^2 x = (1 - \cos x)(1 + \cos x)$.

47. $\dfrac{1 - \cos x}{\sin x} = \dfrac{\sin x}{1 + \cos x}$ *Hint:* $\dfrac{\sin x}{1 + \cos x} = \dfrac{\sin x(1 - \cos x)}{(1 + \cos x)(1 - \cos x)}$.

48. $\dfrac{1 + \sin x}{\cos x} = \dfrac{\cos x}{1 - \sin x}$ *Hint:* $\dfrac{1 + \sin x}{\cos x} = \dfrac{(1 + \sin x)(1 - \sin x)}{\cos x(1 - \sin x)}$

49. $\csc y = \dfrac{\sec y + \csc y}{1 + \tan y}$

50. $\dfrac{1}{\sec y - \tan y} = \sec y + \tan y$

51. $\dfrac{\sec y - 1}{\sec y + 1} = \dfrac{1 - \cos y}{1 + \cos y}$

52. $\dfrac{\cos^2 y}{1 - \sin y} = \dfrac{\cos y}{\sec y - \tan y}$

53. $\sec^2 y + \csc^2 y = \sec^2 y \csc^2 y$

54. $\tan^4 y + \tan^2 y = \sec^4 y - \sec^2 y$

55. $\cos(-\alpha) \tan(-\alpha) \csc \alpha = -1$

56. $\csc(-\alpha) = \cot(-\alpha) \sec(-\alpha)$

57. $\dfrac{\cos(-\alpha) + \sin \alpha}{\sin(-\alpha)} = -(1 + \cot \alpha)$

58. $\dfrac{\cos(-\alpha) - \sin(-\alpha)}{\cos \alpha} = 1 + \tan \alpha$

By using counterexamples show that each equation is not an identity.

59. $\sin x + \cos x \tan x = 2$ **60.** $\sin^2 x + 2 \cos x - \cos^2 x = 1$

61. $2 \sin y \cos y + \sin y = 0$ **62.** $\tan^2 y - 2 \tan y = 0$

B

63. Show that $\csc(-\alpha) = -\csc \alpha$.

64. Show that $\sec(-\alpha) = \sec \alpha$.

65. Show that $\cot(-\alpha) = -\cot \alpha$.

4.2 Sum and Difference Formulas for Cosine

In this section we shall establish several trigonometric identities involving the sum or difference of two angles or two real numbers. We

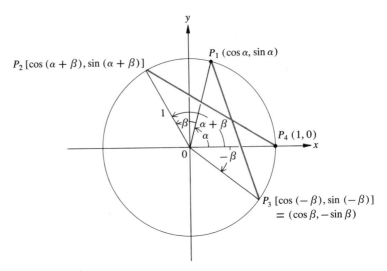

Figure 4.2

first derive a formula for $\cos(\alpha + \beta)$. In Figure 4.2, angles α, $\alpha + \beta$, and $-\beta$ are in standard position, with their sides intersecting the circle of radius 1 at points P_1, P_2, P_3, and P_4. If P_1 has coordinates (x_1, y_1), then, since the radius r of the circle equals 1,

$$\cos \alpha = \frac{x_1}{1} \quad \text{and} \quad \sin \alpha = \frac{y_1}{1}.$$

Hence, the coordinates at P_1 are $x_1 = \cos \alpha$ and $y_1 = \sin \alpha$. We obtain the coordinates at P_2 and P_3 in a similar way. Note that from Equations (1) and (2) in Section 4.1, we have $\sin(-\beta) = -\sin \beta$ and $\cos(-\beta) = \cos \beta$. Since all radii are equal and the central angles $\angle P_4OP_2$ and $\angle P_3OP_1$ are equal (see Appendix A.9),

$$\triangle P_4OP_2 \cong \triangle P_3OP_1$$

and

$$P_4P_2 = P_3P_1.$$

From the distance formula (see Appendix A.4), we have

$$(P_3P_1)^2 = [\cos \alpha - \cos \beta]^2 + [\sin \alpha - (-\sin \beta)]^2$$
$$= (\cos \alpha - \cos \beta)^2 + (\sin \alpha + \sin \beta)^2$$
$$= \cos^2 \alpha - 2 \cos \alpha \cos \beta + \cos^2 \beta$$
$$+ \sin^2 \alpha + 2 \sin \alpha \sin \beta + \sin^2 \beta.$$

Since $\cos^2 \alpha + \sin^2 \alpha = 1$ and $\cos^2 \beta + \sin^2 \beta = 1$,

$$(P_3P_1)^2 = 2 - 2 \cos \alpha \cos \beta + 2 \sin \alpha \sin \beta.$$

Again using the distance formula, we have

$$(P_4P_2)^2 = [\cos(\alpha + \beta) - 1]^2 + [\sin(\alpha + \beta) - 0]^2$$
$$= \cos^2(\alpha + \beta) - 2 \cos(\alpha + \beta) + 1 + \sin^2(\alpha + \beta).$$

Since $\cos^2(\alpha + \beta) + \sin^2(\alpha + \beta) = 1$,

$$(P_4P_2)^2 = 2 - 2 \cos(\alpha + \beta).$$

Since $P_4P_2 = P_3P_1$, we have

$$2 - 2 \cos(\alpha + \beta) = 2 - 2 \cos \alpha \cos \beta + 2 \sin \alpha \sin \beta,$$

which gives

$$\cos(\alpha + \beta) = \cos \alpha \cos \beta - \sin \alpha \sin \beta. \tag{1}$$

Substituting $-\beta$ for β in Equation (1), we have

$$\cos[\alpha + (-\beta)] = \cos \alpha \cos(-\beta) - \sin \alpha \sin(-\beta).$$

Since

$$\cos(-\beta) = \cos \beta \quad \text{and} \quad \sin(-\beta) = -\sin \beta,$$

we obtain

$$\cos(\alpha - \beta) = \cos \alpha \cos \beta + \sin \alpha \sin \beta. \tag{2}$$

These very important relationships for $\cos(\alpha + \beta)$ and $\cos(\alpha - \beta)$ are called the **sum formula** and the **difference formula,** respectively, for the cosine function.

We can, as illustrated in the following examples, find some function values using the sum and difference formulas. Although using Table II, Table III, or a calculator is a more efficient way of finding these function values, such examples give us practice in applying the formulas.

Example   Compute $\cos 15°$.

Solution   Because we know the exact function values of 45° and 30°,

(*continued*)

we replace 15° with 45° − 30° in Equation (2) and obtain

$$\cos 15° = \cos(45° - 30°)$$

$$= \cos 45° \cos 30° + \sin 45° \sin 30°$$

$$= \frac{1}{\sqrt{2}} \cdot \frac{\sqrt{3}}{2} + \frac{1}{\sqrt{2}} \cdot \frac{1}{2} = \frac{\sqrt{3} + 1}{2\sqrt{2}}.$$

Example Compute $\cos \dfrac{7\pi}{12}$.

Solution Since $\dfrac{1}{3} + \dfrac{1}{4} = \dfrac{7}{12}$, we have $\dfrac{7\pi}{12} = \dfrac{\pi}{3} + \dfrac{\pi}{4}$. By Equation (1),

$$\cos \frac{7\pi}{12} = \cos\left(\frac{\pi}{3} + \frac{\pi}{4}\right) = \cos \frac{\pi}{3} \cos \frac{\pi}{4} - \sin \frac{\pi}{3} \sin \frac{\pi}{4}.$$

The appropriate substitutions for the function values yields

$$\cos \frac{7\pi}{12} = \frac{1}{2} \cdot \frac{1}{\sqrt{2}} - \frac{\sqrt{3}}{2} \cdot \frac{1}{\sqrt{2}} = \frac{1 - \sqrt{3}}{2\sqrt{2}}.$$

In general we shall leave such results in radical form. However, you can, if you wish, obtain a rational number approximation. For example, since $\sqrt{2} \approx 1.414$ and $\sqrt{3} \approx 1.732$,

$$\cos \frac{7\pi}{12} \approx \frac{1 - 1.732}{2(1.414)} \approx -0.2588.$$

The sum and difference formulas for the cosine function can be used to establish other identities. Three identities that we will be using are

$$\cos(180° - \alpha) = -\cos \alpha. \tag{3}$$

$$\cos(180° + \alpha) = -\cos \alpha, \tag{4}$$

$$\cos(360° - \alpha) = \cos \alpha. \tag{5}$$

Identities such as these are known as **reduction formulas**. The proof that Equation (3) is an identity is shown here; the proofs of (4) and (5) are left as exercises.

Using the difference formula [Equation (2)] and substituting 180° for α and α for β, we obtain

$$\cos(180° - \alpha) = (\cos 180°)(\cos \alpha) + (\sin 180°)(\sin \alpha).$$

Since $\cos 180° = -1$ and $\sin 180° = 0$, we have

$$\cos(180° - \alpha) = (-1) \cos \alpha + (0) \sin \alpha = -\cos \alpha.$$

Reduction formulas can be used, instead of relying on sketches of reference angles, to rewrite a function value of an angle greater than 90° or less than 0° as a function value of an acute angle.

Examples   Write each expression as the cosine of an acute angle.

a. $\cos 150°$ b. $\cos 225°$

Solutions
a. Since $150° = 180° - 30°$, we use Equation (3) to obtain

$$\cos 150° = \cos(180° - 30°) = -\cos 30°.$$

b. Since $225° = 180° + 45°$, we use Equation (4) to obtain

$$\cos 225° = \cos(180° + 45°) = -\cos 45°.$$

EXERCISE SET 4.2

A

Find the exact value of each expression using Equation (1) or Equation (2) of this section.

1. $\cos 75°$ (Use: $75° = 120° - 45°$)

2. $\cos 105°$ (Use: $105° = 60° + 45°$)

3. $\cos 165°$ (Use: $165° = 120° + 45°$)

4. $\cos 195°$ (Use: $195° = 135° + 60°$)

5. $\cos \dfrac{\pi}{12}$ $\left(\text{Use: } \dfrac{\pi}{12} = \dfrac{\pi}{3} - \dfrac{\pi}{4}\right)$ **6.** $\cos \dfrac{5\pi}{12}$ $\left(\text{Use: } \dfrac{5\pi}{12} = \dfrac{\pi}{6} + \dfrac{\pi}{4}\right)$

Verify that each equation is correct.

Example $\cos 110° \cos 70° - \sin 110° \sin 70° = -1$

Solution   From Equation (1), if we replace α with 110° and β with 70°, we obtain

$$\cos 110° \cos 70° - \sin 110° \sin 70° = \cos(110° + 70°)$$
$$= \cos 180° = -1.$$

7. $\cos 40° \cos 140° - \sin 40° \sin 140° = -1$

8. $\cos 20° \cos 160° - \sin 20° \sin 160° = -1$

9. $\cos 35° \cos 55° - \sin 35° \sin 55° = 0$

10. $\cos 50° \cos 40° - \sin 50° \sin 40° = 0$

11. $\cos 100° \cos 55° + \sin 100° \sin 55° = \dfrac{1}{\sqrt{2}}$

12. $\cos 130° \cos 70° + \sin 130° \sin 70° = \dfrac{1}{2}$

Write each expression as a single function of kx, k an integer.

Example $\cos 2x \cos 3x - \sin 2x \sin 3x$

Solution   From Equation (1),

$$\cos 2x \cos 3x - \sin 2x \sin 3x = \cos(2x + 3x)$$
$$= \cos 5x.$$

13. $\cos 4x \cos 5x - \sin 4x \sin 5x$

14. $\cos x \cos 2x - \sin x \sin 2x$

15. $\cos 8x \cos 6x + \sin 8x \sin 6x$

16. $\cos 5x \cos x + \sin 5x \sin x$

17. $\cos \dfrac{2}{3} x \cos \dfrac{1}{3} x - \sin \dfrac{2}{3} x \sin \dfrac{1}{3} x$

18. $\cos \dfrac{3}{4} x \cos \dfrac{5}{4} x - \sin \dfrac{3}{4} x \sin \dfrac{5}{4} x$

19. $\cos(x + 70°) \cos(x - 70°) - \sin(x + 70°) \sin(x - 70°)$

20. $\cos(65° + x) \cos(65° - x) + \sin(65° + x) \sin(65° - x)$

If angles α and β have the given function values and are in the indicated quadrant, use Equation (1) to find cos(α + β).

Example $\cos \alpha = -\dfrac{1}{\sqrt{5}}$ and $\sin \beta = \dfrac{2}{\sqrt{13}}$; α in II and β in I

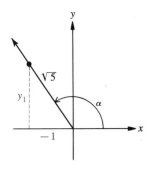

Solution   Since α is in Quadrant II, as shown in the sketch, using the Pythagorean theorem,

$$y_1{}^2 + (-1)^2 = (\sqrt{5})^2,$$

$$y_1{}^2 + 1 = 5,$$

$$y_1{}^2 = 4,$$

$$y_1 = 2 \quad (-2 \text{ does not apply}).$$

Hence, $\sin \alpha = \dfrac{y_1}{\sqrt{5}} = \dfrac{2}{\sqrt{5}}.$

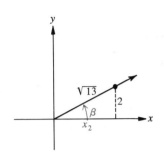

Since β is in Quadrant I, from the sketch,

$$x_2{}^2 + 2^2 = (\sqrt{13})^2,$$

$$x_2{}^2 + 4 = 13,$$

$$x_2{}^2 = 9,$$

$$x_2 = 3 \quad (-3 \text{ does not apply}).$$

Hence, $\cos \beta = \dfrac{x_2}{\sqrt{13}} = \dfrac{3}{\sqrt{13}}.$ Therefore,

$$\cos(\alpha + \beta) = \cos \alpha \cos \beta - \sin \alpha \sin \beta$$

$$= -\frac{1}{\sqrt{5}} \cdot \frac{3}{\sqrt{13}} - \frac{2}{\sqrt{5}} \cdot \frac{2}{\sqrt{13}}$$

$$= -\frac{3}{\sqrt{65}} - \frac{4}{\sqrt{65}} = -\frac{7}{\sqrt{65}}.$$

21. $\cos \alpha = \dfrac{3}{5}$ and $\sin \beta = \dfrac{5}{13}$; α and β in Quadrant I

22. $\cos \alpha = -\dfrac{4}{5}$ and $\sin \beta = -\dfrac{7}{25}$; α in Quadrant III and β in IV

23. $\sin \alpha = \dfrac{1}{\sqrt{10}}$ and $\cos \beta = -\dfrac{4}{\sqrt{17}}$; α in Quadrant II and β in III

24. $\sin \alpha = -\dfrac{5}{\sqrt{29}}$ and $\cos \beta = \dfrac{1}{\sqrt{26}}$; α in Quadrant IV and β in I

Use one of the reduction formulas [Equation (3), (4), or (5)] of this section to write each expression as a function value of an acute angle.

Example   cos 135°

Solution   Using Equation (3), we find that

$$\cos 135° = \cos(180° - 45°) = -\cos 45°.$$

25. cos 120°   **26.** cos 240°   **27.** cos 210°

28. cos 300°   **29.** cos 315°   **30.** cos 330°

Verify that each equation in Exercises 31–35 is an identity.

31. $\cos(180° + \alpha) = -\cos \alpha$ **32.** $\cos(360° - \alpha) = \cos \alpha$

33. $\cos(90° - \alpha) = \sin \alpha$ **34.** $\cos(90° + \alpha) = -\sin \alpha$

35. $\cos 2x = \cos^2 x - \sin^2 x.$ *Hint:* $\cos 2x = \cos(x + x).$

36. Use the results of Exercise 35 to show that

$$\cos 2x = 2 \cos^2 x - 1 = 1 - 2 \sin^2 x.$$

37. Show by counterexample that $\cos(\alpha + \beta) = \cos \alpha + \cos \beta$ is not an identity.

38. Show by counterexample that $\cos(\alpha - \beta) = \cos \alpha - \cos \beta$ is not an identity.

39. Show that $\cos\left(\dfrac{\pi}{2} - \alpha\right) = \sin \alpha.$

40. Use the results of Exercise 39 to show that $\sin\left(\dfrac{\pi}{2} - \alpha\right) = \cos \alpha.$

B

Evaluate each of the following.

Example $\cos\left(\text{Arccot } \dfrac{1}{\sqrt{3}} + \text{Arcsin } \dfrac{1}{\sqrt{2}}\right)$

Solution   Let

$$\alpha = \text{Arccot } \frac{1}{\sqrt{3}} \quad \text{and} \quad \beta = \text{Arcsin } \frac{1}{\sqrt{2}}. \tag{1}$$

Then, using symbols α and β and the sum formula on page 157, we have

$$\cos(\alpha + \beta) = \cos\alpha\cos\beta - \sin\alpha\sin\beta.$$

By inspection of Equations (1), $\alpha = (\pi/3)^R$. Hence,

$$\cos\alpha = \frac{1}{2} \quad \text{and} \quad \sin\alpha = \frac{\sqrt{3}}{2}.$$

Also by inspection of (1), $\beta = (\pi/4)^R$. Thus, we have that

$$\sin\beta = \frac{1}{\sqrt{2}} \quad \text{and} \quad \cos\beta = \frac{1}{\sqrt{2}}.$$

Therefore,

$$\cos\left(\text{Arccot}\,\frac{1}{\sqrt{3}} + \text{Arcsin}\,\frac{1}{\sqrt{2}}\right) = \frac{1}{2}\cdot\frac{1}{\sqrt{2}} - \frac{\sqrt{3}}{2}\cdot\frac{1}{\sqrt{2}}$$

$$= \frac{1 - \sqrt{3}}{2\sqrt{2}}.$$

41. $\cos\left(\text{Arcsin}\,\frac{1}{2} + \text{Arcsec}\,2\right)$ **42.** $\cos\left(\text{Arccos}\,\frac{1}{2} + \text{Arccsc}\,2\right)$

43. $\cos\left(\text{Arctan}\,1 - \text{Arccos}\,\frac{\sqrt{3}}{2}\right)$ **44.** $\cos\left(\text{Arcsin}\,\frac{1}{\sqrt{2}} - \text{Arcsec}\,1\right)$

45. $\cos[\text{Csc}^{-1}(-2) - \text{Sec}^{-1}\sqrt{2}]$ **46.** $\cos[\text{Cos}^{-1}\left(-\frac{1}{\sqrt{2}}\right) - \text{Sin}^{-1}(-1)]$

4.3 Sum and Difference Formulas for Sine

Sum and difference formulas for the sine function can be obtained from the sum and difference formulas for the cosine function. First, however, we consider two relationships between function values for the cosine and sine functions. From the difference formula for the cosine function we have

$$\cos\left(\frac{\pi}{2} - \theta\right) = \cos\frac{\pi}{2}\cos\theta + \sin\frac{\pi}{2}\sin\theta.$$

Replacing $\cos(\pi/2)$ with 0 and $\sin(\pi/2)$ with 1, we have

$$\cos\left(\frac{\pi}{2} - \theta\right) = 0 \cdot \cos \theta + 1 \cdot \sin \theta,$$

$$\cos\left(\frac{\pi}{2} - \theta\right) = \sin \theta. \qquad (1)$$

Replacing θ with $\pi/2 - \theta$ in Equation (1), we obtain

$$\cos\left[\frac{\pi}{2} - \left(\frac{\pi}{2} - \theta\right)\right] = \sin\left(\frac{\pi}{2} - \theta\right),$$

$$\cos\left[\left(\frac{\pi}{2} - \frac{\pi}{2}\right) + \theta\right] = \sin\left(\frac{\pi}{2} - \theta\right),$$

$$\cos \theta = \sin\left(\frac{\pi}{2} - \theta\right),$$

$$\sin\left(\frac{\pi}{2} - \theta\right) = \cos \theta. \qquad (2)$$

In Section 3.5 we noted that the sine and cosine are cofunctions. Equations (1) and (2) also establish this fact because in each case $(\pi/2 - \theta) + \theta = \pi/2$.

Examples

a. $\sin\dfrac{\pi}{3} = \cos\left(\dfrac{\pi}{2} - \dfrac{\pi}{3}\right)$

                $= \cos\dfrac{\pi}{6}$

b. $\cos 46° = \sin(90° - 46°)$

           $= \sin 44°$

Now we consider the sum and difference formulas for the sine function. If we replace θ with $\alpha + \beta$ in Equation (1), we have

$$\sin(\alpha + \beta) = \cos\left[\frac{\pi}{2} - (\alpha + \beta)\right]$$

$$= \cos\left[\left(\frac{\pi}{2} - \alpha\right) - \beta\right],$$

which by the difference formula for the cosine can be written as

$$\sin(\alpha + \beta) = \cos\left(\frac{\pi}{2} - \alpha\right)\cos \beta + \sin\left(\frac{\pi}{2} - \alpha\right)\sin \beta.$$

By Equations (1) and (2),

$$\cos\left(\frac{\pi}{2} - \alpha\right) = \sin \alpha \quad \text{and} \quad \sin\left(\frac{\pi}{2} - \alpha\right) = \cos \alpha.$$

Hence, we have

$$\sin(\alpha + \beta) = \sin \alpha \cos \beta + \cos \alpha \sin \beta. \tag{3}$$

Replacing β with $-\beta$ in Equation (3) yields

$$\sin[\alpha + (-\beta)] = \sin \alpha \cos(-\beta) + \cos \alpha \sin(-\beta).$$

Substituting $\cos \beta$ for $\cos(-\beta)$ and $(-\sin \beta)$ for $\sin(-\beta)$, we have

$$\sin(\alpha - \beta) = \sin \alpha \cos \beta + \cos \alpha(-\sin \beta),$$

from which

$$\sin(\alpha - \beta) = \sin \alpha \cos \beta - \cos \alpha \sin \beta. \tag{4}$$

Example Compute $\sin 15°$.

Solution Since $15° = 45° - 30°$, by Equation (4),

$$\sin 15° = \sin(45° - 30°)$$
$$= \sin 45° \cos 30° - \cos 45° \sin 30°$$
$$= \frac{1}{\sqrt{2}} \cdot \frac{\sqrt{3}}{2} - \frac{1}{\sqrt{2}} \cdot \frac{1}{2} = \frac{\sqrt{3} - 1}{2\sqrt{2}}.$$

Example Compute $\sin \frac{\pi}{12}$.

Solution Observe that $\frac{\pi}{12} = \frac{\pi}{3} - \frac{\pi}{4}$. By using Equation (4),

$$\sin \frac{\pi}{12} = \sin\left(\frac{\pi}{3} - \frac{\pi}{4}\right) = \sin \frac{\pi}{3} \cos \frac{\pi}{4} - \cos \frac{\pi}{3} \sin \frac{\pi}{4}.$$

Making the appropriate substitutions for the function values yields

$$\sin \frac{\pi}{12} = \frac{\sqrt{3}}{2} \cdot \frac{1}{\sqrt{2}} - \frac{1}{2} \cdot \frac{1}{\sqrt{2}} = \frac{\sqrt{3} - 1}{2\sqrt{2}}.$$

The same results are obtained if $\pi/12$ is written as $(\pi/4) - (\pi/6)$.

Again we note that in practical applications, approximations for function values such as $\sin(\pi/12)$ can be found readily by using Table II or a calculator.

The sum and difference formulas for the sine function can be used to establish the following reduction formulas.

$$\sin(180° - \alpha) = \sin \alpha, \tag{5}$$

$$\sin(180° + \alpha) = -\sin \alpha, \tag{6}$$

$$\sin(360° - \alpha) = -\sin \alpha. \tag{7}$$

The proof that Equation (5) is an identity is presented here; the proofs of (6) and (7) are left as exercises.

Using the difference formula, Equation (4), and substituting 180° for α and α for β, we obtain

$$\sin(180° - \alpha) = \sin 180° \cos \alpha - \cos 180° \sin \alpha.$$

Since

$$\sin 180° = 0 \quad \text{and} \quad \cos 180° = -1,$$

we have

$$\sin(180° - \alpha) = 0 \cdot \cos \alpha - (-1)\sin \alpha$$
$$= \sin \alpha.$$

EXERCISE SET 4.3

A

Find the value of each expression using Equation (3) or (4).

1. $\sin 105°$ (Use: $105° = 60° + 45°$)

2. $\sin 75°$ (Use: $75° = 120° - 45°$)

3. $\sin 165°$ (Use: $165° = 210° - 45°$)

4. $\sin 195°$ (Use: $195° = 135° + 60°$)

5. $\sin \dfrac{5\pi}{12}$ $\left(\text{Use: } \dfrac{5\pi}{12} = \dfrac{\pi}{6} + \dfrac{\pi}{4}\right)$

6. $\sin \dfrac{\pi}{12}$ $\left(\text{Use: } \dfrac{\pi}{12} = \dfrac{\pi}{3} - \dfrac{\pi}{4}\right)$

Verify that each equation is correct.

Example   sin 100° cos 80° + cos 100° sin 80° = 0

Solution   From Equation (3) of this section, if we replace α with 100° and β with 80°,

$$\text{sin } 100° \text{ cos } 80° + \text{cos } 100° \text{ sin } 80° = \text{sin}(100° + 80°)$$
$$= \text{sin } 180° = 0.$$

7. sin 20° cos 160° + cos 20° sin 160° = 0

8. sin 40° cos 140° + cos 40° sin 140° = 0

9. sin 50° cos 40° + cos 50° sin 40° = 1

10. sin 35° cos 55° + cos 35° sin 55° = 1

11. $\text{sin } 110° \text{ cos } 80° - \text{cos } 110° \text{ sin } 80° = \dfrac{1}{2}$

12. $\text{sin } 95° \text{ cos } 50° - \text{cos } 95° \text{ sin } 50° = \dfrac{1}{\sqrt{2}}$

Write each expression as a single function of kx, where k is an integer.

Example   sin 2x cos 3x + cos 2x sin 3x

Solution   Using Equation (3),

$$\text{sin } 2x \text{ cos } 3x + \text{cos } 2x \text{ sin } 3x = \text{sin}(2x + 3x)$$
$$= \text{sin } 5x.$$

13. sin x cos 2x + cos x sin 2x

14. sin 4x cos 5x + cos 4x sin 5x

15. sin 5x cos x − cos 5x sin x

16. sin 8x cos 6x − cos 8x sin 6x

17. $\text{sin } \dfrac{3}{4} x \text{ cos } \dfrac{5}{4} x + \text{cos } \dfrac{3}{4} x \text{ sin } \dfrac{5}{4} x$

18. $\text{sin } \dfrac{4}{3} x \text{ cos } \dfrac{1}{3} x - \text{cos } \dfrac{4}{3} x \text{ sin } \dfrac{1}{3} x$

19. sin(50° + x) cos(50° − x) − cos(50° + x) sin(50° − x)

20. sin(x + 60°) cos(x − 60°) + cos(x + 60°) sin(x − 60°)

If angles α and β have the given function values and are in the indicated quadrants, use Equation (3) to find $\sin(\alpha + \beta)$.

Example $\cos \alpha = -\dfrac{1}{\sqrt{5}}$, $\sin \beta = \dfrac{2}{\sqrt{13}}$, α in Quadrant II, β in I

Solution   From the example on page 160, we have $\sin \alpha = 2/\sqrt{5}$ and $\cos \beta = 3/\sqrt{13}$. Therefore, from Equation (3),

$$\sin(\alpha + \beta) = \sin \alpha \cos \beta + \cos \alpha \sin \beta$$

$$= \frac{2}{\sqrt{5}} \cdot \frac{3}{\sqrt{13}} + \left(-\frac{1}{\sqrt{5}}\right) \cdot \frac{2}{\sqrt{13}}$$

$$= \frac{6}{\sqrt{65}} - \frac{2}{\sqrt{65}} = \frac{4}{\sqrt{65}}.$$

21. $\cos \alpha = -\dfrac{4}{5}$, $\sin \beta = -\dfrac{7}{25}$, α in Quadrant III, β in IV

22. $\cos \alpha = \dfrac{3}{5}$, $\sin \beta = \dfrac{5}{13}$, α and β in Quadrant I

23. $\sin \alpha = -\dfrac{5}{\sqrt{29}}$, $\cos \beta = \dfrac{1}{\sqrt{26}}$, α in Quadrant IV, β in I

24. $\sin \alpha = \dfrac{1}{\sqrt{10}}$, $\cos \beta = -\dfrac{4}{\sqrt{17}}$, α in Quadrant II, β in III

Use one of the reduction formulas [Equation (5), (6), or (7)] of this section to write each expression as a function of an acute angle.

Example $\sin 135°$

Solution   By Equation (5),

$$\sin 135° = \sin(180° - 45°) = \sin 45°.$$

25. $\sin 240°$ **26.** $\sin 120°$ **27.** $\sin 150°$

28. $\sin 210°$ **29.** $\sin 330°$ **30.** $\sin 315°$

Verify that each equation is an identity.

31. $\sin(180° + \alpha) = -\sin \alpha$ **32.** $\sin(360° - \alpha) = -\sin \alpha$

33. $\sin(270° - \alpha) = -\cos \alpha$ **34.** $\sin(270° + \alpha) = -\cos \alpha$

35. $\sin 2x = 2 \sin x \cos x.$ *Hint:* $\sin 2x = \sin(x + x).$

36. $\sin(\alpha - 30°) = \dfrac{\sqrt{3} \sin \alpha - \cos \alpha}{2}$

37. Show by a counterexample that $\sin(\alpha - \beta) = \sin \alpha - \sin \beta$ is not an identity.

38. Show by a counterexample that $\sin(\alpha + \beta) = \sin \alpha + \sin \beta$ is not an identity.

B

Evaluate each of the following.

Example $\sin\left(\text{Arcsin} \dfrac{1}{\sqrt{2}} + \text{Arccos} \dfrac{1}{2} \right)$

Solution   Let

$$\alpha = \text{Arcsin} \frac{1}{\sqrt{2}} \quad \text{and} \quad \beta = \text{Arccos} \frac{1}{2}. \tag{8}$$

Then, by using the symbols α and β, and by the sum formula,

$$\sin\left(\text{Arcsin} \frac{1}{\sqrt{2}} + \text{Arccos} \frac{1}{2} \right) = \sin(\alpha + \beta)$$

$$= \sin \alpha \cos \beta + \cos \alpha \sin \beta.$$

By inspection of Equations (1), $\alpha = (\pi/4)^R$, and hence

$$\sin \alpha = \frac{1}{\sqrt{2}} \quad \text{and} \quad \cos \alpha = \frac{1}{\sqrt{2}}.$$

Also, by inspection of (8), $\beta = (\pi/3)^R$, and hence $\cos \beta = 1/2$ and $\sin \beta = \sqrt{3}/2$. Therefore,

$$\sin\left(\text{Arcsin} \frac{1}{\sqrt{2}} + \text{Arccos} \frac{1}{2} \right) = \frac{1}{\sqrt{2}} \cdot \frac{1}{2} + \frac{1}{\sqrt{2}} \cdot \frac{\sqrt{3}}{2}$$

$$= \frac{1}{2\sqrt{2}} + \frac{\sqrt{3}}{2\sqrt{2}} = \frac{1 + \sqrt{3}}{2\sqrt{2}}.$$

39. $\sin(\text{Arcsin } 0 + \text{Arccos } 1)$ **40.** $\sin(\text{Arccos } 0 + \text{Arcsin } 1)$

41. $\sin\left(\text{Arcsin } 0 - \text{Arcsec } \dfrac{2}{\sqrt{3}}\right)$ **42.** $\sin\left(\text{Arccos } 1 - \text{Arcsin } \dfrac{1}{\sqrt{2}}\right)$

43. $\sin\left(\text{Arctan } 1 - \text{Arccos } \dfrac{\sqrt{3}}{2}\right)$ **44.** $\sin\left(\text{Arcsin } \dfrac{1}{2} - \text{Arcsec } 2\right)$

4.4 Sum and Difference Formulas for Tangent

Sum and difference formulas for the tangent function follow from the sum and difference formulas for the sine and cosine functions. Since

$$\tan(\alpha + \beta) = \frac{\sin(\alpha + \beta)}{\cos(\alpha + \beta)},$$

by substituting appropriately, we have

$$\tan(\alpha + \beta) = \frac{\sin\alpha\cos\beta + \cos\alpha\sin\beta}{\cos\alpha\cos\beta - \sin\alpha\sin\beta}.$$

Multiplying each term of the numerator and denominator of the right-hand member by $1/\cos\alpha\cos\beta$ yields

$$\tan(\alpha + \beta) = \frac{\dfrac{\sin\alpha\cos\beta}{\cos\alpha\cos\beta} + \dfrac{\cos\alpha\sin\beta}{\cos\alpha\cos\beta}}{\dfrac{\cos\alpha\cos\beta}{\cos\alpha\cos\beta} - \dfrac{\sin\alpha\sin\beta}{\cos\alpha\cos\beta}},$$

from which, by simplifying the right-hand member, we obtain

$$\tan(\alpha + \beta) = \frac{\tan\alpha + \tan\beta}{1 - \tan\alpha\tan\beta}. \tag{1}$$

By substituting $-\beta$ for β in Equation (1), we have

$$\tan[\alpha + (-\beta)] = \frac{\tan\alpha + \tan(-\beta)}{1 - \tan\alpha\tan(-\beta)}.$$

Substituting $-\tan\beta$ for $\tan(-\beta)$ yields

$$\tan[\alpha + (-\beta)] = \frac{\tan\alpha + (-\tan\beta)}{1 - \tan\alpha(-\tan\beta)},$$

$$\tan(\alpha - \beta) = \frac{\tan\alpha - \tan\beta}{1 + \tan\alpha\tan\beta}. \tag{2}$$

Example Compute tan 75°.

Solution Observe that $75° = 45° + 30°$. Then, using Equation (1) and replacing α with 45° and β with 30°,

$$\tan 75° = \tan(45° + 30°) = \frac{\tan 45° + \tan 30°}{1 - \tan 45° \tan 30°}$$

$$= \frac{1 + \dfrac{1}{\sqrt{3}}}{1 - 1\left(\dfrac{1}{\sqrt{3}}\right)} = \frac{\left(1 + \dfrac{1}{\sqrt{3}}\right) \cdot \sqrt{3}}{\left(1 - \dfrac{1}{\sqrt{3}}\right) \cdot \sqrt{3}} = \frac{\sqrt{3} + 1}{\sqrt{3} - 1}.$$

The sum and difference formulas established in this section can be used to establish the following reduction formulas.

$$\tan(180° - \alpha) = -\tan \alpha, \tag{3}$$

$$\tan(180° + \alpha) = \tan \alpha, \tag{4}$$

$$\tan(360° - \alpha) = -\tan \alpha. \tag{5}$$

The proof that Equation (3) is an identity is presented here; the proofs of (4) and (5) are left as exercises.

Using the difference formula [Equation (2)] and substituting 180° for α and α for β, we obtain

$$\tan(180° - \alpha) = \frac{\tan 180° - \tan \alpha}{1 + \tan 180° \tan \alpha}$$

$$= \frac{0 - \tan \alpha}{1 + (0)\tan \alpha}$$

$$= -\tan \alpha.$$

EXERCISE SET 4.4

A

Use Equation (1) or (2) to find the value of each expression.

1. tan 105° (Use: $105° = 45° + 60°$)

2. tan 15° (Use: $15° = 45° - 30°$)

3. tan 195° (Use: $195° = 240° - 45°$)

4. tan 165° (Use: $165° = 120° + 45°$)

5. $\tan\dfrac{\pi}{12}$ $\left(\text{Use: }\dfrac{\pi}{12}=\dfrac{\pi}{3}-\dfrac{\pi}{4}\right)$ 6. $\tan\dfrac{3\pi}{4}$ $\left(\text{Use: }\dfrac{3\pi}{4}=\pi-\dfrac{\pi}{4}\right)$

Verify that each equation is correct.

Example $\dfrac{\tan 20° + \tan 25°}{1 - \tan 20° \tan 25°} = 1$

Solution   From Equation (1), if we replace α with $20°$ and β with $25°$,

$$\dfrac{\tan 20° + \tan 25°}{1 - \tan 20° \tan 25°} = \tan(20° + 25°)$$

$$= \tan 45° = 1.$$

7. $\dfrac{\tan 50° + \tan 130°}{1 - \tan 50° \tan 130°} = 0$ 8. $\dfrac{\tan 100° + \tan 50°}{1 - \tan 100° \tan 50°} = -\dfrac{1}{\sqrt{3}}$

9. $\dfrac{\tan 140° + \tan 100°}{1 - \tan 140° \tan 100°} = \sqrt{3}$ 10. $\dfrac{\tan 95° + \tan 40°}{1 - \tan 95° \tan 40°} = -1$

11. $\dfrac{\tan 110° - \tan 50°}{1 + \tan 110° \tan 50°} = \sqrt{3}$ 12. $\dfrac{\tan 115° - \tan 70°}{1 + \tan 115° \tan 70°} = 1$

Write each expression as a single function of kx where k is an integer.

Example $\dfrac{\tan 2x + \tan 3x}{1 - \tan 2x \tan 3x}$

Solution   Using Equation (1), we obtain

$$\dfrac{\tan 2x + \tan 3x}{1 - \tan 2x \tan 3x} = \tan(2x + 3x)$$

$$= \tan 5x.$$

13. $\dfrac{\tan 4x + \tan 5x}{1 - \tan 4x \tan 5x}$ 14. $\dfrac{\tan 2x + \tan x}{1 - \tan 2x \tan x}$

15. $\dfrac{\tan 8x - \tan 6x}{1 + \tan 8x \tan 6x}$ 16. $\dfrac{\tan 5x - \tan x}{1 + \tan 5x \tan x}$

17. $\dfrac{\tan \frac{4}{3}x - \tan \frac{1}{3}x}{1 + \tan \frac{4}{3}x \tan \frac{1}{3}x}$ 18. $\dfrac{\tan \frac{5}{4}x + \tan \frac{3}{4}x}{1 - \tan \frac{5}{4}x \tan \frac{3}{4}x}$

Use one of the reduction formulas [Equation (3), (4), or (5)] of this section to write each expression as a function of an acute angle.

Example   tan 135°

Solution   Using Equation (3),

$$\tan 135° = \tan(180° - 45°) = -\tan 45°.$$

19. tan 120°   **20.** tan 240°   **21.** tan 210°

22. tan 150°   **23.** tan 315°   **24.** tan 330°

Verify that each equation is an identity.

25. $\tan(180° + \alpha) = \tan \alpha$ **26.** $\tan(360° - \alpha) = -\tan \alpha$

27. $\tan(90° - \alpha) = \cot \alpha$ **28.** $\cot(90° - \alpha) = \tan \alpha$

29. $\tan 2x = \dfrac{2 \tan x}{1 - \tan^2 x}.$ *Hint:* $\tan 2x = \tan(x + x).$

30. $\tan\left(x + \dfrac{\pi}{4}\right) = \dfrac{1 + \tan x}{1 - \tan x}$

B

31. $\dfrac{\tan(45° - \alpha)}{\tan(45° + \alpha)} = \dfrac{(1 - \tan \alpha)^2}{(1 + \tan \alpha)^2}$ **32.** $\tan \beta = \dfrac{\tan(45° + \beta) - 1}{1 + \tan(45° + \beta)}$

33. $\cot(\alpha + \beta) = \dfrac{\cot \alpha \cot \beta - 1}{\cot \beta + \cot \alpha}$ **34.** $\cot(\alpha - \beta) = \dfrac{\cot \alpha \cot \beta + 1}{\cot \beta - \cot \alpha}$

4.5 Identities Involving cos 2x, sin 2x, and tan 2x

Additional identities follow from the sum and difference formulas developed in Sections 4.2 and 4.3. For example, if α is substituted for β in

$$\cos(\alpha + \beta) = \cos \alpha \cos \beta - \sin \alpha \sin \beta,$$

we obtain

$$\cos(\alpha + \alpha) = \cos \alpha \cos \alpha - \sin \alpha \sin \alpha,$$

$$\cos 2\alpha = \cos^2 \alpha - \sin^2 \alpha. \tag{1}$$

The right-hand member can be written in a variety of convenient forms. Thus, if $1 - \sin^2 \alpha$ is substituted for $\cos^2 \alpha$, we have

$$\cos 2\alpha = (1 - \sin^2 \alpha) - \sin^2 \alpha,$$

$$\mathbf{\cos 2\alpha = 1 - 2 \sin^2 \alpha.} \qquad (2)$$

If $1 - \cos^2 \alpha$ is substituted for $\sin^2 \alpha$ in Equation (1), we have

$$\cos 2\alpha = \cos^2 \alpha - (1 - \cos^2 \alpha),$$

$$\mathbf{\cos 2\alpha = 2 \cos^2 \alpha - 1.} \qquad (3)$$

   Identities (1), (2), and (3), and similar identities that follow for the sine and tangent functions, called **double-angle formulas,** are often helpful for rewriting expressions in more useful forms. You will prove additional identities in the exercises to become familiar with these important relationships.

Example   Show that $\dfrac{1 - \cos 2x}{2 \sin x \cos x} = \tan x$ is an identity.

Solution   From Equation (2), we can substitute $1 - 2 \sin^2 x$ for $\cos 2x$ in the left-hand member to obtain

$$\frac{1 - (1 - 2 \sin^2 x)}{2 \sin x \cos x} = \tan x$$

$$\frac{2 \sin^2 x}{2 \sin x \cos x} = \tan x$$

$$\frac{\sin x}{\cos x} = \tan x$$

$$\tan x = \tan x.$$

Hence, the original equation is an identity.

Example   Show that $2 \sec^2 \beta = \dfrac{5 + \cos 2\beta}{1 + \cos 2\beta} - 1$ is an identity

Solution   From Equation (3), we substitute $2 \cos^2 \beta - 1$ for $\cos 2\beta$ in the right-hand member to obtain

$$2 \sec^2 \beta = \frac{5 + (2 \cos^2 \beta - 1)}{1 + (2 \cos^2 \beta - 1)} - 1$$

$$= \frac{4 + 2 \cos^2 \beta}{2 \cos^2 \beta} - 1$$

$$= \frac{4 + 2 \cos^2 \beta - 2 \cos^2 \beta}{2 \cos^2 \beta}$$

$$= \frac{4}{2 \cos^2 \beta}$$

$$2 \sec^2 \beta = 2 \sec^2 \beta.$$

Hence, the original equation is an identity.

If α is substituted for β in

$$\sin(\alpha + \beta) = \sin \alpha \cos \beta + \cos \alpha \sin \beta,$$

we obtain

$$\sin(\alpha + \alpha) = \sin \alpha \cos \alpha + \cos \alpha \sin \alpha,$$

$$\mathbf{\sin 2\alpha = 2 \sin \alpha \cos \alpha.} \tag{4}$$

Example   Show that $\dfrac{2}{\sin 2\theta} = \tan \theta + \cot \theta$ is an identity.

Solution   Substituting $2 \sin \theta \cos \theta$ for $\sin 2\theta$ in the lefthand member, and $\sin \theta / \cos \theta$ for $\tan \theta$ and $\cos \theta / \sin \theta$ for $\cot \theta$ in the right-hand member yields

$$\frac{2}{2 \sin \theta \cos \theta} = \frac{\sin \theta}{\cos \theta} + \frac{\cos \theta}{\sin \theta}$$

$$= \frac{\sin^2 \theta + \cos^2 \theta}{\sin \theta \cos \theta}$$

$$= \frac{1}{\sin \theta \cos \theta}$$

$$= \frac{2}{2 \sin \theta \cos \theta}.$$

Hence, the original equation is an identity.

If α is substituted for β in

$$\tan(\alpha + \beta) = \frac{\tan \alpha + \tan \beta}{1 - \tan \alpha \tan \beta},$$

we obtain

$$\tan(\alpha + \alpha) = \frac{\tan \alpha + \tan \alpha}{1 - \tan \alpha \tan \alpha},$$

$$\tan 2\alpha = \frac{2 \tan \alpha}{1 - \tan^2 \alpha}. \tag{5}$$

Example Show that $\tan 2x = \dfrac{2 \tan x}{2 - \sec^2 x}$ is an identity.

Solution Substituting $\tan^2 x + 1$ for $\sec^2 x$ yields

$$\tan 2x = \frac{2 \tan x}{2 - (\tan^2 x + 1)}$$

$$= \frac{2 \tan x}{1 - \tan^2 x},$$

which is an identity by Equation (5).

Relationships similar to those developed in this section for sine, cosine, and tangent can be derived for cotangent, secant, and cosecant. However, they are of less importance and will not be considered.

EXERCISE SET 4.5

A

Express each of the following as a single function of kx, or kα, where k is a positive integer. Assume that x or α takes on no value for which the expression is undefined.

Examples

a. $1 - 2 \sin^2 x$

b. $\dfrac{\tan 3x}{1 - \tan^2 3x}$

Solutions

a. From Equation (2),

$$1 - 2 \sin^2 x = \cos 2x.$$

b. From Equation (5),

$$\frac{\tan 3x}{1 - \tan^2 3x} = \frac{1}{2} \cdot \frac{2 \tan 3x}{1 - \tan^2 3x}$$

$$= \frac{1}{2} \tan 2(3x) = \frac{1}{2} \tan 6x.$$

1. $2 \sin x \cos x$

2. $2 \cos^2 x - 1$

3. $\cos^2 x - \sin^2 x$

4. $\dfrac{2 \tan x}{1 - \tan^2 x}$

5. $2 \sin 2x \cos 2x$

6. $\dfrac{4 \tan 2x}{1 - \tan^2 2x}$

7. $\sin \dfrac{x}{2} \cos \dfrac{x}{2}$

8. $4 \sin 3x \cos 3x$

9. $\cos^2 5\alpha - \sin^2 5\alpha$

10. $1 - 2 \sin^2 4\alpha$

11. $4 \cos^2 6\alpha - 2$

12. $2 \sin 5\alpha \cos 5\alpha$

13. $\sin 2\alpha \cos \alpha - \cos 2\alpha \sin \alpha$

14. $\sin 3\alpha \cos 2\alpha + \cos 3\alpha \sin 2\alpha$

15. $\cos 3x \cos 5x + \sin 3x \sin 5x$

16. $\cos 4x \cos 2x - \sin 4x \sin 2x$

Verify that each equation is an identity.

17. $\cos^2 \alpha = \dfrac{1 + \cos 2\alpha}{2}$

18. $\sin^2 \alpha = \dfrac{1 - \cos 2\alpha}{2}$

19. $\cos 2x + 2 \sin^2 x = 1$

20. $\sin 2x \csc x = 2 \cos x$

21. $\dfrac{\sin 2x}{1 + \cos 2x} = \tan x$

22. $\sin 2x = \dfrac{2 \tan x}{1 + \tan^2 x}$

23. $\sec^2 x = \dfrac{2}{1 + \cos 2x}$

24. $\cot x = \dfrac{1 + \cos 2x}{\sin 2x}$

25. $\cos 2\beta = \dfrac{1 - \tan^2 \beta}{1 + \tan^2 \beta}$

26. $\cot^2 \beta = \dfrac{1 + \cos 2\beta}{1 - \cos 2\beta}$

27. $\cot 4x = \dfrac{1 - \tan^2 2x}{2 \tan 2x}$

28. $\cos^4 x - \sin^4 x = \cos 2x$

29. $\sin 3x = 3 \sin x - 4 \sin^3 x$
   Hint: First rewrite $\sin 3x$ as $\sin(2x + x)$.

30. $\cos 3x = 4 \cos^3 x - 3 \cos x$

31. $\sin 4\alpha = (\cos \alpha)(4 \sin \alpha - 8 \sin^3 \alpha)$

32. $\cos 4\alpha = 1 - 8 \sin^2 \alpha \cos^2 \alpha$

Example   If $\sin x = \dfrac{3}{5}$ and $\cos x < 0$, find $\sin 2x$.

Solution   To evaluate

$$\sin 2x = 2 \sin x \cos x, \qquad\qquad (1)$$

(*continued*)

the values for cos x for those values of x for which sin $x = 3/5$ and cos $x < 0$ are needed. Substituting $3/5$ for sin x in

$$\sin^2 x + \cos^2 x = 1$$

gives

$$\left(\frac{3}{5}\right)^2 + \cos^2 x = 1,$$

$$\cos^2 x = 1 - \frac{9}{25} = \frac{16}{25}.$$

Because cos $x < 0$, cos $x = -4/5$. Substituting $3/5$ for sin x and $-4/5$ for cos x in sin $2x = 2$ sin x cos x yields

$$\sin 2x = 2\left(\frac{3}{5}\right)\left(-\frac{4}{5}\right) = -\frac{24}{25}.$$

33. If sin $x = \dfrac{4}{5}$ and cot $x > 0$, find sin $2x$.

34. If sin $x = \dfrac{12}{13}$ and sec $x < 0$, find cos $2x$.

35. If cos $2\alpha = -\dfrac{8}{17}$ and $180° \leq 2\alpha \leq 270°$, find sin α.

36. If cos $2\alpha = \dfrac{5}{13}$ and $270° \leq 2\alpha \leq 360°$, find cos α.

37. If tan $\beta = -\dfrac{3}{4}$, find tan 2β.   **38.** If tan $\beta = \dfrac{5}{12}$, find tan 2β.

4.6 Additional Identities

The identities in this section are less important than some of the identities introduced in the preceding sections. However, they are sometimes useful in rewriting expressions involving trigonometric function values.

In Section 4.5 we observed that

$$\cos 2\alpha = 2 \cos^2 \alpha - 1.$$

Solving this for $\cos^2 \alpha$, we have

$$1 + \cos 2\alpha = 2 \cos^2 \alpha,$$

from which

$$\cos^2 \alpha = \frac{1 + \cos 2\alpha}{2}. \qquad (1)$$

We also noted in Section 4.5 that

$$\cos 2\alpha = 1 - 2 \sin^2 \alpha.$$

Solving this for $\sin^2 \alpha$, we have

$$2 \sin^2 \alpha = 1 - \cos 2\alpha,$$

from which

$$\sin^2 \alpha = \frac{1 - \cos 2\alpha}{2}. \qquad (2)$$

These identities enable us to write the second-degree terms, $\cos^2 \alpha$ and $\sin^2 \alpha$, in terms of first-degree terms. They also enable us to write additional useful identities.

Half-Angle Formulas

Substituting $\alpha/2$ for α in Equation (1) yields

$$\cos^2 \frac{\alpha}{2} = \frac{1 + \cos 2(\alpha/2)}{2},$$

from which

$$\cos^2 \frac{\alpha}{2} = \frac{1 + \cos \alpha}{2}. \qquad (3)$$

Substituting $\alpha/2$ for α in Equation (2) yields

$$\sin^2 \frac{\alpha}{2} = \frac{1 - \cos 2(\alpha/2)}{2},$$

from which

$$\sin^2 \frac{\alpha}{2} = \frac{1 - \cos \alpha}{2}. \qquad (4)$$

Values for $\cos(\alpha/2)$ and $\sin(\alpha/2)$ are positive or negative, depending on the value of $\alpha/2$. Table 1.1 (page 5) can be used to help you select the appropriate sign.

Example   Use Equation (4) to find $\sin \dfrac{\pi}{8}$.

Solution   With $\alpha/2 = \pi/8$ and $\alpha = 2(\pi/8) = \pi/4$, we obtain

$$\sin^2 \frac{\pi}{8} = \frac{1 - \cos \dfrac{\pi}{4}}{2}.$$

Because $0 < \pi/8 < \pi/2$, we use the positive square root for $\sin(\pi/8)$. Then, since $\cos(\pi/4) = 1/\sqrt{2}$,

$$\sin \frac{\pi}{8} = \sqrt{\frac{1 - \dfrac{1}{\sqrt{2}}}{2}} = \sqrt{\frac{\sqrt{2} - 1}{2\sqrt{2}}} = \frac{1}{2}\sqrt{2 - \sqrt{2}}.$$

Formulas for $\tan(\alpha/2)$ also follow directly from identities we have developed. Substituting $\alpha/2$ for α in $\tan \alpha = (\sin \alpha)/(\cos \alpha)$, we have

$$\tan \frac{\alpha}{2} = \frac{\sin \dfrac{\alpha}{2}}{\cos \dfrac{\alpha}{2}}.$$

Multiplying both the numerator and the denominator of the right-hand member by $2 \sin(\alpha/2)$ yields

$$\tan \frac{\alpha}{2} = \frac{2 \sin^2 \dfrac{\alpha}{2}}{2 \sin \dfrac{\alpha}{2} \cos \dfrac{\alpha}{2}}.$$

Substituting $(1 - \cos \alpha)/2$ for $\sin^2(\alpha/2)$ and substituting $\sin 2(\alpha/2)$ for $2 \sin(\alpha/2) \cos(\alpha/2)$, we obtain

$$\tan \frac{\alpha}{2} = \frac{2 \left(\dfrac{1 - \cos \alpha}{2} \right)}{\sin 2 \left(\dfrac{\alpha}{2} \right)},$$

$$\tan \frac{\alpha}{2} = \frac{1 - \cos \alpha}{\sin \alpha}. \tag{5}$$

By multiplying the numerator and the denominator of the right-hand member of Equation (5) by $1 + \cos \alpha$, we obtain

$$\tan \frac{\alpha}{2} = \frac{(1 - \cos \alpha)(1 + \cos \alpha)}{\sin \alpha(1 + \cos \alpha)}$$

$$= \frac{\sin^2 \alpha}{\sin \alpha(1 + \cos \alpha)},$$

from which

$$\tan \frac{\alpha}{2} = \frac{\sin \alpha}{1 + \cos \alpha}. \qquad (6)$$

Example   Use Equation (5) to find $\tan \dfrac{\pi}{8}$.

Solution   If $\pi/8 = \alpha/2$, then $\alpha = \pi/4$ and

$$\tan \frac{\pi}{8} = \frac{1 - \cos \dfrac{\pi}{4}}{\sin \dfrac{\pi}{4}} = \frac{1 - \dfrac{1}{\sqrt{2}}}{\dfrac{1}{\sqrt{2}}}$$

$$= \sqrt{2} - 1.$$

Just as identities such as $\sin 2\alpha = 2 \sin \alpha \cos \alpha$ are sometimes called double-angle formulas, the identities developed above are sometimes called **half-angle formulas.**

Relationships similar to those developed above for sine, cosine, and tangent can be derived for cotangent, secant, and cosecant. They are of less importance and will not be considered.

Product, Sum, and Difference Formulas

The following identities are derived from the sum and difference formulas for the cosine and sine that were developed in Sections 4.2 and 4.3. The proofs are left as exercises.

$$\cos \alpha \cos \beta = \tfrac{1}{2}[\cos(\alpha + \beta) + \cos(\alpha - \beta)], \qquad (7)$$

$$\sin \alpha \sin \beta = -\tfrac{1}{2}[\cos(\alpha + \beta) - \cos(\alpha - \beta)], \qquad (8)$$

$$\sin \alpha \cos \beta = \tfrac{1}{2}[\sin(\alpha + \beta) + \sin(\alpha - \beta)], \qquad (9)$$

$$\cos \alpha \sin \beta = \tfrac{1}{2}[\sin(\alpha + \beta) - \sin(\alpha - \beta)]. \qquad (10)$$

Example   Express cos 5x sin 2x as a sum or difference.

Solution   From Equation (10),

$$\cos 5x \sin 2x = \tfrac{1}{2}[\sin(5x + 2x) - \sin(5x - 2x)]$$
$$= \tfrac{1}{2}(\sin 7x - \sin 3x).$$

The following four identities enable us to express sums and differences of function values in terms of products.

$$\cos \alpha + \cos \beta = 2 \cos\left(\frac{\alpha + \beta}{2}\right) \cos\left(\frac{\alpha - \beta}{2}\right), \qquad (11)$$

$$\cos \alpha - \cos \beta = -2 \sin\left(\frac{\alpha + \beta}{2}\right) \sin\left(\frac{\alpha - \beta}{2}\right), \qquad (12)$$

$$\sin \alpha + \sin \beta = 2 \sin\left(\frac{\alpha + \beta}{2}\right) \cos\left(\frac{\alpha - \beta}{2}\right), \qquad (13)$$

$$\sin \alpha - \sin \beta = 2 \cos\left(\frac{\alpha + \beta}{2}\right) \sin\left(\frac{\alpha - \beta}{2}\right). \qquad (14)$$

Example   Express sin 4α + sin 2α as a product.

Solution   From Equation (13),

$$\sin 4\alpha + \sin 2\alpha = 2 \sin\left(\frac{4\alpha + 2\alpha}{2}\right) \cos\left(\frac{4\alpha - 2\alpha}{2}\right)$$
$$= 2 \sin 3\alpha \cos \alpha.$$

EXERCISE SET 4.6

A

Use the half-angle formulas to find the exact value for each of the following.

Example   sin 105°

Solution   From Equation (4), with $\alpha/2 = 105°$ and $\alpha = 210°$,

$$\sin 105° = \sqrt{\frac{1 - \cos 210°}{2}},$$

where the positive square root is chosen because 105° is in Quadrant II and sin 105° is therefore positive. Since $\cos 210° = -\sqrt{3}/2$,

$$\sin 105° = \sqrt{\frac{1 - (-\sqrt{3}/2)}{2}} = \frac{\sqrt{2 + \sqrt{3}}}{2}.$$

1. $\sin 15°$ **2.** $\cos 15°$ **3.** $\tan 15°$ **4.** $\sin 75°$

5. $\cos 75°$ **6.** $\tan 75°$ **7.** $\cos \dfrac{\pi}{8}$ **8.** $\sin \dfrac{\pi}{12}$

9. $\tan \dfrac{5\pi}{12}$ **10.** $\cos \dfrac{\pi}{12}$ **11.** $\cos \dfrac{7\pi}{12}$ **12.** $\sin \dfrac{7\pi}{12}$

Verify each identity.

13. $\tan \dfrac{x}{2} = \csc x - \cot x$ **14.** $\sin \dfrac{\theta}{2} \cos \dfrac{\theta}{2} = \dfrac{\sin \theta}{2}$

15. $\left(\cos \dfrac{\alpha}{2} - \sin \dfrac{\alpha}{2} \right)^2 = 1 - \sin \alpha$ **16.** $\sin \beta - \cos \beta \tan \dfrac{\beta}{2} = \tan \dfrac{\beta}{2}$

17. $\sin^2 \dfrac{\gamma}{2} = \dfrac{\sec \gamma - 1}{2 \sec \gamma}$ **18.** $\tan \dfrac{x}{2} \sin x = \dfrac{\tan x - \sin x}{\sin x \sec x}$

In Exercises 19–24, assume $0° \leq x < 360°$.

Example   If $\tan x = -\dfrac{3}{4}$ and $\cos x$ is negative, find $\sin \dfrac{x}{2}$.

Solution   Since $\cos x$ and $\tan x$ are both negative, x is an angle in Quadrant II, and because $\tan x = -3/4$, a point on the terminal ray has the x-coordinate -4 and the y-coordinate 3. From the Pythagorean formula (see Appendix A.8),

$$r = \sqrt{x^2 + y^2}$$
$$= \sqrt{(-4)^2 + 3^2} = 5.$$

From Equation (4) with $\cos x = -4/5$, we obtain

$$\sin \dfrac{x}{2} = \sqrt{\frac{1 - (-4/5)}{2}} = \dfrac{3}{\sqrt{10}},$$

where the positive square root is taken because x is in Quadrant II and therefore $x/2$ must be in Quadrant I.

19. If $\sin x = \dfrac{\sqrt{3}}{2}$ and $\cos x > 0$, find $\tan \dfrac{x}{2}$.

20. If $\sin \theta = \dfrac{1}{2}$ and $\sec \theta > 0$, find $\sin \dfrac{\theta}{2}$.

21. If $\cos \alpha = -\dfrac{1}{3}$ and $\tan \alpha > 0$, find $\sin \dfrac{\alpha}{2}$.

22. If $\tan \beta = 3$ and $\sin \beta > 0$, find $\cos \dfrac{\beta}{2}$.

23. If $\tan x = -1$ and $\sin x < 0$, find $\cos \dfrac{x}{2}$.

24. If $\sin \theta = \dfrac{1}{\sqrt{2}}$ and $\cos \theta < 0$, find $\tan \dfrac{\theta}{2}$.

Write each expression as a sum or difference of function values.

Example $\sin 3x \sin x$

Solution   From Equation (8),

$$\sin 3x \sin x = -\tfrac{1}{2}[\cos(3x + x) - \cos(3x - x)]$$
$$= -\tfrac{1}{2}(\cos 4x - \cos 2x).$$

25. $\sin 5° \cos 12°$ **26.** $\cos 7° \cos 20°$ **27.** $\cos 2x \sin x$

28. $\sin 2x \sin 5x$ **29.** $\cos 2x \cos 5x$ **30.** $\sin 6x \cos x$

Write each expression as a product.

Example $\cos 3\alpha - \cos \alpha$

Solution   From Equation (12),

$$\cos 3\alpha - \cos \alpha = -2 \sin\left(\frac{3\alpha + \alpha}{2}\right) \sin\left(\frac{3\alpha - \alpha}{2}\right)$$
$$= -2 \sin 2\alpha \sin \alpha.$$

31. $\cos 20° + \cos 4°$ **32.** $\sin 18° - \sin 6°$ **33.** $\sin 3\alpha + \sin 5\alpha$

34. $\cos \alpha + \cos 5\alpha$ **35.** $\sin 5\alpha - \sin \alpha$ **36.** $\cos 6\alpha - \cos 2\alpha$

B

Verify each of the following identities that are listed in this section.

37. Equation (7)   **38.** Equation (8)   **39.** Equation (9)

40. Equation (10)   **41.** Equation (11)   **42.** Equation (12)

43. Equation (13)   **44.** Equation (14)

4.7 Conditional Equations

In Sections 4.1–4.6 we considered identities—equations that are satisfied by all angle or all real number replacements for which both of the members are defined. We now consider equations that are conditional—that is, they are satisfied only for particular replacements for the variable.

We have already solved many simple conditional equations, such as

$$\sin x = \frac{1}{2},$$

by inspection and by using Table 1.2, Table II or Table III in Appendix C, or a calculator. In this case,

for $0 \le x \le \pi/2$, the solution set is $\{\pi/6\}$;

for $0 \le x < 2\pi$, the solution set is $\{\pi/6, 5\pi/6\}$;

for $x \in A$ (the set of all angles), in degree units, the solution set is

$$\{x \mid x = (30 + k \cdot 360)° \text{ or } x = (150 + k \cdot 360)°\}, \quad k \in J.$$

Perhaps you can determine the solution set of

$$\sin x = \cos x, \quad 0 < x < \frac{\pi}{2}, \tag{1}$$

by inspection—perhaps not. However, you can generate equivalent equations and hopefully you will generate one from which the solution(s) will be evident by inspection. Generally, solutions can be determined most easily from equations that involve *values of one function only*. The identities developed in the preceding sections are useful in obtaining such equivalent equations from equations involving values of more than one function. For example, in (1) above, for $0 < x < \pi/2$, $\cos x \ne 0$. Thus, we can multiply each member by $1/\cos x$ to obtain

$$\frac{\sin x}{\cos x} = 1.$$

Substituting $\tan x$ for $\sin x/\cos x$, we obtain

$$\tan x = 1.$$

Since, in this case, values of x are restricted to $0 < x < \pi/2$, we find the solution set by inspection to be $\{\pi/4\}$.

Because function values ($\cos x$, $\sin x$, etc.) are real numbers, equations that are quadratic in a given trigonometric function value, such as

$$\cos^2 x + \cos x - 2 = 0, \quad x \in A, \tag{2}$$

can be solved by first solving the quadratic equation for the function value involved. To emphasize that we are using a standard algebraic method for solving a quadratic equation, we also show each step of the process, where we let $\cos x = u$ and write Equation (2) as

$$u^2 + u - 2 = 0. \tag{3}$$

Since the left-hand members of Equations (2) and (3) are factorable, the equations can be written equivalently as

$$(\cos x + 2)(\cos x - 1) = 0 \quad \text{or} \quad (u + 2)(u - 1) = 0.$$

Since $\cos x + 2$ cannot equal zero (there is no angle x such that $\cos x = -2$), we seek values of x for which

$$\cos x - 1 = 0 \quad \text{or} \quad u - 1 = 0.$$

From either equation, we have

$$\cos x = 1.$$

By inspection the solution set of $\cos x = 1$ and hence of Equation (2) is

$$\{x \mid x = k \cdot 360°, k \in J\} \quad \text{or} \quad \{x \mid x = k \cdot 2\pi^R, k \in J\}.$$

EXERCISE SET 4.7

Solve each equation. Find all solutions in the interval $0 \le x \le \pi/2$.

Examples

a. $(2 \cos x - \sqrt{3})(\sin x - 1) = 0$ b. $\sqrt{2} \sin x \cos x - \cos x = 0$

Solutions

a. The left-hand member equals 0 if

$$2 \cos x - \sqrt{3} = 0 \qquad \text{or} \qquad \sin x - 1 = 0.$$

From these equations

$$\cos x = \frac{\sqrt{3}}{2} \qquad \text{or} \qquad \sin x = 1,$$

and the solution set is $\{\pi/6, \pi/2\}$.

b. Factoring the left-hand member

$$\cos x(\sqrt{2} \sin x - 1) = 0.$$

The left-hand member equals 0 if

$$\cos x = 0 \qquad \text{or} \qquad \sin x = \frac{1}{\sqrt{2}},$$

and the solution set is $\{\pi/2, \pi/4\}$.

1. $2 \sin x - 1 = 0$ 2. $2 \cos x - 1 = 0$

3. $2 \cos^2 x = 1$ 4. $4 \sin^2 x = 3$

5. $3 \csc^2 x - 3 = 0$ 6. $\sec^2 x = 4$

7. $(2 \cos^2 x - 1)(\sin x - 1) = 0$ 8. $(\sin^2 x - 1)(\sec x - 2) = 0$

9. $\cos x \sin x = 0$ 10. $3 \tan x \sec x = 0$

11. $2 \cos^3 x - \cos x = 0$ 12. $2 \sin^3 x - \sin x = 0$

13. $2 \sin x \cos x + \sin x = 0$ 14. $2 \sin x \cos x - \cos x = 0$

Solve each equation. Find all solutions in the interval $0 \le x < 2\pi$.

Example $2 \cos^2 x + \cos x - 1 = 0$

Solution   Factoring the left-hand member,

$$(2 \cos x - 1)(\cos x + 1) = 0,$$

$$\cos x = \frac{1}{2} \qquad \text{or} \qquad \cos x = -1,$$

and the solution set is $\{\pi/3, 5\pi/3, \pi\}$.

15. $2 \cos^2 x - \cos x - 1 = 0$ **16.** $2 \cos^2 x + 3 \cos x - 2 = 0$

17. $9 \cos^2 x - 21 \cos x - 8 = 0$ **18.** $25 \sin^2 x - 20 \sin x + 4 = 0$

Solve each equation **(a)** *in the interval* $0° \leq x < 360°$ *and* **(b)** *for all* $x \in A$.

Example $\sec x - 2 \cos x = 1$

Solution

a. First write each term using the same function value. Substitute $1/\cos x$ for $\sec x$ to obtain

$$\frac{1}{\cos x} - 2 \cos x = 1.$$

Multiplying each member by $\cos x$ ($\cos x \neq 0$),

$$1 - 2 \cos^2 x = \cos x,$$

from which

$$2 \cos^2 x + \cos x - 1 = 0.$$

This equation is the same as in the preceding example. Thus, the solution set over the interval $0° \leq x < 360°$ is $\{60°, 300°, 180°\}$.

b. For all $x \in A$, the solution set is

$$\{x \mid x = 60° + k \cdot 360°\} \cup \{x \mid x = 180° + k \cdot 360°\}$$

$$\cup \{x \mid x = 300° + k \cdot 360°\}, \quad k \in J,$$

19. $\csc x + \sin x + 2 = 0$ **20.** $2 \cos x + \sec x - 3 = 0$

21. $2 \sin^2 x - \cos x - 1 = 0$ **22.** $2 \cos^2 x - 3 \sin x - 3 = 0$

23. $2 \sin x + \csc x - 3 = 0$ **24.** $\tan x + \cot x + 2 = 0$

B

Solve each equation **(a)** *in the interval* $0° \leq x < 360°$ *and* **(b)** *for all* $x \in A$.   (*Hint: Use the quadratic formula*)

25. $\sin^2 x - \sin x - 1 = 0$ **26.** $\cos^2 x + 5 \cos x + 2 = 0$

27. $3 \cos x - 1 = \sec x$ **28.** $4 \sin x \cos x - 2 \sin x = \tan x$

4.8 Conditional Equations for Multiples

Conditional equations such as

$$2 \sin x \cos x = \frac{\sqrt{3}}{2}, \tag{1}$$

$$\tan 3x = 1, \tag{2}$$

and

$$\cos 2x = \cos^2 x - 1 \tag{3}$$

need further discussion.

The identities involving multiples of the variable are often useful to help solve certain kinds of equations. For example, the solution set of

$$2 \sin x \cos x = \frac{\sqrt{3}}{2}, \tag{1}$$

over the interval $0 \le x \le \pi/2$, can readily be found if $\sin 2x$ is substituted for the left-hand member, $2 \sin x \cos x$, to obtain

$$\sin 2x = \frac{\sqrt{3}}{2}.$$

By inspection we have that

$$2x = \frac{\pi}{3} + k \cdot 2\pi \qquad \text{or} \qquad 2x = \frac{2\pi}{3} + k \cdot 2\pi,$$

$$x = \frac{\pi}{6} + k \cdot \pi \qquad \text{or} \qquad x = \frac{\pi}{3} + k \cdot \pi.$$

If $k = 0$, $x = \pi/6$ or $x = \pi/3$; if $k \ge 1$, then $x > \pi$. Hence, the solution set of Equation (1) over the interval from 0 to $\pi/2$ is $\{\pi/6, \pi/3\}$.

Now consider the solution set of

$$\tan 3x = 1 \tag{2}$$

over the interval $0 \le x < 2\pi$. By inspection we have that

$$3x = \frac{\pi}{4} + k \cdot \pi,$$

and, dividing each term by 3,

$$x = \frac{\pi}{12} + k \cdot \frac{\pi}{3}, \quad k \in J.$$

To find the solution set over the interval $0 \le x < 2\pi$, we take 0, 1, 2, 3, 4, and 5 as replacements for k and obtain

$$\left\{ \frac{\pi}{12}, \frac{5\pi}{12}, \frac{3\pi}{4}, \frac{13\pi}{12}, \frac{17\pi}{12}, \frac{7\pi}{4} \right\}.$$

Note that if $k > 5$, then $x > 2\pi$.

Now consider the equation

$$\cos 2x = \cos^2 x - 1. \qquad (3)$$

One method of solving this equation for $x \in R$ consists of substituting $2 \cos^2 x - 1$ for $\cos 2x$ to obtain the equivalent equations

$$2 \cos^2 x - 1 = \cos^2 x - 1,$$
$$\cos^2 x = 0.$$

Then, we have as the solution set

$$\left\{ x \mid x = \frac{\pi}{2} + k\pi, k \in J \right\}.$$

Alternatively, we could have substituted $(1 + \cos 2x)/2$ for $\cos^2 x$ in the right-hand member of Equation (3) to obtain the equivalent equations

$$\cos 2x = \frac{1 + \cos 2x}{2} - 1,$$
$$2 \cos 2x = 1 + \cos 2x - 2,$$
$$\cos 2x = -1.$$

By inspection, we have that

$$2x = \pi + k \cdot 2\pi, \quad k \in J,$$

from which the solution set is given by

$$\left\{ x \mid x = \frac{\pi}{2} + k\pi, k \in J \right\},$$

as we found above using the other method.

EXERCISE SET 4.8

A

Solve each equation for all x, such that $0 \le x \le \pi/2$.

Example $\cos 3x = \dfrac{1}{2}$

Solution Using Table 1.2 and the fact that the cosine of an angle in Quadrant I or IV is positive, we first consider all possible solutions and obtain

$$3x = \frac{\pi}{3} + k \cdot 2\pi \qquad \text{or} \qquad 3x = \frac{5\pi}{3} + k \cdot 2\pi.$$

From which, dividing each term by 3,

$$x = \frac{\pi}{9} + k \cdot \frac{2\pi}{3} \qquad \text{or} \qquad x = \frac{5\pi}{9} + k \cdot \frac{2\pi}{3}.$$

Since the problem restricts x to the interval $0 \le x \le \pi/2$, we need only the value 0 for k. If $k = 0$, $x = \pi/9$ or $x = 5\pi/9$. Furthermore, since $5\pi/9$ is not in the required interval, the solution set is $\{\pi/9\}$.

1. $\sin 3x = 0$ 2. $\cos 3x = 1$

3. $\tan 4x = -\sqrt{3}$ 4. $\cot 4x = -1$

5. $\sec 5x = 2$ 6. $\csc 5x = \sqrt{2}$

7. $\cos 2x - \sin x = 0$ 8. $\cos 2x + \cos x = 0$

9. $\sin 2x + \sin x = 0$ 10. $\sin 2x - \cos x = 0$

11. $\sin 2x = \cos 2x$ 12. $\sin \dfrac{x}{2} = \tan \dfrac{x}{2}$

13. $\tan \dfrac{x}{2} - \cos x = -1$ 14. $\cos x = \sin \dfrac{x}{2}$

Solve each equation in the interval $0° \le x < 360°$.

Example $\sin 4x = \dfrac{\sqrt{3}}{2}$

Solution By inspection we have $4x = 60°$. However, since $\sin \theta$ is

(continued)

also positive for angles in Quadrant II, we know that $4x = 120°$ will also satisfy the equation. Thus for $k \in J$,

$$4x = 60° + k \cdot 360° \quad \text{or} \quad 4x = 120° + k \cdot 360°.$$

Dividing each member of both equations by 4, we obtain

$$x = 15° + k \cdot 90° \quad \text{or} \quad x = 30° + k \cdot 90°.$$

Since the problem restricts x to the interval $0° \leq x < 360°$, we need only the values of 0, 1, 2, and 3 for k.

If $k = 0$, $x = 15°$ or $x = 30°$,

if $k = 1$, $x = 105°$ or $x = 120°$,

if $k = 2$, $x = 195°$ or $x = 210°$,

if $k = 3$, $x = 285°$ or $x = 300°$,

and the solution set is $\{15°, 30°, 105°, 120°, 195°, 210°, 285°, 300°\}$.

15. $\sin 3x = \dfrac{1}{2}$ **16.** $\cos 4x = -1$

17. $\sin 3x = \cos 3x$ **18.** $\tan 2x = \cot 2x$

19. $\sin^2 2x = 1$ **20.** $\cos^2 2x = 1$

21. $\tan^2 3x = 1$ **22.** $\cot^2 3x = 3$

23. $\left(1 + \cos \dfrac{x}{2}\right) \cos \dfrac{x}{2} = 0$ **24.** $\sin^2 \dfrac{x}{4} - \dfrac{1}{2} \sin \dfrac{x}{4} = 0$

25. $5 \sec 3x = 2 \cos 3x - 3$ **26.** $\tan x \tan 2x = 1$

B

Solve each equation for all x, such that $x \in R$.

27. $\sin 2x = \cos x$ **28.** $2 \cos 2x - 1 = -3 \sin^2 x$

29. $\sin x \cos 3x = 0$ **30.** $(\sin 2x - 1)(\cos 3x + 1) = 0$

31. $\tan 2x - 3 \sec^2 2x = -5$ **32.** $\cos^2 2x + 3 \sin 2x - 3 = 0$

33. $\sin 2x \cos x + \cos 2x \sin x = \dfrac{1}{\sqrt{2}}$

34. $\sin 3x \cos x - \cos 3x \sin x = \dfrac{\sqrt{3}}{2}$

35. Use graphical methods to approximate a positive solution for

$$\cos 2x = x, \quad x \in R.$$

Hint: Graph $y = \cos 2x$ and $y = x$ on the same axes.

36. Use graphical methods to approximate a positive solution for

$$x^2 - 3 \sin \frac{x}{2} = 0, \quad x \in R.$$

Chapter Summary

4.1–4.6 Equations are **identities** if they are satisfied for all real number replacements of the variable for which both members of the equation are defined.

For convenience, the basic identities that have been established are listed inside the back cover.

An equation can be shown *not* to be an identity by replacing the variable with a real number for which the resulting statement is false.

4.7–4.8 **Conditional equations** involving circular function values can be solved by inspection or by generating equivalent equations from which the solutions are evident by inspection. The identities introduced in this chapter are useful in obtaining such equivalent equations.

A list of symbols introduced in this chapter is shown inside the front cover, and important properties are shown inside the back cover.

Review Exercises

A

4.1–4.5 *Express each of the following in terms of the function values* $\sin \alpha$ *and/or* $\cos \alpha$ *and simplify the expression.*

1. $\csc \alpha \tan \alpha$ **2.** $\cot^2 \alpha \sec^2 \alpha$

3. $\sin^2 \alpha (\csc^2 \alpha - 1)$ **4.** $\cot \alpha \cos \alpha \sec^2 \alpha$

Verify that each equation is an identity.

5. $\cos \alpha \csc \alpha = \cot \alpha$

6. $\dfrac{\cos \alpha}{\cot \alpha} = \sin \alpha$

7. $\sin^2 \alpha(1 + \cot^2 \alpha) = 1$

8. $\dfrac{\cos \alpha \csc \alpha}{\cot \alpha} = 1$

9. $\tan \alpha = \dfrac{1}{\cos \alpha \csc \alpha}$

10. $1 + \tan^2 \alpha = \csc^2 \alpha \tan^2 \alpha$

11. $\sin(-\alpha) = -\dfrac{\tan \alpha}{\sec \alpha}$

12. $\tan(-\alpha) = \dfrac{\cos(-\alpha) \sin(-\alpha)}{1 - \sin^2 \alpha}$

13. $\cos(270° + x) = \sin x$

14. $\cos(270° - x) = -\sin x$

15. $\sin(90° + x) = \cos x$

16. $\sin(\alpha - 45°) = \dfrac{\sin \alpha - \cos \alpha}{\sqrt{2}}$

17. $\cos(\alpha - 45°) = \dfrac{\cos \alpha + \sin \alpha}{\sqrt{2}}$

18. $\tan(\alpha - 45°) = \dfrac{\tan \alpha - 1}{1 + \tan \alpha}$

19. $\cos 2x + 1 = 2 \cos^2 x$

20. $\sin 2x = 2 \sin^2 x \cos x \csc x$

21. $\csc x = 2 \cos x \csc 2x$

22. $\cos 2x = \cos^4 x - \sin^4 x$

By counterexamples, show that each equation is not an identity.

23. $\sin \alpha \sec \alpha = 2 \tan \alpha$

24. $\dfrac{1 - \cos \alpha}{\sin \alpha} = \dfrac{1 + \sin \alpha}{\cos \alpha}$

4.6 *Use half-angle formulas to find the exact value for each of the following.*

25. $\cos 105°$

26. $\tan 165°$

Verify the identities in Exercises 27 and 28.

27. $\cos^2 \dfrac{x}{2} = \dfrac{\sin^2 x}{2(1 - \cos x)}$

28. $\sin^2 \dfrac{x}{2} = \dfrac{\csc x - \cot x}{2 \csc x}$

29. Express $\cos x \cos 5x$ in terms of sums of function values.

30. Express $\sin 6x + \sin 4x$ in terms of products of function values.

4.7 *Solve each equation in the interval $0 \le x \le \pi/2$.*

31. $2 \sin x - \sqrt{3} = 0$

32. $\csc^2 x = 4$

33. $\sec x - 2 \cos x = 0$ **34.** $\cot x \csc x = 0$

Solve each equation in the interval $0° \leq x < 360°$.

35. $\cot^2 x - 2 \csc^2 x + 5 = 0$ **36.** $\sec^2 x - 4 \cos^2 x = 0$

4.8 *Solve each equation in the interval* $0° \leq x < 360°$.

37. $\cos 3x = \dfrac{1}{\sqrt{2}}$ **38.** $\sin 4x = \dfrac{\sqrt{3}}{2}$

39. $\sin 2x - \tan x = 0$ **40.** $\tan 2x = \tan x$

5 VECTORS

5.1 Geometric Vectors

Some physical quantities, such as length and mass, are characterized by *magnitude alone*. If units of measure are specified, the quantities can be represented by real numbers and associated with points in a number line. In the description of other physical quantities, such as force, velocity, and acceleration, *direction as well as magnitude* is required. Such a quantity can be represented by a pair of real numbers and associated with a line segment in the form of an arrow with length representing the magnitude and pointing in an assigned direction.

Definition 5.1 *A two-dimensional* **geometric vector*** *designated by* $\vec{v}$ *is a line segment with a specified direction.*

If the end points of a geometric vector are named, it is sometimes convenient to specify the vector by using these names. For example, in Figure 5.1 the geometric vector can also be designated by $\overrightarrow{PQ}$, where the point named P is called the **initial point** and the point named Q is called the **terminal point.** For discussion purposes, the geometric vector in Figure 5.1 is shown in the framework of a rectangular coordinate system.

Sometimes a geometric vector is simply represented by **v** without using the arrow above the symbol. We are using the arrow to differen-

Figure 5.1

---

* The term *geometric vector* is used to differentiate this notion of a directed line segment from a vector as an ordered pair of real numbers introduced in Section 5.3.

tiate this symbol for a geometric vector from the symbol v as a variable for a real number. Also the arrow emphasizes the fact that a geometric vector has *magnitude* and *direction*.

Magnitude and Direction

We shall assume that each geometric vector in the plane has a length that is a real number that depends on the unit of measurement.

Definition 5.2   *For all geometric vectors $\vec{v}$, the* **norm** (*or* **magnitude**) *of $\vec{v}$ is the length of $\vec{v}$ and is designated by $\|\vec{v}\|$.*

When a geometric vector is considered in relation to a rectangular coordinate system, the following concept is useful.

Definition 5.3   *The* **direction angle** *of a geometric vector $\vec{v}$ is an angle α, $-180° < \alpha \le 180°$, such that the initial side of α is the ray from the initial point of $\vec{v}$ parallel to the x-axis and directed in the positive x direction; the terminal side of α is the ray from the initial point of $\vec{v}$ and containing $\vec{v}$.*

Figure 5.2

Figure 5.2 shows $\|\vec{v}\|$ and the direction angle α associated with a vector $\vec{v}$. From a vector viewpoint, the real number $\|\vec{v}\|$ is called a **scalar.**

Definition 5.4   *For all geometric vectors $\vec{v}$, the geometric vector $-\vec{v}$ has the same magnitude as $\vec{v}$ and has a direction angle whose measure differs from the measure of the direction angle of $\vec{v}$ by 180°.*

Figure 5.3 shows two vectors $\vec{v}$ and $-\vec{v}$.

Figure 5.3

Definition 5.5   *Two geometric vectors $\vec{v}_1$ and $\vec{v}_2$ are* **equivalent** *if they have the same magnitude and the same direction angle.*

Figure 5.4 illustrates three equivalent vectors. We use the symbol = to indicate that two vectors are equivalent.

If we can imagine "sliding" a geometric vector so that it remains parallel to its original position in the plane, then any geometric vector can "slide" onto any vector equivalent to it.

Figure 5.4

Operations

Geometric vectors are very useful in setting up mathematical models of practical problems. However, before this can be done, certain operations must be defined.

Figure 5.5

Definition 5.6   *For all geometric vectors $\vec{v}_1$ and $\vec{v}_2$, such that the terminal point of $\vec{v}_1$ is the initial point of $\vec{v}_2$, $\vec{v}_1 + \vec{v}_2$ is the geometric vector having the same initial point as $\vec{v}_1$ and the same terminal point as $\vec{v}_2$. $\vec{v}_1 + \vec{v}_2$ is called the* **sum** *(or* **resultant***) of $\vec{v}_1$ and $\vec{v}_2$.*

As indicated in Figure 5.5a, if $\vec{v}_1$ and $\vec{v}_2$ are not in the relative locations required by Definition 5.6, we "slide" one of them, say $\vec{v}_2$, parallel to its original position into the correct location and then find the sum $\vec{v}_1 + \vec{v}_2$.

Because a triangle is formed by $\vec{v}_1$, $\vec{v}_2$, and $\vec{v}_1 + \vec{v}_2$, we sometimes say that geometric vectors are added according to "the triangle law." From the properties of a parallelogram, we have that, if $\vec{v}_1$ and $\vec{v}_2$ have the same initial point, as shown in Figure 5.5b, the sum $\vec{v}_1 + \vec{v}_2$ is a diagonal of the parallelogram with adjacent sides $\vec{v}_1$ and $\vec{v}_2$. Therefore, we sometimes also say that geometric vectors are added according to "the parallelogram law." Figure 5.5c shows the sum $\vec{v}_3 + \vec{v}_4$ if $\vec{v}_3$ and $\vec{v}_4$ are collinear (vectors lie on the same line).

Note that the symbol "+" in a vector sum is being used in a different sense from that of its ordinary usage to pair two real numbers in a sum, although the operation is commonly referred to as the "addition" of geometric vectors.

Example   Construct the sum $\vec{v}_1 + \vec{v}_2$.

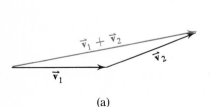

(a)

Solution   "Slide" the initial point of $\vec{v}_2$ onto the terminal point of $\vec{v}_1$. The sum $\vec{v}_1 + \vec{v}_2$ is the geometric vector from the initial point of $\vec{v}_1$ to the terminal point of $\vec{v}_2$ (figure a).

(b)

Alternate Solution   "Slide" the initial point of $\vec{v}_2$ onto the initial point of $\vec{v}_1$ and form a parallelogram. The sum $\vec{v}_1 + \vec{v}_2$ is the diagonal of the parallelogram (figure b).

Definition 5.7   *For all geometric vectors $\vec{v}$ and any real number c, $c\vec{v}$ is a geometric vector with magnitude $\|c\vec{v}\| = |c| \cdot \|\vec{v}\|$, having the same direction angle as $\vec{v}$ if $c > 0$ and the same direction angle as $-\vec{v}$ if $c < 0$. The geometric vector $c\vec{v}$ is called a **scalar multiple** of $\vec{v}$.*

Example   As shown in the figure, $2\vec{v}$ and $\frac{1}{2}\vec{v}$ are geometric vectors in the same direction as $\vec{v}$ such that $\|2\vec{v}\| = 2\|\vec{v}\|$ and $\|\frac{1}{2}\vec{v}\| = \frac{1}{2}\|\vec{v}\|$, while $-2\vec{v}$ is in the opposite direction such that $\|-2\vec{v}\| = |-2|\,\|\vec{v}\| = 2\|\vec{v}\|$.

EXERCISE SET 5.1

A

In Exercises 1–40, use the geometric vectors below.

If $\|\vec{v}_1\| = 1$, estimate the magnitude and the measure of the direction angle for each of the following geometric vectors, where $\vec{v}_1$ is in the direction of the positive x-axis.

1. $\vec{v}_2$ **2.** $\vec{v}_3$ **3.** $\vec{v}_4$ **4.** $\vec{v}_5$ **5.** $\vec{v}_6$ **6.** $\vec{v}_7$

Using freehand methods, draw a single vector representing each of the following sums.

Example $(\vec{v}_1 + \vec{v}_3) + \vec{v}_7$

Solution   See figure.

7. $\vec{v}_1 + \vec{v}_2$	**8.** $\vec{v}_1 + \vec{v}_3$	**9.** $\vec{v}_1 + \vec{v}_4$
10. $\vec{v}_1 + \vec{v}_5$	**11.** $\vec{v}_1 + \vec{v}_6$	**12.** $\vec{v}_1 + \vec{v}_7$
13. $\vec{v}_2 + \vec{v}_3$	**14.** $\vec{v}_2 + \vec{v}_4$	**15.** $(\vec{v}_2 + \vec{v}_5) + \vec{v}_6$
16. $(\vec{v}_2 + \vec{v}_6) + \vec{v}_7$	**17.** $(\vec{v}_2 + \vec{v}_3) + \vec{v}_5$	**18.** $\vec{v}_3 + (\vec{v}_4 + \vec{v}_7)$

Using freehand methods, draw each of the following.

19. $-\vec{v}_1$	**20.** $-\vec{v}_3$	**21.** $2\vec{v}_7$
22. $4\vec{v}_1$	**23.** $-2\vec{v}_5$	**24.** $-\vec{v}_6$
25. $\frac{1}{2}\vec{v}_3$	**26.** $-\frac{1}{3}\vec{v}_4$	**27.** $2\vec{v}_1 + 3\vec{v}_5$
28. $4\vec{v}_7 + 2\vec{v}_6$	**29.** $\frac{1}{2}\vec{v}_4 + \vec{v}_7$	**30.** $\vec{v}_2 + \frac{3}{4}\vec{v}_3$
31. $2\vec{v}_3 + (-3\vec{v}_1)$	**32.** $\vec{v}_7 + (-2\vec{v}_2)$	

B

By appropriate freehand sketches show that each statement is true.

33. $\vec{v}_2 + \vec{v}_3 = \vec{v}_3 + \vec{v}_2$ **34.** $\vec{v}_5 + \vec{v}_4 = \vec{v}_4 + \vec{v}_5$

35. $(\vec{v}_6 + \vec{v}_7) + \vec{v}_2 = \vec{v}_6 + (\vec{v}_7 + \vec{v}_2)$ **36.** $\vec{v}_3 + (\vec{v}_7 + \vec{v}_5) = (\vec{v}_3 + \vec{v}_7) + \vec{v}_5$

37. $2(\vec{v}_3 + \vec{v}_5) = 2\vec{v}_3 + 2\vec{v}_5$ **38.** $(2 + 3)\vec{v}_7 = 2\vec{v}_7 + 3\vec{v}_7$

39. $\frac{1}{3}\vec{v}_1 + 2\vec{v}_1 = \frac{7}{3}\vec{v}_1$ **40.** $\vec{v}_2 + (-2\vec{v}_2) = -\vec{v}_2$

5.2 Applications of Geometric Vectors

The solution to many kinds of practical problems involving such quantities as velocities, accelerations, forces, and directed line segments can be found by means of geometric vectors.

Projections

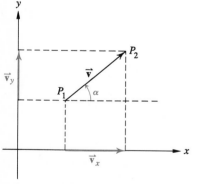

Figure 5.6

First, consider the *projections* of a geometric vector on the x- and y-axes of a Cartesian coordinate system. Figure 5.6 depicts a geometric vector $\vec{v}$ and perpendicular lines drawn to the x- and y-axes from the endpoints P_1 and P_2 of $\vec{v}$. The geometric vector projections $\vec{v}_x$ and $\vec{v}_y$ of $\vec{v}$ on the x-axis and y-axis, respectively, are called the **rectangular components** of $\vec{v}$; $\vec{v}_x$ is called the **horizontal component** of $\vec{v}$, and $\vec{v}_y$ is called the **vertical component**. These components are determined by the magnitude of $\vec{v}$ and its direction. Furthermore,

$$\vec{v} = \vec{v}_x + \vec{v}_y.$$

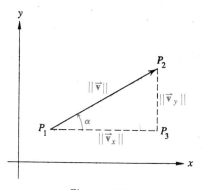

Figure 5.7

In Figure 5.7, $\overline{P_1P_3}$ is drawn parallel to the x-axis, and $\overline{P_2P_3}$ is drawn parallel to the y-axis. Since

$$|\sin \alpha| = \frac{\|\vec{v}_y\|}{\|\vec{v}\|},$$

$$\|\vec{v}_y\| = \|\vec{v}\| \cdot |\sin \alpha|. \tag{1}$$

Also, since

$$|\cos \alpha| = \frac{\|\vec{v}_x\|}{\|\vec{v}\|},$$

$$\|\vec{v}_x\| = \|\vec{v}\| \cdot |\cos \alpha|. \tag{2}$$

In Figure 5.7, α is shown to be a positive acute angle. From Definition 5.3, we have that $-180° < \alpha \le 180°$ and hence $\cos \alpha$ or $\sin \alpha$ may be negative. Therefore because $\|\vec{v}_x\|$, $\|\vec{v}_y\|$, and $\|\vec{v}\|$ are all positive, we use $|\sin \alpha|$ and $|\cos \alpha|$ in Equations (1) and (2).

If the geometric vectors $\vec{v}_x$ and $\vec{v}_y$ are known, the magnitude $\|\vec{v}\|$ and direction angle α of $\vec{v}$ can be determined from the relationships in a right triangle, as shown in Figure 5.7:

$$\|\vec{v}\| = \sqrt{\|\vec{v}_x\|^2 + \|\vec{v}_y\|^2},$$

and

$$|\sin \alpha| = \frac{\|\vec{v}_y\|}{\|\vec{v}\|} \qquad \text{or} \qquad |\cos \alpha| = \frac{\|\vec{v}_x\|}{\|\vec{v}\|}.$$

Example The horizontal component, $\vec{v}_x$, has its initial point at (4, 0) with $\|\vec{v}_x\| = 6$. The vertical component, $\vec{v}_y$, has its initial point at (0, 3) with $\|\vec{v}_y\| = 8$. Find α and $\|\vec{v}\|$ and sketch $\vec{v}$. Assume $\vec{v}_x$ and $\vec{v}_y$ are directed in a positive direction.

Solution The magnitude

$$\|\vec{v}\| = \sqrt{\|\vec{v}_x\|^2 + \|\vec{v}_y\|^2}$$
$$= \sqrt{6^2 + 8^2} = \sqrt{100} = 10.$$

Because

$$\cos \alpha = \frac{6}{10} = 0.6000,$$

$$\alpha \approx 53.1°.$$

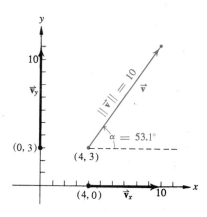

Thus, the geometric vector $\vec{v}$ has its initial point at (4, 3), a direction angle whose measure is approximately 53.1°, and a magnitude of 10.

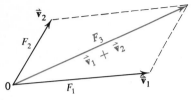

Figure 5.8

Force

Consider two forces, F_1 and F_2, acting on a particle at the point O, as in Figure 5.8. Since a force has magnitude and direction, we can represent it with a geometric vector, with magnitude given in terms of the units of force and with direction angle given by the direction of the force. It is shown in physics that the two forces represented by $\vec{v}_1$ and $\vec{v}_2$ can be replaced by a single equivalent force, F_3, associated with the vector $\vec{v}_1 + \vec{v}_2$, the resultant of the forces represented by $\vec{v}_1$ and $\vec{v}_2$. The resultant $\vec{v}_1 + \vec{v}_2$ can be obtained, as discussed in Section 5.1, by constructing the parallelogram with adjacent sides $\vec{v}_1$ and $\vec{v}_2$ and drawing the diagonal; $\vec{v}_1 + \vec{v}_2$ is then associated with the resultant force F_3.

Example Two forces, the first one of 5 pounds and the second of 12 pounds, act on a body at right angles to each other. Find the magnitude of the resultant force and the measure of the angle that the resultant force makes with the 5-pound force.

Solution Because $\|\vec{v}_1\| = 5$ and $\|\vec{v}_2\| = 12$,

$$\|\vec{v}\| = \sqrt{5^2 + 12^2} = \sqrt{169} = 13,$$

and

$$\cos \alpha = \frac{5}{13} \approx 0.3846.$$

Hence, $\alpha = 67.4°$. Thus, the magnitude of the resultant force is 13 pounds, and the angle it makes with the 5-pound force has a measure of approximately $67.4°$.

In cases where the measure of an angle between two forces is not $90°$, it is sometimes convenient to use the Law of Cosines and the Law of Sines in order to find the resultant force.

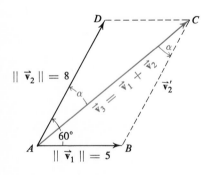

Example A force of 5 pounds and another force of 8 pounds act on an object at an angle of $60°$ with respect to each other. Find the magnitude of the resultant force and the angle it forms with respect to the 8-pound force.

Solution The figure shows the forces of 5 pounds and 8 pounds represented by the geometric vectors $\vec{v}_1$ and $\vec{v}_2$, respectively, and the resultant $\vec{v}_3 = \vec{v}_1 + \vec{v}_2$. Since $\vec{v}_2'$ is equivalent to $\vec{v}_2$, and since the consecutive angles of a parallelogram are supplementary,

$$\angle ABC = 180° - 60° = 120°,$$

and it follows from the Law of Cosines that

$$\|\vec{\mathbf{v}}_3\|^2 = \|\vec{\mathbf{v}}_1\|^2 + \|\vec{\mathbf{v}}_2\|^2 - 2\|\vec{\mathbf{v}}_1\| \cdot \|\vec{\mathbf{v}}_2\| \cos 120°$$

$$= 5^2 + 8^2 - 2(5)(8)(-\cos 60°)$$

$$= 25 + 64 + 80(0.5000) = 129.$$

Therefore, $\|\vec{\mathbf{v}}_3\| = \sqrt{129} \approx 11.4$. From the Law of Sines,

$$\frac{\sin \alpha}{\|\vec{\mathbf{v}}_1\|} = \frac{\sin 120°}{\|\vec{\mathbf{v}}_3\|},$$

or, equivalently,

$$\sin \alpha = \frac{\|\vec{\mathbf{v}}_1\| \sin 120°}{\|\vec{\mathbf{v}}_3\|}$$

$$\approx \frac{5(0.8660)}{11.4} \approx 0.3798.$$

Hence, $\alpha \approx 22.3°$. Thus, the forces of 5 and 8 pounds, acting at an angle of 60° with respect to each other, can be represented by the single resultant force of 11.4 pounds. The angle it makes with the 8-pound force has a measure of approximately 22.3°.

Velocity

Geometric vectors also can facilitate the solution of problems involving velocities and accelerations. As examples, we shall look at several air navigation problems. First, however, we consider some terminology that is commonly used. The **heading** of an airplane is the direction in which it is pointed, and the **course** is the direction in which it is actually moving over the ground. Its **air speed** is the speed relative to the air, and its **ground speed** is the speed relative to the ground. The two directions and two speeds may differ because of wind effect.

If we use one geometric vector, say $\vec{\mathbf{v}}_1$, to represent the heading and air speed of an airplane (see Figure 5.9) and another, say $\vec{\mathbf{v}}_2$, to represent the wind direction and speed, then $\vec{\mathbf{v}}_3 = \vec{\mathbf{v}}_1 + \vec{\mathbf{v}}_2$ represents the course and ground speed. The angle α between the geometric vectors $\vec{\mathbf{v}}_1$ and $\vec{\mathbf{v}}_3$ is called the **drift angle.** The measures of the angles for the heading, wind, and course directions in air navigation are generally taken clockwise from the ray directed toward true north. The angle is called the **bearing** and has a positive measure. In graphical representa-

Figure 5.9

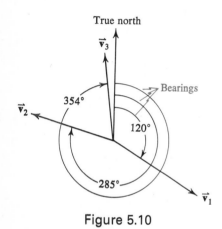

Figure 5.10

tions, we shall use the positive y-axis as the true north direction, and the positive x-axis as the true east direction. For example, in Figure 5.10, the bearing of the geometric vector $\vec{v}_1$ is 120°, that of $\vec{v}_2$ is 285°, and that of $\vec{v}_3$ is 354°.*

Example An airplane is headed northeast (bearing 45°) with an air speed of 500 miles per hour, with a wind blowing from the southeast (bearing 315°) at a speed of 75 miles per hour. Find the drift angle, the ground speed, and the course of the plane.

Solution The figure on page 205 shows three vectors: $\vec{v}_1$ representing the heading and air speed, $\vec{v}_2$ representing the wind direction and speed, and $\vec{v}_3$ representing the course and ground speed. From geometry we have that

$$\angle ABC = 315° - 45° - 180° = 90°.$$

Because $\angle ABC$ is a right angle,

$$\tan \alpha = \frac{75}{500} = 0.1500,$$

and the drift angle $\alpha \approx 8.5°$. The bearing, or direction, of the course is

$$45° - \alpha = 45° - 8.5° = 36.5°.$$

---

* Other types of bearings, each of which has its own reference, or initial, ray from which the angle is measured, are also defined. A bearing used in surveying is designated by an acute angle measured to the east or west of a ray pointing toward true north or true south, for example, N 35° E, N 38° W, S 22° E, and S 47° W.

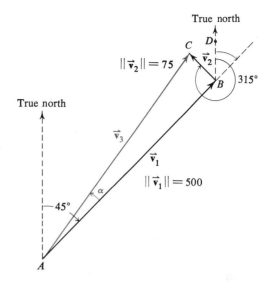

Now, because $\cos \alpha = 500/\|\vec{\mathbf{v}}_3\|$,

$$\|\vec{\mathbf{v}}_3\| = \frac{500}{\cos 8.5°} \approx \frac{500}{0.9890} \approx 506.$$

Thus, the ground speed (magnitude of the course vector) is approximately 506 miles per hour.

EXERCISE SET 5.2

A

The direction angle α and $\|\vec{\mathbf{v}}\|$ are given. Find $\|\vec{\mathbf{v}}_x\|$ and $\|\vec{\mathbf{v}}_y\|$.

Example $\alpha = 60°$ and $\|\vec{\mathbf{v}}\| = 8$

Solution   The figure shows the geometric vector $\vec{\mathbf{v}}$ and its rectangular components $\vec{\mathbf{v}}_x$ and $\vec{\mathbf{v}}_y$. From Equations (1) and (2) on page 201,

$$\|\vec{\mathbf{v}}_x\| = \|\vec{\mathbf{v}}\| \,|\cos 60°| = 8\left(\frac{1}{2}\right) = 4,$$

$$\|\vec{\mathbf{v}}_y\| = \|\vec{\mathbf{v}}\| \,|\sin 60°| = 8\left(\frac{\sqrt{3}}{2}\right) = 4\sqrt{3}.$$

1. $\alpha = 45°$ and $\|\vec{\mathbf{v}}\| = 5\sqrt{2}$ **2.** $\alpha = 30°$ and $\|\vec{\mathbf{v}}\| = 6$

3. $\alpha = 90°$ and $\|\vec{\mathbf{v}}\| = 15$ **4.** $\alpha = 120°$ and $\|\vec{\mathbf{v}}\| = 2$

5. $\alpha = -30°$ and $\|\vec{v}\| = 12$ **6.** $\alpha = -45°$ and $\|\vec{v}\| = 2\sqrt{2}$

7. $\alpha = -120°$ and $\|\vec{v}\| = 8$ **8.** $\alpha = -150°$ and $\|\vec{v}\| = 4$

In Exercises 9–14, the two given forces act on a point in a plane at an angle with the specified measure. Find the magnitude of the resultant force and the angles the resultant force makes with the given forces.

Example Forces of 10 to 20 kilograms act on a point at an angle of 45° with respect to each other.

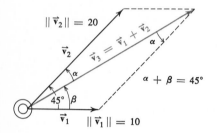

Solution The figure shows the given forces $\vec{v}_1$ and $\vec{v}_2$ and the resultant $\vec{v}_3 = \vec{v}_1 + \vec{v}_2$. Since $\alpha + \beta = 45°$, the measure of the angle opposite $\vec{v}_3$ is 135°. From the fact that $\cos 135° = -\cos 45°$ and from the Law of Cosines,

$$\|\vec{v}_3\|^2 = 10^2 + 20^2 - 2(10)(20)(-\cos 45°)$$
$$\approx 100 + 400 + 283 \approx 783,$$

and by means of a calculator or by using interpolation from Table I, $\|\vec{v}_3\| \approx 28.0$. From the Law of Sines,

$$\frac{\sin \alpha}{\|\vec{v}_1\|} = \frac{\sin 135°}{\|\vec{v}_3\|},$$

so

$$\sin \alpha = \frac{\|\vec{v}_1\| \sin 135°}{\|\vec{v}_3\|} \approx \frac{10(0.7071)}{28.0} \approx 0.2525.$$

Hence, $\alpha \approx 14.6°$. If $\alpha + \beta = 45°$, then

$$\beta \approx 45° - 14.6° = 30.4°.$$

Thus, the resultant force is approximately 28.0 kilograms. The angles this force makes with the force of 10 kilograms and with the force of 20 kilograms have measures of approximately 30.4° and 14.6°, respectively.

9. Forces of 3 and 4 pounds, acting at an angle of 90° with respect to each other.

10. Forces of 5 and 7 pounds, acting at an angle of 30° with respect to each other.

11. Forces of 15 and 20 kilograms, acting at an angle of 75° with respect to each other.

12. Forces of 8 and 11 kilograms, acting at an angle of 132° 48′ with respect to each other.

13. Forces of 6 and 10 kilograms acting at an angle of 120° with respect to each other.

14. Forces of 20 and 30 kilograms, acting at an angle of 100° with respect to each other.

15. The resultant of two forces acting at an angle of 90° with respect to each other is 50 kilograms. If one of the forces is 30 kilograms, find the other force and the angle it makes with the resultant.

16. Two equal forces acting at an angle of 60° with respect to each other have a resultant of 80 kilograms. Find the magnitude of each force.

17. Two forces acting at an angle of 60° with respect to each other have a resultant of 50 pounds. If one force acts at an angle of 20° with respect to the resultant, find the magnitude of each force.

18. Two forces, one of 100 kilograms and the other 200 kilograms, have a resultant of 250 kilograms. Find the angle formed by the two forces.

Example An auto weighing 1500 kilograms is on a slope that makes an angle of 9° 30′ with the horizontal. Find the force that pulls the auto down the hill.

Solution The force due to gravity can be resolved into two forces, one force in the direction of the incline and one force perpendicular to the plane. See the figure. In this case, $\overrightarrow{AB}$, the force due to gravity, is resolved into $\overrightarrow{AC}$ along the incline and $\overrightarrow{CB}$, perpendicular to $\overrightarrow{AC}$. From geometry, $\angle B = \angle D$ because the sides of $\angle B$ are perpendicular to the sides of $\angle D$. Thus,

$$\sin 9° \, 30′ = \frac{\|\overrightarrow{AC}\|}{1500},$$

from which

$$\|\overrightarrow{AC}\| = 1500 \sin 9° \, 30′ \approx 248.$$

Hence, a force of 248 kilograms pulls the auto down the hill.

19. An auto, weighing 1750 kilograms, is on a slope that makes an angle of 8° 24′ with the horizontal. Find the force that pulls the auto down the hill.

20. A steel ball, weighing 50 kilograms, is on an inclined surface. What angle does the plane make with the horizontal if a force of 10 kilograms is pulling the ball down the surface?

21. A force of 110 kilograms is needed to keep a weight of 200 kilograms from sliding down an inclined plane. What angle does the plane make with the horizontal?   *Note:* The force that keeps it from sliding is opposite to the force pulling it down the plane, and has the same magnitude.

22. A force of 200 kilograms is needed to keep a weight of 320 kilograms from sliding down an inclined ramp. What angle does the plane make with the horizontal?

23. A bullet has an acceleration of 2 meters per second^2 in a direction making an angle of 35° with the horizontal. Find the horizontal and vertical components ($\|\vec{v}_x\|$ and $\|\vec{v}_y\|$) of its acceleration.

24. A space rocket has an acceleration of 4.2 meters per second^2 in a direction making an angle of 73° with the horizontal. Find the horizontal and vertical components of the rocket's acceleration.

25. A crew can row a boat at a speed of 9.2 kilometers per hour in still water. If the crew heads across a river at right angles to the current and finds its "drift angle" to be 6°, find the speed of the current.

26. A man can swim at a speed of 2 kilometers per hour in still water. If he heads across a river at right angles to a current of 5 kilometers per hour, find his speed in relation to the land and the direction in which he actually moves.

27. An airplane is headed southeast (bearing 135°) with an air speed of 600 miles per hour, with the wind blowing from the northeast (bearing 225°) at a speed of 120 miles per hour. Find the drift angle, the ground speed, and the course of the airplane.

28. Solve Exercise 27 if the wind is from the southwest (bearing 45°) at a speed of 60 miles per hour.

29. An airplane is headed on a bearing of 250° with an air speed of 425 miles per hour. The course has a bearing of 262°. The ground speed is 475 miles per hour. Find the drift angle, the wind direction, and the wind speed.

30. Solve Exercise 29 if the course has a bearing of 241°.

31. A pilot wishes to fly on a course bearing 90° and with a ground speed of 600 kilometers per hour. If a wind is blowing from the north (bearing 180°) with a speed of 50 kilometers an hour, what must be the heading and air speed of the aircraft?

32. Solve Exercise 31 if the wind is from the northwest (bearing 135°).

Ex. 35

Ex. 36

B

33. Two ships leave a harbor at the same time, the first traveling at 20 knots (nautical miles per hour) on a course bearing 40°, and the second at 25 knots on a course bearing 300°. After one hour, how far apart are they and what is the bearing of a course from the first ship to the second?

34. Three forces of 25, 35, and 45 kilograms act in directions having bearings of 240°, 290°, and 340°, respectively. Find a force, acting due east, and a force, acting due south, that would counterbalance these three forces.

35. A 100-kilogram weight hangs from a rope that makes an angle of 90° where it is attached to the weight (see figure). What is the tension (force) on each half of the rope?

36. A 50-kilogram weight hangs from a rope whose two ends are tied at 60° angles to a support (see figure). What is the tension on each half of the rope?

5.3 Vectors as Ordered Pairs

In Sections 5.1 and 5.2 we considered geometric vectors. In this section we will consider the more general notion of a two-dimensional vector as an ordered pair of real numbers, some of its properties, and the close relationship that exists between such a vector and a geometric vector in the plane.

Geometric vectors whose initial points are located at a fixed position in the plane are called **bound geometric vectors,** or **position vectors.** The terminal point of such a geometric vector with initial point at the origin has coordinates that are the components of exactly one ordered pair (a, b) of real numbers. This relationship, shown in Figure 5.11, suggests the following definition.

Figure 5.11

Definition 5.8 *A* **two-dimensional vector** **v** *is an ordered pair of real numbers*

$$\mathbf{v} = (a, b), \quad where \; a, b \in R.$$

The set of all such vectors is designated by **V.**

For a vector $\mathbf{v} = (a, b)$, the numbers a and b are called the **scalar components** of **v**.

Notice that boldface type *without* an arrow above the symbol is being used to differentiate a vector **v**, an ordered pair of real numbers, from a geometric vector $\vec{\mathbf{v}}$.

Example   The figure shows the geometric vectors associated with the vectors $\mathbf{v}_1 = (2, 3)$, $\mathbf{v}_2 = (-3, 5)$, $\mathbf{v}_3 = (-5, -1)$, and $\mathbf{v}_4 = (0, -4)$, respectively.

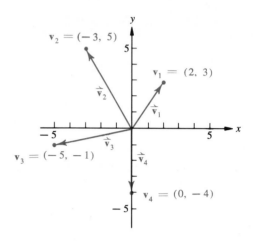

The following definitions are suggested by the close association of a vector with a geometric vector.

Definition 5.9   *For all* $\mathbf{v}_1$, $\mathbf{v}_2 \in \mathbf{V}$, *where* $\mathbf{v}_1 = (a_1, b_1)$ *and* $\mathbf{v}_2 = (a_2, b_2)$,

$$\mathbf{v}_1 = \mathbf{v}_2 \quad \text{if and only if } a_1 = a_2 \text{ and } b_1 = b_2.$$

Definition 5.10   *For all* $\mathbf{v} \in \mathbf{V}$, *where* $\mathbf{v} = (a, b)$, *the* **norm** *or* **magnitude** *of* **v** *is*

$$\|\mathbf{v}\| = \|(a, b)\| = \sqrt{a^2 + b^2}.$$

Definition 5.11   *For all* $\mathbf{v} \in \mathbf{V}$, *where* $\mathbf{v} = (a, b)$ *and* $\|\mathbf{v}\| \neq 0$, *the* **direction angle** *of* **v** *is the angle* α *such that*

$$\cos \alpha = \frac{a}{\|\mathbf{v}\|} \quad \text{and} \quad \sin \alpha = \frac{b}{\|\mathbf{v}\|},$$

where $-180° < \alpha \leq 180°$.

Although Definition 5.11 defines the direction angle of $\mathbf{v} = (a, b)$ in terms of both $\cos \alpha$ and $\sin \alpha$, in practice we generally determine only one function value in order to find α. This is possible because the quadrant in which **v** lies can readily be determined from the ordered pair (a, b).

Example By Definition 5.10, the norm of the vector $\mathbf{v} = (2, -5)$ is

$$\|\mathbf{v}\| = \sqrt{2^2 + (-5)^2} = \sqrt{29}.$$

By Definition 5.11,

$$\sin \alpha = \frac{-5}{\sqrt{29}} \approx -0.9285.$$

and because $(2, -5)$ is in Quadrant IV, then $-90° < \alpha < 0°$, and

$$\alpha \approx -68.2° = -68° \; 12'.$$

Notice that the norm of a vector **v** is the length of the corresponding geometric vector $\vec{v}$, and its direction angle is the angle α such that $-180° < \alpha \le 180°$, associated with the geometric vector.

EXERCISE SET 5.3

A

Find real numbers x and y for which each statement is true.

Example $(x, -y) = (-2, -8)$

Solution By Definition 5.9, $x = -2$ and $y = 8$.

1. $(x, y) = (-3, 6)$ **2.** $(-x, y) = (5, 1)$

3. $(2x, 7) = (-7, -y)$ **4.** $(6, 3y) = (x, -6)$

5. $(x + y, x - y) = (-4, 0)$ **6.** $(2x - y, x + 2y) = (0, -5)$

For each ordered pair **(a)** *sketch each corresponding geometric vector with initial point at the origin and* **(b)** *find the norm and the direction angle (to the nearest six minutes) of each vector.*

Example $(-2, 3)$

Solution

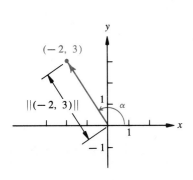

   a. See the figure.   *(continued)*

b. By Definition 5.10.

$$\|(-2, 3)\| = \sqrt{(-2)^2 + (3)^2} = \sqrt{13}.$$

By Definition 5.11,

$$\sin \alpha = \frac{3}{\sqrt{13}} \approx 0.8321,$$

and because $(-2, 3)$ is in Quadrant II, $90° < \alpha < 180°$, and

$$\alpha \approx 123.7° = 123° \, 42'.$$

7. $(3, 4)$ **8.** $(-3, 4)$ **9.** $(1, 1)$ **10.** $(-1, 1)$

11. $(-3, -3)$ **12.** $(0, -5)$ **13.** $(4, 0)$ **14.** $(\sqrt{3}, 1)$

Given the following norms and direction angles, find the vector **v**, *and sketch the corresponding geometric vector.*

Example $\|\mathbf{v}\| = 5$ and $\alpha = 30°$

Solution By Definition 5.11, if $\mathbf{v} = (a, b)$, then

$$a = \|\mathbf{v}\| \cos \alpha,$$
$$b = \|\mathbf{v}\| \sin \alpha.$$

Thus,

$$\mathbf{v} = (5 \cos 30°, 5 \sin 30°) = \left(\frac{5\sqrt{3}}{2}, \frac{5}{2}\right).$$

15. $\|\mathbf{v}\| = 2\sqrt{2}$ and $\alpha = 45°$ **16.** $\|\mathbf{v}\| = 2$ and $\alpha = 60°$

17. $\|\mathbf{v}\| = 1$ and $\alpha = 90°$ **18.** $\|\mathbf{v}\| = 4$ and $\alpha = 150°$

19. $\|\mathbf{v}\| = 5$ and $\alpha = -150°$ **20.** $\|\mathbf{v}\| = 3\sqrt{2}$ and $\alpha = -30°$

B

21. Use Definition 5.11 to show that the direction angles of (a, b) and $(-b, a)$ differ by 90°, given $a, b > 0$.

22. Show that if $a, b, c, d > 0$ and $ac - bd = 0$, then the direction angles of (a, b) and $(-c, d)$ differ by 90°.

5.4 Fundamental Operations

Two basic operations on vectors are closely related to the operations on geometric vectors that have been defined in Section 5.1.

Vector Addition

As was the case for geometric vectors, the operation of forming the sum of two vectors is called **vector addition.**

Definition 5.12   *For all* $\mathbf{v}_1, \mathbf{v}_2 \in \mathbf{V}$, *where* $\mathbf{v}_1 = (a_1, b_1)$ *and* $\mathbf{v}_2 = (a_2, b_2)$ *the* **sum** $\mathbf{v}_1 + \mathbf{v}_2$ *is a vector such that*

$$\mathbf{v}_1 + \mathbf{v}_2 = (a_1, b_1) + (a_2, b_2) = (a_1 + a_2, b_1 + b_2).$$

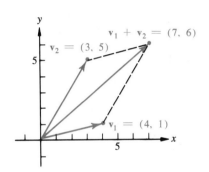

Example   Given that $\mathbf{v}_1 = (4, 1)$ and $\mathbf{v}_2 = (3, 5)$,

$$\mathbf{v}_1 + \mathbf{v}_2 = (4, 1) + (3, 5)$$
$$= (4 + 3, 1 + 5)$$
$$= (7, 6).$$

The corresponding geometric vectors for $\mathbf{v}_1$, $\mathbf{v}_2$, and their sum $\mathbf{v}_1 + \mathbf{v}_2$ are shown in the figure.

Note that, in the above example, the resultant $\mathbf{v}_1 + \mathbf{v}_2$ is associated with the geometric vector that is one of the diagonals of a parallelogram.

Multiplication of a Vector by a Scalar

The second basic operation on vectors concerns multiplication of a scalar (real number) and a vector and is also related to the similar operation on geometric vectors.

Definition 5.13   *For all* $\mathbf{v} \in \mathbf{V}$, *where* $\mathbf{v} = (a, b)$ *and* $c \in R$,

$$c\mathbf{v} = c(a, b) = (ca, cb).$$

Example   If $\mathbf{v} = (1, 3)$, $c_1 = 2$, and $c_2 = -2$, then

$$c_1\mathbf{v} = 2(1, 3) = (2, 6)$$

and

$$c_2\mathbf{v} = -2(1, 3) = (-2, -6).$$

Notice from the above example that $c\mathbf{v}$ has a magnitude $|c| \cdot \|\mathbf{v}\|$ if c is a positive or negative real number. The direction angles of $\mathbf{v}$ and $c\mathbf{v}$ are the same if c is positive, and they differ by $180°$ if c is negative.

Properties of Vectors

The following two definitions establish the identity element and the additive inverse element in our system of vectors.

Definition 5.14   *The* **zero vector** *is*

$$\mathbf{0} = (0, 0).$$

Any direction may be assigned to the zero vector.
Since

$$\mathbf{v} + \mathbf{0} = (a, b) + (0, 0)$$
$$= (a + 0), b + 0)$$
$$= (a, b) = \mathbf{v},$$

the zero vector is an *additive identity element.*

Definition 5.15   *For all* $\mathbf{v} \in \mathbf{V}$, *where* $\mathbf{v} = (a, b),$

$$-\mathbf{v} = -(a, b) = (-a, -b).$$

Since

$$\mathbf{v} + (-\mathbf{v}) = (a, b) + (-a, -b)$$
$$= [a + (-a), b + (-b)]$$
$$= (0, 0) = \mathbf{0},$$

$-\mathbf{v}$ is an *additive inverse element.*

The properties of a set of vectors under the operations of vector addition and multiplication of a vector by a scalar listed in Theorem 5.1 follow from the properties of real numbers and the definitions we have made.

Theorem 5.1   *If* $\mathbf{v}_1, \mathbf{v}_2, \mathbf{v}_3 \in \mathbf{V}$, *and* $c, d \in R$, *then*

I. $\mathbf{v}_1 + \mathbf{v}_2 \in \mathbf{V}$ Closure law for addition

II. $\mathbf{v}_1 + \mathbf{v}_2 = \mathbf{v}_2 + \mathbf{v}_1$ Commutative law for addition

III. $(\mathbf{v}_1 + \mathbf{v}_2) + \mathbf{v}_3 = \mathbf{v}_1 + (\mathbf{v}_2 + \mathbf{v}_3)$ Associative law of addition

IV. *There exists an element* $\mathbf{0}$ *in* $\mathbf{V}$ Identity law of addition
such that $\mathbf{v}_1 + \mathbf{0} = \mathbf{v}_1$

V. *For each* $\mathbf{v}_1 \in \mathbf{V}$ *there exists*   Additive inverse law
$-\mathbf{v}_1$ *such that* $\mathbf{v}_1 + (-\mathbf{v}_1) = \mathbf{0}$

VI. $c\mathbf{v}_1 \in \mathbf{V}$ Closure law for multiplication

VII. $(c + d)\mathbf{v}_1 = c\mathbf{v}_1 + d\mathbf{v}_1$ Distributive law for a vector
multiple over a scalar sum

VIII. $c(\mathbf{v}_1 + \mathbf{v}_2) = c\mathbf{v}_1 + c\mathbf{v}_2$ Distributive law for a scalar
multiple over a vector sum

IX. $c(d\mathbf{v}_1) = (cd)\mathbf{v}_1$ Associative law for a scalar
multiple

X. $1 \cdot \mathbf{v}_1 = \mathbf{v}_1$ Identity law for a scalar
multiple

The proofs of parts IV and V of this theorem were given immediately following Definitions 5.14 and 5.15. The proofs of some other parts are left as exercises.

Difference of Two Vectors

The difference of two vectors, $\mathbf{v}_2 - \mathbf{v}_1$, is defined similarly to the difference of two real numbers.

Definition 5.16   *For all vectors* $\mathbf{v}_1$ *and* $\mathbf{v}_2$, *the* **difference** $\mathbf{v}_2 - \mathbf{v}_1$ *is a vector such that*

$$\mathbf{v}_2 - \mathbf{v}_1 = \mathbf{v}_2 + (-\mathbf{v}_1).$$

Example   Given that $\mathbf{v}_1 = (2, 5)$ and $\mathbf{v}_2 = (7, 1)$,

$$\mathbf{v}_2 - \mathbf{v}_1 = (7, 1) - (2, 5)$$
$$= (7, 1) + (-2, -5)$$
$$= (7 - 2, 1 - 5)$$
$$= (5, -4).$$

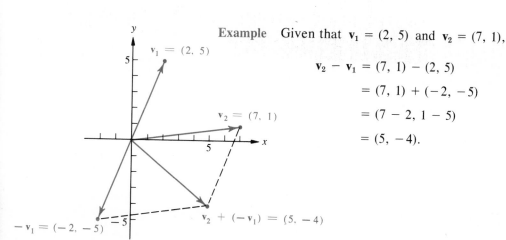

Quotient of a Vector and a Scalar

The quotient of a vector divided by a scalar is defined in terms of a product in much the same way as is the quotient of two real numbers.

Definition 5.17   *For all* $\mathbf{v} \in V$ *and* $c \in R$ $(c \neq 0)$,

$$\frac{\mathbf{v}}{c} = \frac{1}{c}\mathbf{v}.$$

Example   If $\mathbf{v} = (2, 4)$, $c_1 = 2$, and $c_2 = -2$, then

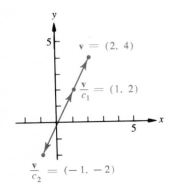

$$\frac{\mathbf{v}}{c_1} = \frac{(2, 4)}{2} = \frac{1}{2}(2, 4)$$

$$= (1, 2),$$

$$\frac{\mathbf{v}}{c_2} = \frac{(2, 4)}{-2} = -\frac{1}{2}(2, 4)$$

$$= (-1, -2).$$

$a\mathbf{i} + b\mathbf{j}$ Form

If vectors $\mathbf{v}_1 = (1, 0)$ and $\mathbf{v}_2 = (0, 1)$, called **unit vectors**, are designated $\mathbf{i}$ and $\mathbf{j}$, respectively, then each vector

$$\mathbf{v} = (a, b)$$

$$= (a, 0) + (0, b)$$

$$= a(1, 0) + b(0, 1)$$

$$= a\mathbf{i} + b\mathbf{j}.$$

Here again the real numbers a and b are called the **scalar components** of the vector.

Examples   Express each vector as the sum of scalar multiples of $\mathbf{i}$ and $\mathbf{j}$ and sketch the corresponding geometric vectors.

a. $(-4, 0)$ b. $(-4, 3)$

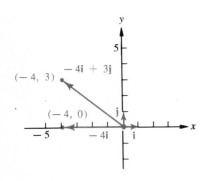

Solutions

a. $(-4, 0) = -4(1, 0)$ b. $(-4, 3) = (-4, 0) + (0, 3)$

$= -4\mathbf{i}$ $= -4(1, 0) + 3(0, 1)$

$= -4\mathbf{i} + 3\mathbf{j}$

Example Find the norm and the direction angle of $5\mathbf{i} - 3\mathbf{j}$.

Solution $5\mathbf{i} - 3\mathbf{j} = 5(1, 0) - 3(0, 1) = (5, -3)$. Thus,

$$\|5\mathbf{i} - 3\mathbf{j}\| = \|(5, -3)\|,$$

from which, by Definition 5.10, we have

$$\|5\mathbf{i} - 3\mathbf{j}\| = \sqrt{5^2 + (-3)^2} = \sqrt{34}.$$

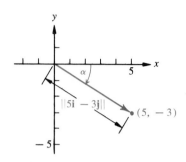

From Definition 5.11,

$$\sin \alpha = \frac{-3}{\sqrt{34}} \approx -0.5145.$$

Furthermore, $(5, -3)$ corresponds to a point in Quadrant IV. Hence

$$\alpha \approx -31.0°.$$

EXERCISE SET 5.4

A

Write the sum of each pair of vectors as an ordered pair and show the corresponding geometric vectors.

Example $\mathbf{v}_1 = (2, -5)$ and $\mathbf{v}_2 = (-4, 2)$

Solution $\mathbf{v}_1 + \mathbf{v}_2 = (2, -5) + (-4, 2)$

$$= (2 + (-4), -5 + 2)$$

$$= (-2, -3)$$

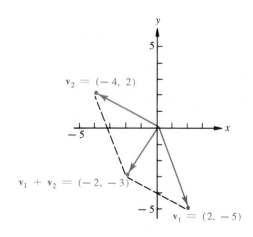

1. $v_1 = (-4, 0)$ and $v_2 = (0, 6)$ **2.** $v_1 = (-6, 0)$ and $v_2 = (0, 1)$

3. $v_1 (1, -4)$ and $v_2 = (2, 5)$ **4.** $v_1 = (7, -8)$ and $v_2 = (-3, -7)$

5. $v_1 = (-5, 3)$ and $v_2 = (1, -2)$ **6.** $v_1 = (-6, 6)$ and $v_2 = (3, -3)$

Let $v_1 = (3, 6)$, $v_2 = (5, -1)$, $v_3 = (-4, 2)$, $c_1 = 2$, *and* $c_2 = -3$. *Write each expression as an ordered pair and show the corresponding geometric vectors.*

Example $c_1 v_2 + c_1 v_3$

Solution $c_1 v_2 + c_1 v_3 = 2(5, -1) + 2(-4, 2)$

$$= (10, -2) + (-8, 4)$$

$$= (10 + (-8), -2 + 4)$$

$$= (2, 2)$$

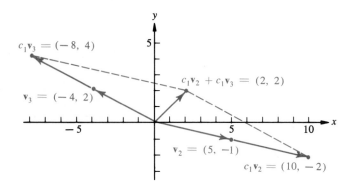

7. $-v_1$ **8.** $-v_2$ **9.** $v_3 + 0$

10. $0 - v_1$ **11.** $c_1 v_1$ **12.** $c_2 v_2$

13. $c_2 v_1 + v_3$ **14.** $c_1 v_2 + v_1$ **15.** $c_1 v_1 + c_2 v_2$

16. $c_1 v_2 + c_2 v_3$ **17.** $c_1 (v_1 + v_2)$ **18.** $c_2 (v_2 + v_3)$

19. $c_1 v_2 - v_1$ **20.** $c_2 v_3 - v_2$ **21.** $c_2 v_2 - c_1 v_3$

22. $c_2 v_3 - c_1 v_1$ **23.** $c_2 (v_2 - v_3)$ **24.** $c_1 (v_3 - v_1)$

25. $\dfrac{v_2}{c_1}$ **26.** $\dfrac{v_3}{c_2}$ **27.** $\dfrac{v_1}{c_1} - \dfrac{v_2}{c_2}$

28. $\dfrac{v_2}{c_2} - \dfrac{v_3}{c_1}$ **29.** $\dfrac{1}{4} c_1 v_1 - \dfrac{1}{3} c_2 v_3$ **30.** $\dfrac{1}{8} c_1 v_2 + \dfrac{1}{6} c_2 v_1$

*Express each vector as a sum of scalar multiples of **i** and **j**.*

Example (2, 9)

Solution   (2, 9) = (2, 0) + (0, 9)

$$= 2(1, 0) + 9(0, 1)$$

$$= 2\mathbf{i} + 9\mathbf{j}$$

31. (3, 5)   **32.** (−2, 1)   **33.** (1, −4)

34. (−2, −3)   **35.** (−3, 0)   **36.** (0, 4)

Find the norm and the direction angle, to the nearest six minutes, of each vector. Sketch the corresponding geometric vector.

Example 2**i** − 3**j**

Solution   2**i** − 3**j** = 2(1, 0) − 3(0, 1)

$$= (2, 0) + (0, -3) = (2, -3)$$

Hence, by Definition 5.10,

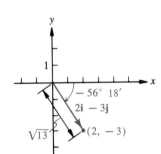

$$\|2\mathbf{i} - 3\mathbf{j}\| = \|(2, -3)\|$$

$$= \sqrt{2^2 + (-3)^2}$$

$$= \sqrt{13}.$$

From Definition 5.11,

$$\sin \alpha = \frac{-3}{\sqrt{13}} \approx -0.8321.$$

Since (2, −3) is in Quadrant IV, −90° < α < 0°. Thus,

$$\alpha \approx -56.3° = -56° \; 18'.$$

37. 4**i** − 4**j**   **38.** $\sqrt{3}\mathbf{i} + \mathbf{j}$ **39.** 2**i** + **j**   **40.** −**i** − 5**j**

41. −**i** − 3**j**   **42.** −6**i** + **j**   **43.** −**i** + $\sqrt{3}\mathbf{j}$ **44.** 3**i** − 2**j**

B

Let $\mathbf{v}_1 = (a_1, b_1)$, $\mathbf{v}_2 = (a_2, b_2)$, *and* $\mathbf{v}_3 = (a_3, b_3)$.

45. Prove Theorem 5.1-I.   *Hint:* Refer to the closure law of addition for real numbers, and use Definition 5.12.

46. Prove Theorem 5.1-II.   *Hint:* Refer to the commutative law of addition for real numbers, and use Definitions 5.12 and 5.9.

47. Prove Theorem 5.1-III.

48. Prove Theorem 5.1-VI.   *Hint:* Refer to the closure law of multiplication, and use Definition 5.13.

49. Prove Theorem 5.1-VII.

50. Prove Theorem 5.1-IX.

5.5 Inner Products

In Section 5.4 we considered two basic operations, vector addition and the multiplication of a vector by a scalar. The result of either operation is a vector and the set of vectors **V** is said to be closed for each of these operations. Another operation on two vectors is defined in such a way as to be useful in a variety of problems related to physical and geometric concepts.

Definition 5.18   *For all* $\mathbf{v}_1$, $\mathbf{v}_2 \in \mathbf{V}$, $\mathbf{v}_1 = (a_1, b_1)$ *and* $\mathbf{v}_2 = (a_2, b_2)$, *the* **inner product**

$$\mathbf{v}_1 \cdot \mathbf{v}_2 = (a_1, b_1) \cdot (a_2, b_2) = a_1 a_2 + b_1 b_2. \tag{1}$$

Since the symbol for the operation is a dot, the inner product is also called a **dot product.** Notice that the dot as used here has a different meaning than when it is used for the operation of multiplication in the set of real numbers.

Examples

a. If $\mathbf{v}_1 = (2, 3)$ and $\mathbf{v}_2 = (-5, 4)$, then

$$\mathbf{v}_1 \cdot \mathbf{v}_2 = (2, 3) \cdot (-5, 4)$$
$$= (2)(-5) + (3)(4) = 2.$$

b. If $\mathbf{v}_1 = 3\mathbf{i} - 4\mathbf{j}$ and $\mathbf{v}_2 = \mathbf{i} + 2\mathbf{j}$, then

$$\mathbf{v}_1 \cdot \mathbf{v}_2 = (3\mathbf{i} - 4\mathbf{j}) \cdot (\mathbf{i} + 2\mathbf{j})$$
$$= (3)(1) + (-4)2 = -5.$$

Notice that the set of vectors **V** is not closed for this operation. The inner product of two vectors is a scalar, not a vector. For this reason the inner product is also called the **scalar product.**

Another useful form of the inner product can be obtained from the Law of Cosines.

Theorem 5.2 *If* $\mathbf{v}_1 = (a_1, b_1)$ *and* $\mathbf{v}_2 = (a_2, b_2)$, *where* $\mathbf{v}_1$ *and* $\mathbf{v}_2$ *are nonzero vectors, and* γ *is the angle formed by the geometric vectors corresponding to* $\mathbf{v}_1$ *and* $\mathbf{v}_2$, *then*

$$\mathbf{v}_1 \cdot \mathbf{v}_2 = \|\mathbf{v}_1\| \, \|\mathbf{v}_2\| \cos \gamma. \qquad (2)$$

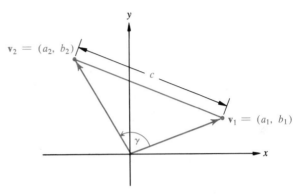

Figure 5.12

Proof Consider the line segment with length c drawn between the points corresponding to (a_1, b_1) and (a_2, b_2), as shown in Figure 5.12. From the Law of Cosines,

$$c^2 = \|\mathbf{v}_1\|^2 + \|\mathbf{v}_2\|^2 - 2\|\mathbf{v}_1\| \, \|\mathbf{v}_2\| \cos \gamma,$$

from which, for nonzero vectors $\mathbf{v}_1$ and $\mathbf{v}_2$,

$$\cos \gamma = \frac{\|\mathbf{v}_1\|^2 + \|\mathbf{v}_2\|^2 - c^2}{2\|\mathbf{v}_1\| \, \|\mathbf{v}_2\|}.$$

Substituting $\sqrt{a_1^2 + b_1^2}$ for $\|\mathbf{v}_1\|$, $\sqrt{a_2^2 + b_2^2}$ for $\|\mathbf{v}_2\|$, and

$$\sqrt{(a_2 - a_1)^2 + (b_2 - b_1)^2}$$

for c and simplifying, we obtain

$$\cos \gamma = \frac{a_1 a_2 + b_1 b_2}{\|\mathbf{v}_1\| \, \|\mathbf{v}_2\|}.$$

Substituting $\mathbf{v}_1 \cdot \mathbf{v}_2$ for $a_1 a_2 + b_1 b_2$ from Definition 5.18 yields

$$\mathbf{v}_1 \cdot \mathbf{v}_2 = \|\mathbf{v}_1\| \, \|\mathbf{v}_2\| \cos \gamma.$$

We can now express the inner product of two vectors $v_1 = (a_1, b_1)$ and $v_2 = (a_2, b_2)$ either, as shown in Equation (1), in terms of their scalar components or, as in Equation (2), in terms of the norms of the two vectors and the cosine of the angle γ formed by their corresponding geometric vectors.

Example   Given that $\|v_1\| = 3$, and v_1 has a direction angle, $\alpha_1 = 20°$, $\|v_2\| = 8$, and v_2 has a direction angle, $\alpha_2 = 170°$, find $v_1 \cdot v_2$.

Solution   From Theorem 5.2,

$$v_1 \cdot v_2 = (3)(8) \cos(170° - 20°) = (3)(8) \cos 150°$$

$$= 24 \left(-\frac{\sqrt{3}}{2} \right) = -12\sqrt{3}.$$

Scalar Projections

The property of inner products exhibited for two nonzero vectors in Equation (2) is particularly useful in several equivalent forms.

Theorem 5.3   *If* $v_1 = (a_1, b_1)$ *and* $v_2 = (a_2, b_2)$, *where* v_1 *and* v_2 *are nonzero vectors, and* γ *is the angle formed by the geometric vectors corresponding to* v_1 *and* v_2, *then*

$$\text{I. } \cos \gamma = \frac{v_1 \cdot v_2}{\|v_1\| \, \|v_2\|},$$

$$\text{II. } \|v_1\| \cos \gamma = \frac{v_1 \cdot v_2}{\|v_2\|},$$

$$\text{III. } \|v_2\| \cos \gamma = \frac{v_1 \cdot v_2}{\|v_1\|}.$$

Theorem 5.3-I enables us to find the angle γ between any two nonzero vectors.

Example   The angle γ between the geometric vectors corresponding to $(2, 3)$ and $(0, 2)$ is given by

$$\cos \gamma = \frac{(2, 3) \cdot (0, 2)}{\|(2, 3)\| \, \|(0, 2)\|} = \frac{2 \cdot 0 + 3 \cdot 2}{\sqrt{4 + 9}\sqrt{0 + 4}}$$

$$= \frac{3}{\sqrt{13}} \approx 0.8321.$$

Thus, $\gamma \approx 33.7° = 33° \, 42'$.

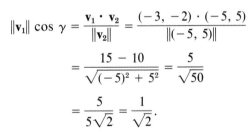

Figure 5.13

In Section 5.2 we obtained projections of a vector on the x- and y-axes of a Cartesian coordinate system. Parts II and III of Theorem 5.3 now give us a way to find the projection of a vector on any other vector.

The product $\|\mathbf{v}_1\| \cos \gamma$ is called the **scalar projection** of $\mathbf{v}_1$ on $\mathbf{v}_2$ and the product $\|\mathbf{v}_2\| \cos \gamma$ is called the scalar projection of $\mathbf{v}_2$ on $\mathbf{v}_1$. In a geometric sense, these can be interpreted as the lengths of the line segments shown in Figure 5.13 (a and b).

Example Given that $\mathbf{v}_1 = (-3, -2)$ and $\mathbf{v}_2 = (-5, 5)$, the scalar projection of $\mathbf{v}_1$ on $\mathbf{v}_2$ (Theorem 5.3-II) is

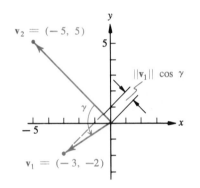

$$\|\mathbf{v}_1\| \cos \gamma = \frac{\mathbf{v}_1 \cdot \mathbf{v}_2}{\|\mathbf{v}_2\|} = \frac{(-3, -2) \cdot (-5, 5)}{\|(-5, 5)\|}$$

$$= \frac{15 - 10}{\sqrt{(-5)^2 + 5^2}} = \frac{5}{\sqrt{50}}$$

$$= \frac{5}{5\sqrt{2}} = \frac{1}{\sqrt{2}}.$$

The scalar projection of $\mathbf{v}_2$ on $\mathbf{v}_1$ (Theorem 5.3-III) is

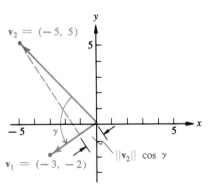

$$\|\mathbf{v}_2\| \cos \gamma = \frac{\mathbf{v}_1 \cdot \mathbf{v}_2}{\|\mathbf{v}_1\|} = \frac{(-3, -2) \cdot (-5, 5)}{\|(-3, -2)\|}$$

$$= \frac{15 - 10}{\sqrt{(-3)^2 + (-2)^2}} = \frac{5}{\sqrt{13}}.$$

Orthogonal Vectors

If $\mathbf{v}_1$ and $\mathbf{v}_2$ are nonzero vectors and are perpendicular, then $\|\mathbf{v}_1\| \neq 0$, $\|\mathbf{v}_2\| \neq 0$, $\cos \gamma = 0$, and

$$\mathbf{v}_1 \cdot \mathbf{v}_2 = \|\mathbf{v}_1\| \, \|\mathbf{v}_2\| \cos \gamma = 0.$$

We also note that for $0° \le \gamma \le 180°$, $\cos \gamma = 0$ only if $\gamma = 90°$. From Definition 5.18,

$$\mathbf{v}_1 \cdot \mathbf{v}_2 = a_1 a_2 + b_1 b_2.$$

Hence, we can test for the orthogonality (perpendicularity) of two vectors directly from their scalar components.

Theorem 5.4   *The vectors* $\mathbf{v}_1 = (a_1, b_1)$ *and* $\mathbf{v}_2 = (a_2, b_2)$ *are orthogonal if and only if*

$$\mathbf{v}_1 \cdot \mathbf{v}_2 = a_1 a_2 + b_1 b_2 = \mathbf{0}.$$

Examples

   a. $(2, -4)$ and $(6, 3)$ are orthogonal because

$$(2, -4) \cdot (6, 3) = (2)(6) + (-4)(3) = 0.$$

   b. $-\mathbf{i} - 2\mathbf{j}$ and $4\mathbf{i} - 2\mathbf{j}$ are orthogonal because

$$(-\mathbf{i} - 2\mathbf{j}) \cdot (4\mathbf{i} - 2\mathbf{j}) = (-1)(4) + (-2)(-2) = 0.$$

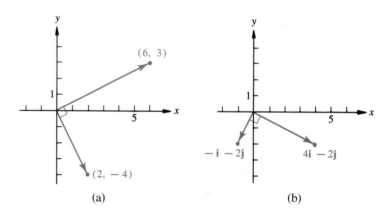

(a)   (b)

Applications

If a force is applied to an object so as to cause motion in a particular direction, and if the force is applied throughout the motion and in the same direction as the motion, then the product of the magnitude of the force (F) and the distance (d) the object moves is called **work.** In many situations, the direction of an applied force is not the same as the direction in which the object moves. In this case, the work is the product of the magnitude of the *component of the force in the direction of motion* and the distance the object moves. Since the inner product of two vectors can be used to find such a product whether or not the two vectors have the same direction, we provide a more general definition of work in Definition 5.19.

Definition 5.19   *If* **F** *is a force vector and* **d** *a displacement vector, then the work W is given by*

$$W = \mathbf{F} \cdot \mathbf{d}.$$

Example   A force of 40 kilograms at an angle of 30° to the horizontal is used to move a box 8 meters on a level floor. Find the work done.

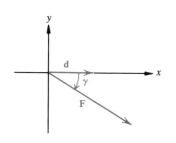

Solution   The figure shows the vectors in a Cartesian system. Since $\|\mathbf{F}\| = 40$ kilograms, $\|\mathbf{d}\| = 8$ meters, and $\gamma = 30°$,

$$W = \mathbf{F} \cdot \mathbf{d} = \|\mathbf{F}\|\,\|\mathbf{d}\| \cos \gamma$$

$$= (40)(8) \cos 30°$$

$$= (40)(8) \left(\frac{\sqrt{3}}{2}\right)$$

$$= 160\sqrt{3} \approx 277.$$

If the force magnitude is measured in kilograms and the displacement magnitude in meters, as in this case, the work is measured in meter-kilograms. Hence the work done is approximately 277 meter-kilograms.

Example   How much work is done in lifting an 80-pound weight to a height of 3 feet?

Solution   Since the force and displacement vectors are in the same direction, the angle $\gamma = 0°$ and $\cos \gamma = 1$. Hence,

$$W = \mathbf{F} \cdot \mathbf{d} = \|\mathbf{F}\|\,\|\mathbf{d}\| \cos \gamma = (80)(3)(1) = 240.$$

Hence, the work done is 240 foot-pounds. In this case the work is simply the product of the force times the distance.

EXERCISE SET 5.5

A

Find the inner product, $\mathbf{v}_1 \cdot \mathbf{v}_2$, of the given vectors.

Examples

   a. $\mathbf{v}_1 = (7, -9)$ and $\mathbf{v}_2 = (-6, -5)$

   b. $\mathbf{v}_1 = -9\mathbf{i} + 8\mathbf{j}$ and $\mathbf{v}_2 = 3\mathbf{i} - 2\mathbf{j}$

Solutions   From Definition 5.18,

   a. $\mathbf{v}_1 \cdot \mathbf{v}_2 = (7, -9) \cdot (-6, -5)$

           $= (7)(-6) + (-9)(-5) = 3$

   b. $\mathbf{v}_1 \cdot \mathbf{v}_2 = (-9\mathbf{i} + 8\mathbf{j}) \cdot (3\mathbf{i} - 2\mathbf{j})$

           $= (-9)(3) + (8)(-2) = -43$

1. $\mathbf{v}_1 = (6, 0)$ and $\mathbf{v}_2 = (8, 10)$ **2.** $\mathbf{v}_1 = (9, 3)$ and $\mathbf{v}_2 = (8, -5)$

3. $\mathbf{v}_1 = (7, -8)$ and $\mathbf{v}_2 = (2, 2)$ **4.** $\mathbf{v}_1 = (3, 0)$ and $\mathbf{v}_2 = (0, -5)$

5. $\mathbf{v}_1 = 9\mathbf{i} - 4\mathbf{j}$ and $\mathbf{v}_2 = 5\mathbf{i}$ **6.** $\mathbf{v}_1 = 8\mathbf{j}$ and $\mathbf{v}_2 = 7\mathbf{i} + 7\mathbf{j}$

7. $\mathbf{v}_1 = \mathbf{i} - 2\mathbf{j}$ and $\mathbf{v}_2 = 3\mathbf{i} - 5\mathbf{j}$ **8.** $\mathbf{v}_1 = -4\mathbf{i} + 3\mathbf{j}$ and $\mathbf{v}_2 = 10\mathbf{j}$

Find the exact value of $\mathbf{v}_1 \cdot \mathbf{v}_2$ given the norms and direction angles for $\mathbf{v}_1$ and $\mathbf{v}_2$.

Example $\|\mathbf{v}_1\| = 10$, $\alpha_1 = 75°$ and $\|\mathbf{v}_2\| = 3$, $\alpha_2 = 45°$

Solution   From Theorem 5.2,

$$\mathbf{v}_1 \cdot \mathbf{v}_2 = (10)(3) \cos(75° - 45°)$$

$$= 30 \cos 30°$$

$$= 30 \left(\frac{\sqrt{3}}{2} \right) = 15\sqrt{3}.$$

9. $\|\mathbf{v}_1\| = 8$, $\alpha_1 = 60°$ and $\|\mathbf{v}_2\| = 9$, $\alpha_2 = 15°$

10. $\|\mathbf{v}_1\| = 7$, $\alpha_1 = 160°$ and $\|\mathbf{v}_2\| = 6$, $\alpha_2 = -170°$

11. $\|\mathbf{v}_1\| = 5$, $\alpha_1 = -155°$ and $\|\mathbf{v}_2\| = \frac{3}{10}$, $\alpha_2 = 145°$

12. $\|\mathbf{v}_1\| = \frac{1}{2}$, $\alpha_1 = -60°$ and $\|\mathbf{v}_2\| = 10$, $\alpha_2 = -150°$

Determine the angle γ, *where* $0° \le \gamma \le 180°$, *to the nearest six minutes, formed by each pair of vectors.*

Example $\mathbf{v}_1 = (1, -7)$ and $\mathbf{v}_2 = (9, -1)$

Solution   From Theorem 5.3-I,

$$\cos \gamma = \frac{(1, -7) \cdot (9, -1)}{\sqrt{1^2 + (-7)^2} \sqrt{9^2 + (-1)^2}}$$

$$= \frac{16}{\sqrt{50}\sqrt{82}} = \frac{16}{5\sqrt{2} \cdot \sqrt{2} \cdot \sqrt{41}} = \frac{8}{5\sqrt{41}} \approx 0.2499,$$

from which $\gamma \approx 75.5° = 75° \, 30'$.

13. $\mathbf{v}_1 = (3, 0)$ and $\mathbf{v}_2 = (-7, 3)$ **14.** $\mathbf{v}_1 = (1, -3)$ and $\mathbf{v}_2 = (8, -2)$

15. $\mathbf{v}_1 = (4, 0)$ and $\mathbf{v}_2 = (0, -2)$ **16.** $\mathbf{v}_1 = (-2, 0)$ and $\mathbf{v}_2 = (0, -3)$

17. $\mathbf{v}_1 = 9\mathbf{i} + 4\mathbf{j}$ and $\mathbf{v}_2 = 2\mathbf{i}$ **18.** $\mathbf{v}_1 = -4\mathbf{i} - 8\mathbf{j}$ and $\mathbf{v}_2 = \mathbf{i} - 5\mathbf{j}$

Find the scalar projection of $\mathbf{v}_1$ *on* $\mathbf{v}_2$ *and of* $\mathbf{v}_2$ *on* $\mathbf{v}_1$ *for the given vectors. Sketch the corresponding geometric vectors and show the scalar projections.*

Example $\mathbf{v}_1 = (1, 2)$ and $\mathbf{v}_2 = (-3, 4)$

Solution   From Theorem 5.3-II, the scalar projection of $\mathbf{v}_1$ on $\mathbf{v}_2$ is

$$\|\mathbf{v}_1\| \cos \gamma = \frac{\mathbf{v}_1 \cdot \mathbf{v}_2}{\|\mathbf{v}_2\|} = \frac{(1)(-3) + (2)(4)}{\sqrt{(-3)^2 + (4)^2}}$$

$$= \frac{-3 + 8}{\sqrt{25}} = \frac{5}{5} = 1.$$

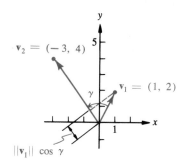

$\mathbf{v}_2 = (-3, 4)$

$\mathbf{v}_1 = (1, 2)$

$\|\mathbf{v}_1\| \cos \gamma$

From Theorem 5.3-III, the scalar projection of $\mathbf{v}_2$ on $\mathbf{v}_1$ is

$$\|\mathbf{v}_2\| \cos \gamma = \frac{\mathbf{v}_1 \cdot \mathbf{v}_2}{\|\mathbf{v}_1\|} = \frac{5}{\sqrt{1^2 + 2^2}} = \frac{5}{\sqrt{5}} = \sqrt{5}.$$

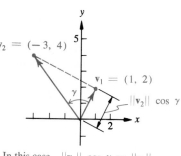

$\mathbf{v}_2 = (-3, 4)$

$\mathbf{v}_1 = (1, 2)$

$\|\mathbf{v}_2\| \cos \gamma$

In this case, $\|\mathbf{v}_2\| \cos \gamma = \|\mathbf{v}_1\|$.

19. $\mathbf{v}_1 = -4\mathbf{i}$ and $\mathbf{v}_2 = -5\mathbf{i} - 2\mathbf{j}$ **20.** $\mathbf{v}_1 = \mathbf{i} - 6\mathbf{j}$ and $\mathbf{v}_2 = -5\mathbf{j}$

21. $\mathbf{v}_1 = (2, 3)$ and $\mathbf{v}_2 = (-4, 5)$ **22.** $\mathbf{v}_1 = (-9, 10)$ and $\mathbf{v}_2 = (2, 4)$

23. $\mathbf{v}_1 = (-3, 5)$ and $\mathbf{v}_2 = (3, -1)$ **24.** $\mathbf{v}_1 = (-7, 4)$ and $\mathbf{v}_2 = (3, -6)$

25. $\mathbf{v}_1 = 3\mathbf{i}$ and $\mathbf{v}_2 = 2\mathbf{j}$ **26.** $\mathbf{v}_1 = 2\mathbf{i}$ and $\mathbf{v}_2 = -2\mathbf{j}$

Verify that the following pairs of vectors are orthogonal.

Example $\mathbf{i} + 4\mathbf{j}$ and $8\mathbf{i} - 2\mathbf{j}$

Solution $(\mathbf{i} + 4\mathbf{j}) \cdot (8\mathbf{i} - 2\mathbf{j}) = (1)(8) + (4)(-2)$

$$= 8 - 8 = 0.$$

Hence, by Theorem 5.4, the vectors are orthogonal.

27. $(0, 5)$ and $(-3, 0)$ **28.** $(-2, 2)$ and $(5, 5)$

29. $(-4, 1)$ and $(1, 4)$ **30.** $(9, 1)$ and $(-1, 9)$

31. $6\mathbf{i} - 9\mathbf{j}$ and $3\mathbf{i} + 2\mathbf{j}$ **32.** $-3\mathbf{i} + \sqrt{3}\mathbf{j}$ and $\mathbf{i} + \sqrt{3}\mathbf{j}$

Find the work done, given each force vector and displacement vector.

Example $\mathbf{F} = (1, 5)$ and $\mathbf{d} = (-2, 3)$

Solution   By Definition 5.19,

$$W = \mathbf{F} \cdot \mathbf{d} = (1, 5) \cdot (-2, 3)$$
$$= 1 \cdot (-2) + 5 \cdot 3 = 13$$

33. $\mathbf{F} = (3, 6)$ and $\mathbf{d} = (4, 2)$

34. $\mathbf{F} = (5, -2)$ and $\mathbf{d} = (-1, -7)$

35. $\mathbf{F} = 7\mathbf{i} - 2\mathbf{j}$ and $\mathbf{d} = 4\mathbf{i} - 4\mathbf{j}$

36. $\mathbf{F} = -12\mathbf{i} + 3\mathbf{j}$ and $\mathbf{d} = -3\mathbf{i} + 12\mathbf{j}$

37. A small wagon is pulled horizontally a distance of 100 meters by a short rope. If the rope is at an angle of 30° to the horizontal and a constant force of 20 kilograms is used, find the work done.

38. How much work is done in moving a string of cars 500 meters along a track by a truck exerting a force of 2000 kilograms at an angle of 20° to the direction of the track?

39. In Exercise 38 how much work is done if the force is applied in the direction of motion?

40. How much work is done by a 175-pound man climbing 12 feet up a vertical ladder?

B

41. Show that $\mathbf{v}_1 \cdot \mathbf{v}_1 = \|\mathbf{v}_1\|^2$.   **42.** Show that $\mathbf{v}_1 \cdot \mathbf{v}_2 = \mathbf{v}_2 \cdot \mathbf{v}_1$.

43. Show that $c(\mathbf{v}_1 \cdot \mathbf{v}_2) = (c\mathbf{v}_1) \cdot \mathbf{v}_2$.

44. Show that $\mathbf{v}_1 \cdot (\mathbf{v}_2 + \mathbf{v}_3) = \mathbf{v}_1 \cdot \mathbf{v}_2 + \mathbf{v}_1 \cdot \mathbf{v}_3$.

Chapter Summary

5.1   A **geometric vector** $\vec{\mathbf{v}}$ is a line segment with a specified direction. Its **norm** or **magnitude** is designated by $\|\vec{\mathbf{v}}\|$. The **direction angle** is the angle α, where $-180° < \alpha \leq 180°$, such that:

> The initial side of α is the ray from the initial point of $\vec{\mathbf{v}}$ parallel to the x-axis and directed in the positive x direction; the terminal side of α is the ray from the initial point of $\vec{\mathbf{v}}$ and containing $\vec{\mathbf{v}}$.

The **sum** $\vec{\mathbf{v}}_1 + \vec{\mathbf{v}}_2$ is defined as the geometric vector having as its initial point the initial point of $\vec{\mathbf{v}}_1$ and as its terminal point the terminal point of $\vec{\mathbf{v}}_2$, and where the terminal point of $\vec{\mathbf{v}}_1$ is the initial point of $\vec{\mathbf{v}}_2$. When viewed in this way, geometric vectors are said to be added according to "the triangle law." When viewed as the diagonal of a parallelogram with adjacent sides $\vec{\mathbf{v}}_1$ and $\vec{\mathbf{v}}_2$, geometric vectors are said to be added according to "the parallelogram law."

If $\vec{\mathbf{v}}$ is any geometric vector and c is any real number (scalar), then $c\vec{\mathbf{v}}$ is a geometric vector collinear with $\vec{\mathbf{v}}$ with magnitude $|c| \cdot \|\vec{\mathbf{v}}\|$.

5.2   The magnitudes of the **geometric vector projections,** $\vec{\mathbf{v}}_x$ and $\vec{\mathbf{v}}_y$, of $\vec{\mathbf{v}}$ on the x-axis and y-axis, respectively, are given by

$$\|\vec{\mathbf{v}}_x\| = \|\vec{\mathbf{v}}\| \cdot |\cos \alpha| \qquad \text{and} \qquad \|\vec{\mathbf{v}}_y\| = \|\vec{\mathbf{v}}\| \cdot |\sin \alpha|.$$

Geometric vectors can help to visualize and thus facilitate the solution of problems involving such quantities as force, velocity, and acceleration, since these quantities have both magnitude and direction.

5.3   A **two-dimensional vector** $\mathbf{v}$ is an ordered pair of real numbers. That is, if $a, b \in R$, then $\mathbf{v} = (a, b)$. The set of all such vectors is designated by **V.** Each vector in the set corresponds to a unique bound geometric vector with initial point at the origin.

For all $\mathbf{v}_1, \mathbf{v}_2 \in \mathbf{V}$, where $\mathbf{v}_1 = (a_1, b_1)$ and $\mathbf{v}_2 = (a_2, b_2)$,

$$\mathbf{v}_1 = \mathbf{v}_2 \text{ if and only if } a_1 = a_2 \text{ and } b_1 = b_2;$$

the **norm,** or **magnitude,** of $\mathbf{v} = (a, b)$ is the real number (scalar)

$$\|\mathbf{v}\| = \sqrt{a^2 + b^2};$$

for $\|\mathbf{v}\| \neq 0$, the **direction angle** of $\mathbf{v} = (a, b)$ is the angle α such that

$$\cos \alpha = \frac{a}{\|\mathbf{v}\|} \quad \text{and} \quad \sin \alpha = \frac{b}{\|\mathbf{v}\|} \quad (-180° < \alpha \leq 180°).$$

The **norm** (or **magnitude**) of a vector, $\|\mathbf{v}\|$, is the length of the associated geometric vector $\vec{v}$ and the **direction angle** of the vector is the angle α, where $-180° < \alpha \leq 180°$, measured from the positive x-axis to the geometric vector corresponding to $\mathbf{v}$.

5.4 For all $\mathbf{v}_1, \mathbf{v}_2 \in \mathbf{V}$, where $\mathbf{v}_1 = (a_1, b_1)$, $\mathbf{v}_2 = (a_2, b_2)$, and $c \in R$,

$\mathbf{v}_1 + \mathbf{v}_2 = (a_1, b_1) + (a_2, b_2) = (a_1 + a_2, b_1 + b_2)$, the sum of $\mathbf{v}_1$ and $\mathbf{v}_2$;

$c\mathbf{v} = c(a_1, b_1) = (ca_1, cb_1)$, a scalar multiple of $\mathbf{v}$.

The **zero vector** $\mathbf{0} = (0, 0)$ is the additive identity for addition and the vector $-\mathbf{v} = (-a, -b)$ is the additive inverse of $\mathbf{v} = (a, b)$.

Vector addition and multiplication of a vector by a scalar have ten basic properties that are listed in Theorem 5.1.

For all $\mathbf{v}_1, \mathbf{v}_2 \in \mathbf{V}$, where $\mathbf{v}_1 = (a_1, b_1)$, $\mathbf{v}_2 = (a_2, b_2)$, and $c \in R$,

$\mathbf{v}_1 - \mathbf{v}_2 = \mathbf{v}_1 + (-\mathbf{v}_2)$, the **difference** of $\mathbf{v}_2$ subtracted from $\mathbf{v}_1$;

$\dfrac{\mathbf{v}_1}{c} = \dfrac{1}{c}\,\mathbf{v}_1 \ (c \neq 0)$, the **quotient** of a vector divided by a scalar.

If $\mathbf{i} = (1, 0)$ and $\mathbf{j} = (0, 1)$, then each vector $\mathbf{v}$ can be expressed as

$$\mathbf{v} = (a, b) = a\mathbf{i} + b\mathbf{j}.$$

5.5 The **inner (dot, scalar) product** of vectors $\mathbf{v}_1$ and $\mathbf{v}_2$ is

$$\mathbf{v}_1 \cdot \mathbf{v}_2 = (a_1, b_1) \cdot (a_2, b_2) = a_1a_2 + b_1b_2.$$

If γ is the angle between the geometric vectors corresponding to $\mathbf{v}_1$ and $\mathbf{v}_2$, then

$$\mathbf{v}_1 \cdot \mathbf{v}_2 = \|\mathbf{v}_1\| \|\mathbf{v}_2\| \cos \gamma.$$

Equivalently,

$$\cos \gamma = \frac{\mathbf{v}_1 \cdot \mathbf{v}_2}{\|\mathbf{v}_1\| \|\mathbf{v}_2\|};$$

$$\|\mathbf{v}_1\| \cos \gamma = \frac{\mathbf{v}_1 \cdot \mathbf{v}_2}{\|\mathbf{v}_2\|}, \text{ the scalar projection of } \mathbf{v}_1 \text{ on } \mathbf{v}_2;$$

$$\|\mathbf{v}_2\| \cos \gamma = \frac{\mathbf{v}_1 \cdot \mathbf{v}_2}{\|\mathbf{v}_1\|}, \text{ the scalar projection of } \mathbf{v}_2 \text{ on } \mathbf{v}_1.$$

The vectors $v_1 = (a_1, b_1)$ and $v_2 = (a_2, b_2)$ are **orthogonal** if and only if the inner product

$$v_1 \cdot v_2 = a_1a_2 + b_1b_2 = 0.$$

A list of symbols introduced in this chapter is shown inside the front cover, and important properties are shown inside the back cover.

Review Exercises

A

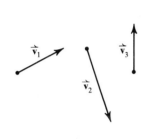

5.1 *Use free-hand methods and the geometric vectors shown at the left to draw a single vector to represent each of the following.*

1. $(\vec{v}_1 + \vec{v}_2) + \vec{v}_3$ **2.** $-3\vec{v}_1$ **3.** $2\vec{v}_2 + \vec{v}_3$ **4.** $2\vec{v}_1 - 3\vec{v}_3$

5.2 **5.** If the direction angle $\alpha = 60°$, and $\|\vec{v}\| = 12$, find $\|\vec{v}_x\|$ and $\|\vec{v}_y\|$.

6. If $\vec{v}_x$ and $\vec{v}_y$ are directed in a positive direction; $\|\vec{v}_x\| = 4$, with initial point at $(1, 0)$; and $\|\vec{v}_y\| = 3$, with initial point at $(0, 2)$, find $\|\vec{v}\|$ and the direction angle α.

7. The resultant of two forces acting at an angle of 90° with respect to each other is 130 kilograms. If one of the forces is 50 kilograms, find the other force and the angle it makes with the resultant.

8. A man can swim at a speed of 3 miles per hour in still water. If he heads across a river at right angles to a current of 6 miles per hour, find his speed in relation to the land and the direction in which he actually moves.

9. An airplane is headed on a bearing of 280° with an air speed of 800 kilometers per hour. The course has a bearing of 292°. The ground speed is 860 kilometers per hour. Find the wind direction and wind speed.

10. A force of 150 kilograms is needed to keep a steel ball weighing 250 kilograms from rolling down an inclined plane. What angle does the plane make with the horizontal?

5.3 *Find real numbers x and y for which each statement is true.*

11. $(x, y) = (-1, 3)$ **12.** $(x + y, x - y) = (5, 3)$

(a) *Sketch the geometric vector corresponding to each vector, and* (b) *find the norm and the direction angle (to the nearest six minutes) of each vector.*

13. $(-4, 3)$ **14.** $(5, -5)$

Given the following norms and direction angles, find the vector **v.**

15. $\|\mathbf{v}\| = 10$ and $\alpha = -135°$ **16.** $\|\mathbf{v}\| = 2$ and $\alpha = 150°$

5.4   *Write the sum of each pair of vectors as an ordered pair.*

17. $\mathbf{v}_1 = (4, -5)$ and $\mathbf{v}_2 = (8, 1)$

18. $\mathbf{v}_1 = (-3, 7)$ and $\mathbf{v}_2 = (-7, 3)$

Let $\mathbf{v}_1 = (3, -2)$, $\mathbf{v}_2 = (5, 4)$, $\mathbf{v}_3 = (1, -3)$, $c_1 = 2$, *and* $c_2 = -1$. *Express each of the following as an ordered pair.*

19. $\mathbf{v}_2 - c_2\mathbf{v}_1$ **20.** $c_1(\mathbf{v}_3 + \mathbf{v}_2)$ **21.** $\dfrac{\mathbf{v}_3}{c_2}$ **22.** $\dfrac{\mathbf{v}_2}{c_1\|\mathbf{v}_1\|}$

Express each vector as the sum of scalar multiples of **i** *and* **j.**

23. $(7, -9)$ **24.** $(-8, -1)$

Find the norm and direction angle (to the nearest six minutes) of each vector.

25. $-10\mathbf{i} + 4\mathbf{j}$ **26.** $7\mathbf{i} - 9\mathbf{j}$

5.5   *Find the inner product* $\mathbf{v}_1 \cdot \mathbf{v}_2$ *for given vectors.*

27. $\mathbf{v}_1 = (6, 6)$ and $\mathbf{v}_2 = (-5, -4)$

28. $\mathbf{v}_1 = 8\mathbf{i} - \mathbf{j}$ and $\mathbf{v}_2 = 9\mathbf{i} - 3\mathbf{j}$

29. $\|\mathbf{v}_1\| = 8$ and $\alpha_1 = 60°$; $\|\mathbf{v}_2\| = 4$ and $\alpha_2 = 30°$

30. $\|\mathbf{v}_1\| = 10$ and $a_1 = -45°$; $\|\mathbf{v}_2\| = 5$ and $\alpha_2 = -15°$

Determine the angle γ *to the nearest 6', where* $0° \le \gamma \le 180°$, *formed by each pair of vectors.*

31. $\mathbf{v}_1 = (-7, 5)$ and $\mathbf{v}_2 = (1, -5)$

32. $\mathbf{v}_1 = -7\mathbf{i} - \mathbf{j}$ and $\mathbf{v}_2 = -8\mathbf{i} + 9\mathbf{j}$

Find the scalar projections of v_1 *on* v_2 *and of* v_2 *on* v_1.

33. $v_1 = (1, 7)$ and $v_2 = (10, -1)$

34. $v_1 = 9i + 2j$ and $v_2 = -8i - 5j$

Verify that each pair of vectors is orthogonal.

35. $(-4, -5)$ and $\left(4, -\dfrac{16}{5}\right)$ **36.** $7i + 6j$ and $5i - \dfrac{35}{6}j$

6

COMPLEX NUMBERS; POLAR COORDINATES

The set of real numbers does not contain an element whose square is a negative real number. Thus, any symbol of the form $\sqrt{-b}$, $b \in R$, $b > 0$, does not represent a real number, and equations such as

$$x^2 + 4 = 0 \qquad \text{equivalent to} \qquad x = \pm\sqrt{-4} \qquad (1)$$

and

$$x^2 - 2x + 5 = 0 \qquad \text{equivalent to} \qquad x = \frac{2 \pm \sqrt{-16}}{2} \qquad (2)$$

have no solutions in this set. In this chapter we consider a set of numbers, called the **set of complex numbers** and designated by C, that does provide solutions to such equations.

6.1 Sums and Products

The elements in the set C that we now consider are represented by various symbols. In this section we consider one form that is frequently used. In the following sections we consider other symbolic forms for these numbers.

Definition 6.1 *For all a, $b \in R$, a **complex number** is*

$$z = a + bi, \qquad \text{where} \quad i^2 = -1.$$

In this chapter we shall restrict the use of the variable z to represent elements in the set C. It is sometimes convenient to refer to a as the **real part** of the complex number and b as the **imaginary part,** with i the **imaginary unit.**

Properties of Equality

Equality in the set of complex numbers is established as follows.

Definition 6.2 *For every pair of complex numbers $z_1 = a_1 + b_1 i$ and $z_2 = a_2 + b_2 i$,*

$$z_1 = z_2 \quad \text{if and only if} \quad a_1 = a_2 \text{ and } b_1 = b_2.$$

Example $2x + y^2 i = 8 + 9i$ if and only if $2x = 8$ and $y^2 = 9$ or, equivalently, $x = 4$ and $y = \pm 3$.

Properties similar to the equality axioms in the set of real numbers R (see Appendix A.2) and the substitution law are valid for the set of complex numbers. These laws follow from the corresponding properties for real numbers. Thus, if z_1, z_2, $z_3 \in C$, then

a. $z_1 = z_1$	Reflexive law
b. If $z_1 = z_2$, then $z_2 = z_1$	Symmetric law
c. If $z_1 = z_2$ and $z_2 = z_3$, then $z_1 = z_3$	Transitive law

Computing Sums and Products

If complex numbers are treated as if i were a variable and $a + bi$ were a binomial in the variable i, then the sum or product of two complex numbers can be found by applying the ordinary rules of the algebra of real numbers. Thus,

$$(2 + 3i) + (5 - 2i) = (2 + 5) + (3 - 2)i$$
$$= 7 + i;$$
$$(2 + 3i)(5 - 2i) = 10 + 11i - 6i^2.$$

However, replacing i^2 with -1, we have

$$(2 + 3i)(5 - 2i) = 10 + 11i - 6(-1)$$
$$= 16 + 11i.$$

More formally we have the following definition.

Definition 6.3 *If* $z_1 = a_1 + b_1 i$ *and* $z_2 = a_2 + b_2 i$, *then*

$$z_1 + z_2 = (a_1 + a_2) + (b_1 + b_2)i,$$

and

$$z_1 z_2 = (a_1 a_2 - b_1 b_2) + (a_1 b_2 + a_2 b_1)i.$$

Using such an approach for sums and products, we find that

1. C will contain elements $a + 0i$, or a, that can be identified with the real numbers for these operations, and
2. C will contain elements $0 + bi$, or bi, whose squares are negative real numbers.

For example,

$$(2) + (3) = (2 + 0i) + (3 + 0i)$$
$$= 5 + 0i = 5,$$
$$(2)(3) = (2 + 0i)(3 + 0i)$$
$$= 6 + 0i + 0i^2 = 6,$$
$$(3i)^2 = 9i^2 = -9.$$

Because the complex number $a + bi$, where $b = 0$, behaves like the real number a, we shall simply write a for $a + 0i$ as convenient and refer to a or $a + 0i$ as a real number.

If $b \neq 0$, the complex number $a + bi$ is called an **imaginary number** and for the special case where $a = 0$ and $b \neq 0$, the complex number is called a **pure imaginary number.** The relationship of the set C and other sets of numbers is shown in Figure 6.1. For example, 3 and -5 are elements of C that are real; $2 + 5i$ and $5i$ are elements of C that are imaginary numbers. Furthermore, $5i$ is a pure imaginary number.

Figure 6.1

Periodic Property of i

Powers of the imaginary unit i have an interesting periodic property. Observe that

$$i^1 = i,$$

$$i^2 = -1$$

$$i^3 = i^2 \cdot i = -1 \cdot i = -i,$$

$$i^4 = i^2 \cdot i^2 = (-1)(-1) = 1,$$

$$i^5 = i^4 \cdot i = 1 \cdot i = i,$$

$$i^6 = i^4 \cdot i^2 = 1 \cdot (-1) = -1,$$

$$i^7 = i^4 \cdot i^3 = 1 \cdot (-i) = -i,$$

etc.

Thus, any integral power of i can be expressed as one of the numbers i, -1, $-i$, or 1.

Radical Notation

Another notation used to represent a complex number involves the square root symbol. In the set C, we make the following definition.

Definition 6.4 *For all $b \in R$, $b > 0$,*

$$\sqrt{-b} = \sqrt{-1}\sqrt{b} = i\sqrt{b}.$$

Observe that for the special case where $b = 1$,

$$\sqrt{-1} = \sqrt{-1}\sqrt{1} = i \cdot 1 = i.$$

Note that for a and b, positive real numbers,

$$\sqrt{-a}\sqrt{-b} = (i\sqrt{a})(i\sqrt{b}) = i^2\sqrt{a}\sqrt{b} = -\sqrt{ab},$$

a negative real number. Hence, the property of real numbers

$$\sqrt{a}\sqrt{b} = \sqrt{ab}, \quad a, b \geq 0,$$

is not applicable for imaginary numbers. For example,

$$\sqrt{-4}\sqrt{-9} \neq \sqrt{(-4)(-9)}.$$

In this case,

$$\sqrt{-4}\sqrt{-9} = 2i \cdot 3i = 6i^2 = -6.$$

To avoid difficulty in rewriting products, expressions of the form $\sqrt{-b}$ ($b > 0$) should first be expressed in the form $\sqrt{b}\, i$ or $i\sqrt{b}$.

Examples

a. $\sqrt{-3}(5 + \sqrt{-3})$

$= i\sqrt{3}(5 + i\sqrt{3})$

$= 5i\sqrt{3} + i^2(3)$

$= 5i\sqrt{3} + (-1)(3)$

$= -3 + 5i\sqrt{3}$

b. $(3 - \sqrt{-2})(3 + \sqrt{-2})$

$= (3 - i\sqrt{2})(3 + i\sqrt{2})$

$= 9 - i^2(2)$

$= 9 - (-1)(2)$

$= 11$

EXERCISE SET 6.1

A

Find real numbers x and y for which each statement is true.

Example By Definition 6.2, $x + 2yi = -5 + 8i$ if and only if

$$x = -5 \quad \text{and} \quad 2y = 8,$$

or, equivalently, if

$$x = -5 \quad \text{and} \quad y = 4.$$

1. $-5x + yi = -5 - 3i$
2. $x + 4i = 2yi$
3. $y + 4xi = 8 - 2i$
4. $x - 4i = 2y - x^2i$

Write each expression in the form a + bi.

Example $(3 + 2i) + (1 - 3i) = (3 + 1) + [2 + (-3)]i$
$$= 4 - i.$$

5. $(4 + 8i) + (-3 + 2i)$
6. $(-6 + 6i) + (4 + 2i)$
7. $(-9 - 5i) + (-1 - 6i)$
8. $(-4 + 3i) + (5 - i)$
9. $(3 + 3i) + (-4 + 3i)$
10. $(-1 + 6i) + (2 - 2i)$
11. $(a + bi) + (-a - bi)$
12. $(a + bi) + (a - bi)$

Examples

a. $2(1 - 5i) = 2(1) + 2(-5)i$ b. $-3(4 + i) = -3(4) - 3(1)i$

$\qquad\qquad = 2 - 10i$ $\qquad\qquad = -12 - 3i$

13. $4(3 - 3i)$ **14.** $5(2 + 4i)$ **15.** $-6(6 + 2i)$

16. $-4(8 - i)$ **17.** $\dfrac{1}{2}(4 + 6i)$ **18.** $\dfrac{2}{3}(9 - 6i)$

Example $(-3 + 4i)(1 + 6i) = -3 + 4i - 18i + 24i^2$

$\qquad\qquad\qquad\qquad = -3 - 14i + 24(-1) = -27 - 14i.$

19. $(-3 + 8i)(1 + 2i)$ **20.** $(4 + 2i)(-8 - 2i)$

21. $(-6 - i)(-9 + 8i)$ **22.** $(-3 - 9i)(3 + 4i)$

23. $(5 - 6i)(4 + i)$ **24.** $(5 + i)(-1 + i)$

25. $(a + bi)(a - bi)$ **26.** $(a + bi)(a + bi)$

Write each expression as one of the complex numbers, i, -1, $-i$, or 1.

27. i^5 **28.** i^8 **29.** i^{10} **30.** i^{11}

31. i^{14} **32.** i^{16} **33.** i^{19} **34.** i^{23}

Write each expression in the form bi or $a + bi$.

Examples

a. $\sqrt{-16} = \sqrt{16}\sqrt{-1}$ b. $4 + \sqrt{-8} = 4 + \sqrt{4}\sqrt{2}\sqrt{-1}$

$\qquad\quad = 4i$ $\qquad\qquad\quad = 4 + 2\sqrt{2}i$

35. $\sqrt{-25}$ **36.** $\sqrt{-49}$ **37.** $\sqrt{-12}$ **38.** $\sqrt{-27}$

39. $1 + \sqrt{-9}$ **40.** $2 - \sqrt{-64}$ **41.** $3 - \sqrt{-20}$ **42.** $5 + \sqrt{-48}$

Examples

a. $\sqrt{-9}(2 - 3\sqrt{-9}) = 3i(2 - 3 \cdot 3i)$

$\qquad\qquad\qquad\quad = 3i(2 - 9i)$

$\qquad\qquad\qquad\quad = 6i - 27i^2 = 27 + 6i$

(continued)

b. $(1 + \sqrt{-5})(1 - 2\sqrt{-5}) = (1 + \sqrt{5}i)(1 - 2\sqrt{5}i)$

$$= 1 + \sqrt{5}i - 2\sqrt{5}i - 2(\sqrt{5})^2i^2$$

$$= 1 - \sqrt{5}i - 2 \cdot 5(-1)$$

$$= 11 - \sqrt{5}i$$

43. $\sqrt{-4}(1 - 2\sqrt{-4})$ **44.** $\sqrt{-8}(3 + 4\sqrt{-2})$

45. $\sqrt{-16}(2 + \sqrt{-4})$ **46.** $\sqrt{-9}(3 - \sqrt{-25})$

47. $(\sqrt{-50} + 2)\sqrt{-10}$ **48.** $(\sqrt{-48} - 1)\sqrt{-21}$

49. $(5 + 2\sqrt{-4})(3 - \sqrt{-4})$ **50.** $(1 - 4\sqrt{-9})(7 + 2\sqrt{-9})$

51. $(2 + \sqrt{-3})(3 - \sqrt{-3})$ **52.** $(3 - \sqrt{-7})(3 + \sqrt{-7})$

53. Show that $2i$ and $-2i$ satisfy $x^2 + 4 = 0$.

54. Show that $1 + 2i$ and $1 - 2i$ satisfy $x^2 - 2x + 5 = 0$.

B

55. Show that $\left(-\dfrac{1}{2} + i\dfrac{\sqrt{3}}{2}\right)^3 = 1$ and $\left(-\dfrac{1}{2} - i\dfrac{\sqrt{3}}{2}\right)^3 = 1$.

56. Show that $\left(\dfrac{1}{2} + i\dfrac{\sqrt{3}}{2}\right)^3 = -1$ and $\left(\dfrac{1}{2} - i\dfrac{\sqrt{3}}{2}\right)^3 = -1$.

Find a and b for which each statement in Exercises 57 and 58 is true.

57. $(a + bi)^2 = -1$.   *Hint:* First express the given equation as $a^2 - b^2 + 2abi = -1$ and then use Definition 6.2.

58. $(a + bi)^2 = 1$.

The formula $e^{ix} = \cos x + i \sin x$, where $e = 2.718 \ldots$, is called **Euler's formula** *(it is usually derived in a course in calculus). Use this formula to show that the following equations are identities.*

59. $e^{\pi i} = -1$ **60.** $e^{-ix} = \cos x - i \sin x$

61. $\sin x = \dfrac{e^{ix} - e^{-ix}}{2i}$ **62.** $\cos x = \dfrac{e^{ix} + e^{-ix}}{2}$

63. $\sin^2 x + \cos^2 x = 1$.   *Hint:* Use Exercises 61 and 62.

6.2 Differences and Quotients

The operations of addition and multiplication of complex numbers have been defined so that many of the properties of real numbers are valid in the set of complex numbers.

Two other useful operations, subtraction and division, are defined in terms of addition and multiplication. These definitions are similar to the definitions for a difference and a quotient in the set of real numbers.

Definition 6.5   *For all* $z_1, z_2 \in C$, *the* **difference**

$$z_1 - z_2 = z_1 + (-z_2).$$

Example $(3 + 4i) - (5 + 2i) = (3 + 4i) + (-5 - 2i)$

$$= (3 - 5) + (4 - 2)i = -2 + 2i.$$

Definition 6.6   *For all* $z_1, z_2 \in C$ *where* $z_2 \neq 0$, *the* **quotient**

$$\frac{z_1}{z_2} = z_1 \left(\frac{1}{z_2} \right).$$

Since the axioms used for the real numbers together with equality axioms are also valid in C, for each property that follows from these axioms in the set R (see Appendix A.2), there is a corresponding property in the set C. One such property,

If $z_1, z_2, z_3 \in C$, *such that* $z_2, z_3 \neq 0$, *then*

$$\frac{z_1}{z_2} = \frac{z_1 z_3}{z_2 z_3}, \tag{1}$$

is particularly useful in rewriting quotients in the set C. We first make the following definition.

Definition 6.7   *For all* $z = a + bi$, *the* **conjugate** *of z is*

$$\bar{z} = a - bi.$$

Examples
   a. The conjugate of $5 + 4i$ is $5 - 4i$.

   b. The conjugate of $2 - 3i$ is $2 + 3i$.

A quotient of complex numbers, z_1/z_2, can be expressed in the form $a + bi$ by first multiplying both the numerator and the denominator by the conjugate of the denominator. If the denominator is a pure imaginary number, then it is necessary only to multiply the numerator and denominator by i. If the denominator is a real number and the numerator is of the form $a + bi$, then it is necessary only to write the quotient as two terms.

Examples

a. $\dfrac{3}{1 + 2i} = \dfrac{3(1 - 2i)}{(1 + 2i)(1 - 2i)}$

$= \dfrac{3 - 6i}{1 - 4i^2}$

$= \dfrac{3 - 6i}{5} = \dfrac{3}{5} - \dfrac{6}{5} i$

b. $\dfrac{4 - i}{2 - 3i} = \dfrac{(4 - i)(2 + 3i)}{(2 - 3i)(2 + 3i)}$

$= \dfrac{8 + 10i - 3i^2}{4 - 9i^2}$

$= \dfrac{11 + 10i}{13} = \dfrac{11}{13} + \dfrac{10}{13} i$

c. $\dfrac{3 - i}{3i} = \dfrac{(3 - i)i}{3i \cdot i} = \dfrac{3i - i^2}{3i^2}$

$= \dfrac{3i + 1}{-3} = -\dfrac{1}{3} - i$

d. $\dfrac{4 + 5i}{7} = \dfrac{4}{7} + \dfrac{5}{7} i$

In Example a, note that the product of the complex number $1 + 2i$ and its conjugate $1 - 2i$ is the real number 5. In Example b, note that the product of the complex number $2 - 3i$ and its conjugate $2 + 3i$ is the real number 13. In fact, observe that for all $a + bi \in C$,

$$(a + bi)(a - bi) = a^2 - b^2 i^2 = a^2 + b^2,$$

a real number.

As we noted in Section 6.1, to avoid difficulty in rewriting products, expressions of the form $\sqrt{-b}$ ($b > 0$) should first be expressed in the form $\sqrt{b} i$ or $i\sqrt{b}$. Hence, quotients of this form should also be rewritten before using Equation (1).

Examples

a. $\dfrac{5}{\sqrt{-4}} = \dfrac{5}{2i}$

$= \dfrac{5 \cdot i}{2i \cdot i}$

$= \dfrac{5i}{2(-1)}$

$= -\dfrac{5}{2} i$

b. $\dfrac{4}{3 - \sqrt{-2}} = \dfrac{4(3 + i\sqrt{2})}{(3 - i\sqrt{2})(3 + i\sqrt{2})}$

$= \dfrac{12 + 4i\sqrt{2}}{9 - i^2(2)}$

$= \dfrac{12 + 4i\sqrt{2}}{9 - (-1)(2)}$

$= \dfrac{12}{11} + \dfrac{4\sqrt{2}}{11} i$

EXERCISE SET 6.2

A

Express each difference in the form a + bi.

Example $(1 - 4i) - (-1 + 10i) = (1 - 4i) + (1 - 10i)$

$$= (1 + 1) + (-4 - 10)i = 2 - 14i$$

1. $(6 + i) - (-7 + 5i)$ **2.** $(-7 - 3i) - (-5 + 5i)$

3. $(3 - i) - (1 - 3i)$ **4.** $(3 + 2i) - (-5 + 8i)$

5. $(5 + 2i) - 3i$ **6.** $4 - (2 - 3i)$

Write the conjugate of each complex number in the form a + bi.

Examples a. $z = -3 + 4i$ b. $z = 5 - 2i$

Solutions a. $\bar{z} = -3 - 4i$ b. $\bar{z} = 5 + 2i$

7. $6 + 3i$ **8.** $5 - 5i$ **9.** $-3 - 3i$

10. $-4 + i$ **11.** $3i$ **12.** 7

Express each quotient in the form a + bi.

Examples

a. $\dfrac{8 - 2i}{8i} = \dfrac{(8 - 2i)i}{8i \cdot i}$ b. $\dfrac{-4}{-3 + i} = \dfrac{(-4)(-3 - i)}{(-3 + i)(-3 - i)}$

$\qquad\qquad = \dfrac{8i - 2i^2}{8i^2}$ $\qquad\qquad = \dfrac{12 + 4i}{9 - i^2}$

$\qquad\qquad = \dfrac{8i + 2}{-8} = -\dfrac{1}{4} - i$ $\qquad\qquad = \dfrac{6}{5} + \dfrac{2}{5}i$

13. $\dfrac{-9 - 6i}{-4i}$ **14.** $\dfrac{-2 + 3i}{3i}$ **15.** $\dfrac{4}{2 - 9i}$ **16.** $\dfrac{2}{-8 + 5i}$

17. $\dfrac{2 + i}{4 + i}$ **18.** $\dfrac{2 - 5i}{-1 + 6i}$ **19.** $\dfrac{-5 + 9i}{6 - 2i}$ **20.** $\dfrac{3 - 2i}{3 + 2i}$

Examples

a. $\dfrac{3}{\sqrt{-2}} = \dfrac{3(i)}{i\sqrt{2}(i)}$

$ = \dfrac{3i}{i^2\sqrt{2}}$

$ = \dfrac{3i}{(-1)\sqrt{2}}$

$ = -\dfrac{3}{\sqrt{2}}\,i$

b. $\dfrac{5}{2 + \sqrt{-3}} = \dfrac{5(2 - i\sqrt{3})}{(2 + i\sqrt{3})(2 - i\sqrt{3})}$

$ = \dfrac{10 - 5i\sqrt{3}}{4 - i^2(3)}$

$ = \dfrac{10 - 5i\sqrt{3}}{4 - (-1)(3)}$

$ = \dfrac{10}{7} - \dfrac{5\sqrt{3}}{7}\,i$

21. $\dfrac{1}{\sqrt{-5}}$ **22.** $\dfrac{2}{\sqrt{-7}}$ **23.** $\dfrac{4}{\sqrt{-8}}$

24. $\dfrac{7}{\sqrt{-12}}$ **25.** $\dfrac{3}{4 + \sqrt{-5}}$ **26.** $\dfrac{7}{5 - \sqrt{-3}}$

27. $\dfrac{6}{\sqrt{-2} + 3}$ **28.** $\dfrac{4}{\sqrt{-7} - 6}$ **29.** $\dfrac{6}{\sqrt{2} + \sqrt{-5}}$

30. $\dfrac{10}{\sqrt{3} - \sqrt{-6}}$ **31.** $\dfrac{2}{\sqrt{5} + \sqrt{-8}}$ **32.** $\dfrac{3}{\sqrt{6} - \sqrt{-12}}$

6.3 Graphical Representation

The elements in $\{a + bi \mid a, b \in R\}$ can be placed in a one-to-one correspondence with the set of points in a plane by associating a with the abscissa of a point and b with the ordinate. In this way each point in a plane can be viewed as the graph of a complex number. A plane on which complex numbers are thus represented is called a **complex plane.** The elements in $\{a + 0i \mid a \in R\}$, or simply $\{a \mid a \in R\}$, are associated with the points on the x-axis, called the **real axis** and the elements in $\{0 + bi \mid b \in R\}$, or simply $\{bi \mid b \in R\}$, are associated with points on the y-axis, called the **imaginary axis.**

Examples Graph each number z, its negative, and its conjugate.

a. $z = 3 - 2i$ b. $z = -2 - 4i$

Solutions

a. The negative of $3 - 2i$ is $-3 + 2i$; the conjugate is $3 + 2i$.

b. The negative of $-2 - 4i$ is $2 + 4i$; the conjugate is $-2 + 4i$.

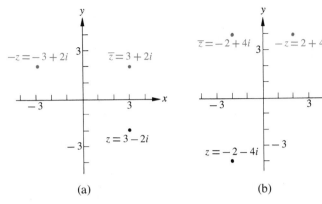

(a)   (b)

Sometimes the graph of a complex number is shown as a geometric vector with its initial point located at the origin. With this representation, complex numbers can be added graphically by the parallelogram law applicable to geometric vectors.

Examples Represent each sum graphically using geometric vectors and check the results by analytic methods.

a. $(2 + 3i) + (4 - 5i)$ b. $(2 + 2i) + (-4 + 5i)$

Solutions

a.   b.

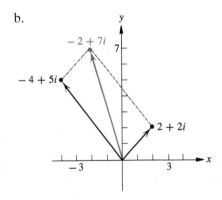

a. Check: $(2 + 3i) + (4 - 5i) = 6 - 2i$

b. Check: $(2 + 2i) + (-4 + 5i) = -2 + 7i$

Complex Numbers as Ordered Pairs

The elements in both the set $C = \{a + bi \mid a, b \in R\}$ and the elements in the set $\{(a, b) \mid a, b \in R\}$ have now been associated with the points in a plane. Hence, elements in C can also be associated with, and represented by, ordered pairs of real numbers (a, b).

Examples

a. $2 + 3i = (2, 3)$

b. $-5 = -5 + 0i = (-5, 0)$

c. $6i = 0 + 6i = (0, 6)$

Absolute Value and Argument

Corresponding to the norm $\|\vec{v}\|$ and the direction angle α for each geometric vector $\vec{v}$, there are a real number and a *set* of angles associated with each complex number.

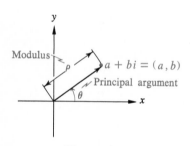

Figure 6.2

Definition 6.8 *For all $z \in C$, the **absolute value** or **modulus** of z, where $z = a + bi = (a, b)$, is*

$$\rho = |z| = |a + bi|$$
$$= |(a, b)| = \sqrt{a^2 + b^2}.$$

The modulus ρ (the Greek letter "rho") is the distance from the origin to the graph of (a, b), as shown in Figure 6.2.

Definition 6.9 *Full all $z \in C$, an **argument** or **amplitude** of z, where $z = a + bi = (a, b)$, denoted by $\arg(a + bi)$ or $\arg(a,b)$, is an angle θ such that*

$$\cos \theta = \frac{a}{\sqrt{a^2 + b^2}} = \frac{a}{\rho} \quad and \quad \sin \theta = \frac{b}{\sqrt{a^2 + b^2}} = \frac{b}{\rho} \quad (a^2 + b^2 \neq 0).$$

Thus, $\arg(a + bi)$ is an angle θ with initial side the positive x-axis and terminal side the ray from the origin through the graph of (a, b), as shown in Figure 6.2.

If θ is an argument of $a + bi$, then for $k \in J$, so is $(\theta + k \cdot 360)°$. The angle θ with the least nonnegative measure is sometimes called the

principal argument. For $a + bi = 0 + 0i$, any angle θ can be used as an argument.

Example Find the absolute value and principal argument of $\sqrt{3} + i$.

Solution $\rho = |\sqrt{3} + i| = \sqrt{(\sqrt{3})^2 + 1^2} = \sqrt{3 + 1} = 2;$

$$\cos \theta = \frac{a}{\rho} = \frac{\sqrt{3}}{2} \quad \text{and} \quad \sin \theta = \frac{b}{\rho} = \frac{1}{2}.$$

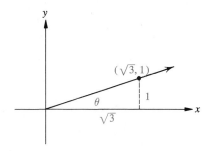

Because both $\cos \theta$ and $\sin \theta$ are positive, θ is in Quadrant I, and hence $\theta = 30°$.

There is another method that is often used to determine θ. Consider the number $a + bi = \sqrt{3} + i$ from the example above. First plot the point $(a, b) = (\sqrt{3}, 1)$ and form angle θ. From the sketch, θ is in Quadrant I, and $\tan \theta = 1/\sqrt{3}$. Hence $\theta = 30°$.

EXERCISE SET 6.3

A

Express each complex number as an ordered pair.

1. $-1 + 6i$ 2. $5 - 9i$ 3. $8 + i$

4. $-2 + 7i$ 5. $6i$ 6. -5

Express each complex number in the form $a + bi$.

7. $(-8, 7)$ 8. $(0, 5)$ 9. $(-4, 0)$

10. $(6, -3)$ 11. $(7, -\sqrt{2})$ 12. $(-\sqrt{3}, 1)$

Graph each complex number z, its negative −z, and its conjugate z̄.

Examples

a. $-5 - 4i$ b. $(3, 2)$

Solutions

a. The negative is $5 + 4i$; the conjugate is $-5 + 4i$.

b. The negative is $(-3, -2)$; the conjugate is $(3, -2)$.

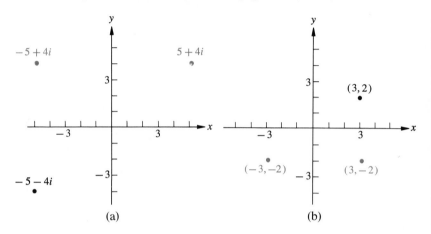

(a)   (b)

13. $2 - 3i$ **14.** $-6 + 6i$ **15.** 5 **16.** $2i$

17. $(4, 6)$ **18.** $(-5, -3)$ **19.** $(-1, 0)$ **20.** $(0, 3)$

Represent each sum graphically. Check results by algebraic methods.

Example $(8 + 3i) + (1 - 5i)$

Solution

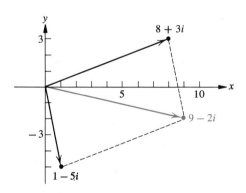

Check: $(8 + 3i) + (1 - 5i) = (8 + 1) + (3 - 5)i = 9 - 2i.$

21. $2 + (-3 + 6i)$ **22.** $(7 - i) + 2i$

23. $(4 - 7i) + (-8 + 2i)$ **24.** $(2 + 4i) + (1 - 5i)$

25. $(-6 + 7i) + (5 - 3i)$ **26.** $(-3 - 5i) + (3 - 2i)$

Find the absolute value and principal argument of each complex number.

Examples

a. $-7 + 5i$ b. $(3, 9)$

Solutions   From Definitions 6.8 and 6.9,

   a. $\rho = |-7 + 5i| = \sqrt{(-7)^2 + 5^2} = \sqrt{74}$;

$$\cos \theta = -\frac{7}{\sqrt{74}} \approx -0.8137 \quad \text{and} \quad \sin \theta = \frac{5}{\sqrt{74}} \approx 0.5812.$$

Because $\cos \theta$ is negative and $\sin \theta$ is positive, θ is in Quadrant II; hence, $\theta \approx 144.5°$.

   b. $\rho = |(3, 9)| = \sqrt{3^2 + 9^2} = \sqrt{90} = 3\sqrt{10}$;

$$\cos \theta = \frac{3}{3\sqrt{10}} \approx 0.3162 \quad \text{and} \quad \sin \theta = \frac{9}{3\sqrt{10}} \approx 0.9487.$$

Because $\cos \theta$ and $\sin \theta$ are both positive, θ is in Quadrant I; hence, $\theta \approx 71.6°$.

27. $5 + 2i$ **28.** $6 + 8i$ **29.** $-2 - 2i$ **30.** $8 - 3i$

31. 7 **32.** -4 **33.** $-5i$ **34.** $6i$

35. $(3, -9)$ **36.** $(-6, -2)$ **37.** $(4, 0)$ **38.** $(0, -7)$

39. Determine the conditions that a and b must satisfy if the graph of the complex number $a + bi$ is
    a. on the real axis.   **b.** on the imaginary axis.
    c. above the real axis.   **d.** below the real axis.

40. What condition does $a^2 + b^2$ satisfy if the graph of $a + bi$ is
    a. on a circle with radius of length 5?
    b. inside a circle with radius of length 5?
    c. outside a circle with radius of length 5?

B

Graphically, the multiplication or division of a complex number a + bi by the complex number i produces a 90° rotation of the geometric vector corresponding to a + bi, counterclockwise for multiplication and clockwise for division. Graph

(a) *the given complex number a + bi,* **(b)** *i · (a + bi), and* **(c)** $\dfrac{a + bi}{i}$.

Example $2 + 3i$

Solutions

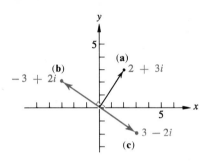

b. $i \cdot (2 + 3i) = 2i + 3i^2$

$$= -3 + 2i$$

c. $\dfrac{2 + 3i}{i} = \dfrac{(2 + 3i) \cdot i}{i \cdot i}$

$$= \dfrac{2i + 3i^2}{i^2}$$

$$= \dfrac{2i - 3}{-1} = 3 - 2i$$

41. $5 + 4i$ **42.** $1 - 2i$ **43.** $-6 + i$

44. $-3 - 4i$ **45.** 2 **46.** $-5i$

6.4 Trigonometric Form

In previous sections we have represented complex numbers in the form $a + bi$, $a + \sqrt{-b^2}$, and (a, b). It is sometimes convenient to represent a complex number in terms of its absolute value $\rho = \sqrt{a^2 + b^2}$ and its argument θ. From Definition 6.9,

$$\cos \theta = \frac{a}{\rho} \quad \text{and} \quad \sin \theta = \frac{b}{\rho}.$$

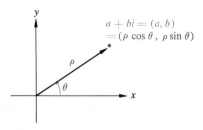

Therefore, as shown in Figure 6.3,

$$a = \rho \cos \theta \quad \text{and} \quad b = \rho \sin \theta,$$

from which we have

$$a + bi = \rho \cos \theta + (\rho \sin \theta)i,$$

$$\boldsymbol{a + bi = \rho(\cos \theta + i \sin \theta).}$$

Figure 6.3

(The expression $\cos \theta + i \sin \theta$ is sometimes abbreviated as cis θ.)

The sine and cosine functions are periodic with period of 360° or $2\pi^R$. Hence, it is also true that

$$a + bi = \rho[\cos(\theta + k \cdot 360°) + i \sin(\theta + k \cdot 360°)], \quad k \in J,$$

or

$$a + bi = \rho[\cos(\theta + k \cdot 2\pi^R) + i \sin(\theta + k \cdot 2\pi^R)], \quad k \in J$$

where θ is the angle of smallest nonnegative measure. Either equation is called the **trigonometric form** of a complex number.

Example   Represent $-2 + 2i$ in trigonometric form.

Solution   From Definition 6.8,

$$\rho = |-2 + 2i| = \sqrt{(-2)^2 + 2^2} = \sqrt{8} = 2\sqrt{2}.$$

From Definition 6.9,

$$\cos \theta = \frac{-2}{2\sqrt{2}} = -\frac{1}{\sqrt{2}} \quad \text{and} \quad \sin \theta = \frac{2}{2\sqrt{2}} = \frac{1}{\sqrt{2}}.$$

Thus, θ is in Quadrant II and $\theta = 135°$. For $k \in J$,

$$-2 + 2i = 2\sqrt{2}[\cos(135° + k \cdot 360°) + i \sin(135° + k \cdot 360°)].$$

For $k = 0$,

$$-2 + 2i = 2\sqrt{2}(\cos 135° + i \sin 135°).$$

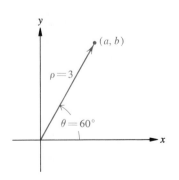

Example   Represent $3(\cos 60° + i \sin 60°)$ graphically and express the number in the form $a + bi$.

Solution   Since

$$a = \rho \cos \theta$$
$$= 3 \cos 60°$$
$$= 3\left(\frac{1}{2}\right) = \frac{3}{2},$$

(continued)

and

$$b = \rho \sin \theta = 3 \sin 60° = 3 \left(\frac{\sqrt{3}}{2}\right) = \frac{3\sqrt{3}}{2},$$

we have

$$3(\cos 60° + i \sin 60°) = \frac{3}{2} + \frac{3\sqrt{3}}{2} i.$$

Products and Quotients

Products and quotients of complex numbers expressed in trigonometric form can be found quite readily. If

$$z_1 = \rho_1(\cos \theta_1 + i \sin \theta_1) \quad \text{and} \quad z_2 = \rho_2(\cos \theta_2 + i \sin \theta_2),$$

then

$$
\begin{aligned}
z_1 \cdot z_2 &= \rho_1(\cos \theta_1 + i \sin \theta_1) \cdot \rho_2(\cos \theta_2 + i \sin \theta_2) \\
&= \rho_1 \rho_2 [(\cos \theta_1 \cos \theta_2 - \sin \theta_1 \sin \theta_2) \\
&\qquad\qquad + i(\cos \theta_1 \sin \theta_2 + \sin \theta_1 \cos \theta_2)].
\end{aligned}
$$

Substituting $\cos(\theta_1 + \theta_2)$ for $\cos \theta_1 \cos \theta_2 - \sin \theta_1 \sin \theta_2$ and then $\sin(\theta_1 + \theta_2)$ for $\cos \theta_1 \sin \theta_2 + \sin \theta_1 \cos \theta_2$, we have

$$z_1 \cdot z_2 = \rho_1 \rho_2 [\cos(\theta_1 + \theta_2) + i \sin(\theta_1 + \theta_2)]. \tag{1}$$

It can also be shown in a similar way that

$$\frac{z_1}{z_2} = \frac{\rho_1}{\rho_2} [\cos(\theta_1 - \theta_2) + i \sin(\theta_1 - \theta_2)], \quad z_2 \neq (0, 0). \tag{2}$$

Example   Express $6(\cos 75° + i \sin 75°) \cdot 3(\cos 15° + i \sin 15°)$ in the form $a + bi$.

Solution   From Equation (1),

$$
\begin{aligned}
6(\cos 75° + i \sin 75°) \cdot 3(\cos 15° &+ i \sin 15°) \\
&= 6 \cdot 3[\cos(75° + 15°) + i \sin(75° + 15°)] \\
&= 18(\cos 90° + i \sin 90°) \\
&= 18(0 + i) = 18i.
\end{aligned}
$$

Example Express $\dfrac{6(\cos 75° + i \sin 75°)}{3(\cos 15° + i \sin 15°)}$ in the form $a + bi$.

Solution From Equation (2),

$$\frac{6(\cos 75° + i \sin 75°)}{3(\cos 15° + i \sin 15°)} = \frac{6}{3}\left[\cos(75° - 15°) + i \sin(75° - 15°)\right]$$

$$= 2(\cos 60° + i \sin 60°)$$

$$= 2\left(\frac{1}{2} + i\frac{\sqrt{3}}{2}\right) = 1 + \sqrt{3}i.$$

EXERCISE SET 6.4

A

Represent each complex number in trigonometric form, using the angle with least nonnegative measure.

Example $\sqrt{3} - i$

Solution From Definition 6.8, $\rho = |\sqrt{3} - i| = \sqrt{3 + 1} = 2$. From Definition 6.9, $\cos \theta = \sqrt{3}/2$ and $\sin \theta = -1/2$. Hence θ is in Quadrant IV and $\theta = 330°$. Therefore,

$$\sqrt{3} - i = 2[\cos(330° + k \cdot 360°) + i \sin(330° + k \cdot 360°)], \quad k \in J.$$

For $k = 0$, we obtain

$$\sqrt{3} - i = 2(\cos 330° + i \sin 330°).$$

1. $-2 + 2\sqrt{3}i$ **2.** $6 + 6i$ **3.** $-5\sqrt{3} - 5i$ **4.** $3\sqrt{3} + 3i$

5. $2 - 2i$ **6.** $-4 - 4i$ **7.** -8 **8.** $-9i$

Represent each complex number graphically and write as $a + bi$.

Example $6(\cos 315° + i \sin 315°)$

Solution Since

$$a = \rho \cos \theta = 6\left(\frac{\sqrt{2}}{2}\right) = 3\sqrt{2},$$

and

$$b = \rho \sin \theta = 6\left(\frac{-\sqrt{2}}{2}\right) = -3\sqrt{2},$$

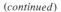
(*continued*)

we have

$$a + bi = 3\sqrt{2} - 3\sqrt{2}\, i.$$

9. $2(\cos 240° + i \sin 240°)$ **10.** $2(\cos 90° + i \sin 90°)$

11. $2(\cos 135° + i \sin 135°)$ **12.** $3(\cos 30° + i \sin 30°)$

13. $\cos(-45°) + i \sin(-45°)$ **14.** $\cos(-210°) + i \sin(-210°)$

15. $\frac{1}{2}(\cos 150° + i \sin 150°)$ **16.** $\frac{3}{4}(\cos 330° + i \sin 330°)$

Express each product in the form a + bi.

Example $2(\cos 140° + i \sin 140°) \cdot 5(\cos 70° + i \sin 70°)$

Solution   From Equation (1) in this section,

$$2(\cos 140° + i \sin 140°) \cdot 5(\cos 70° + i \sin 70°)$$

$$= 2 \cdot 5[\cos(140° + 70°) + i \sin(140° + 70°)]$$

$$= 10(\cos 210° + i \sin 210°)$$

$$= 10\left[\frac{-\sqrt{3}}{2} + i\left(-\frac{1}{2}\right)\right] = -5\sqrt{3} - 5i.$$

17. $5(\cos 100° + i \sin 100°) \cdot 2(\cos 35° + i \sin 35°)$

18. $3(\cos 130° + i \sin 130°) \cdot \frac{2}{3}(\cos 140° + i \sin 140°)$

19. $4(\cos 85° + i \sin 85°) \cdot \frac{3}{4}(\cos 245° + i \sin 245°)$

20. $4(\cos 20° + i \sin 20°) \cdot \frac{1}{2}(\cos 40° + i \sin 40°)$

21. $2(\cos 40° + i \sin 40°) \cdot (\cos 95° + i \sin 95°)$

22. $2(\cos 5° + i \sin 5°) \cdot 3(\cos 40° + i \sin 40°)$

Express each quotient in the form a + bi.

Example $\dfrac{6(\cos 85° + i \sin 85°)}{2(\cos 40° + i \sin 40°)}$

Solution   From Equation (2) in this section,

$$\frac{6(\cos 85° + i \sin 85°)}{2(\cos 40° + i \sin 40°)} = \frac{6}{2}[\cos(85° - 40°) + i \sin(85° - 40°)]$$

$$= 3(\cos 45° + i \sin 45°)$$

$$= \frac{3}{\sqrt{2}} + \frac{3}{\sqrt{2}}\, i.$$

23. $\dfrac{8(\cos 260° + i \sin 260°)}{2(\cos 80° + i \sin 80°)}$

24. $\dfrac{6(\cos 215° + i \sin 215°)}{3(\cos 80° + i \sin 80°)}$

25. $\dfrac{2(\cos 255° + i \sin 255°)}{5(\cos 15° + i \sin 15°)}$

26. $\dfrac{2(\cos 280° + i \sin 280°)}{3(\cos 70° + i \sin 70°)}$

27. $\dfrac{3(\cos 70° + i \sin 70°)}{\cos 130° + i \sin 130°}$

28. $\dfrac{\cos 19° + i \sin 19°}{4(\cos 259° + i \sin 259°)}$

29. Write $[2(\cos 20° + i \sin 20°)]^3$ in the form $a + bi$.

30. Write $\left(\dfrac{1}{\sqrt{2}} + \dfrac{1}{\sqrt{2}} i\right)^3$ in the form $a + bi$.

31. Show that if

$$a + bi = \rho(\cos \theta + i \sin \theta),$$

then $\qquad (a + bi)^2 = \rho^2(\cos 2\theta + i \sin 2\theta).$

32. Use the result of Exercise 31 to show that if

$$a + bi = \rho(\cos \theta + i \sin \theta),$$

then $\qquad (a + bi)^3 = \rho^3(\cos 3\theta + i \sin 3\theta).$

33. Use the result of Exercise 32 to show that if

$$a + bi = \rho(\cos \theta + i \sin \theta),$$

then $\qquad (a + bi)^4 = \rho^4(\cos 4\theta + i \sin 4\theta).$

34. Using the results of Exercises 31–33, what can you conjecture about $(a + bi)^n$, $n \in N$, if $a + bi = \rho(\cos \theta + i \sin \theta)$?

35. Show that $\cos \theta + i \sin \theta$ and $\cos(-\theta) + i \sin(-\theta)$ are conjugates of each other.

36. Show that $\cos \theta + i \sin \theta$ and $\cos(-\theta) + i \sin(-\theta)$ are reciprocals of each other.

6.5 DeMoivre's Theorem; Powers and Roots

Consider the complex number $z = a + bi = \rho(\cos \theta + i \sin \theta)$. From Equation (1) in Section 6.4.

$$[\rho(\cos \theta + i \sin \theta)]^2 = \rho(\cos \theta + i \sin \theta) \cdot \rho(\cos \theta + i \sin \theta)$$

$$= \rho^2[\cos(\theta + \theta) + i \sin(\theta + \theta)]$$

$$= \rho^2(\cos 2\theta + i \sin 2\theta);$$

$$[\rho(\cos\theta + i\sin\theta)]^3 = \rho^2(\cos 2\theta + i\sin 2\theta) \cdot \rho(\cos\theta + i\sin\theta)$$
$$= \rho^3[\cos(2\theta + \theta) + i\sin(2\theta + \theta)]$$
$$= \rho^3(\cos 3\theta + i\sin 3\theta).$$

It can be shown that similar results are valid for each such power for $n \in N$. That is, if $z = \rho(\cos\theta + i\sin\theta)$ and $n \in N$, then

$$z^n = \rho^n (\cos n\theta + i\sin n\theta). \qquad (1)$$

This statement is known as **DeMoivre's theorem.** The proof of the statement and extensions of it which are presented in this section involve the process of mathematical induction and will not be shown. However, the informal argument above should make the validity of Equation (1) plausible.

Example   Express $(\sqrt{3} + i)^5$ in the form $a + bi$.

Solution   From Definition 6.8,

$$\rho = |\sqrt{3} + i| = \sqrt{3 + 1} = 2.$$

By Definition 6.9, $\cos\theta = \sqrt{3}/2$ and $\sin\theta = 1/2$. Therefore θ is in Quadrant I and $\theta = 30°$. Thus,

$$(\sqrt{3} + i)^5 = [2(\cos 30° + i\sin 30°)]^5$$
$$= 2^5(\cos 5 \cdot 30° + i\sin 5 \cdot 30°)$$
$$= 32(\cos 150° + i\sin 150°)$$
$$= 32\left(-\frac{\sqrt{3}}{2} + \frac{1}{2}i\right) = -16\sqrt{3} + 16i.$$

Equation (1) was stated for powers with natural number exponents. If this statement is to be valid for integral exponents, consistent meanings must be assigned to z^0 and z^{-n} for $n \in N$.
Substituting 0 for n in Equation (1), we have

$$z^0 = \rho^0(\cos 0 \cdot \theta + i\sin 0 \cdot \theta) = 1 \cdot (\cos 0 + i\sin 0)$$
$$= 1 \cdot (1 + 0) = 1.$$

Substituting $-n$ for n in Equation (1), we have

$$z^{-n} = \rho^{-n}[\cos(-n\theta) + i\sin(-n\theta)].$$

Since $\cos(-n\theta) = \cos n\theta$ and $\sin(-n\theta) = -\sin n\theta$, we have

$$z^{-n} = \frac{1}{\rho^n} \cdot (\cos n\theta - i \sin n\theta).$$

Multiplying the numerator and the denominator of the right-hand member by the conjugate of the numerator yields

$$z^{-n} = \frac{1}{\rho^n} \cdot \frac{(\cos n\theta - i \sin n\theta) \cdot (\cos n\theta + i \sin n\theta)}{\cos n\theta + i \sin n\theta}$$

$$= \frac{1}{\rho^n} \cdot \frac{\cos^2 n\theta + \sin^2 n\theta}{\cos n\theta + i \sin n\theta}$$

$$= \frac{1}{\rho^n} \cdot \frac{1}{\cos n\theta + i \sin n\theta} = \frac{1}{\rho^n(\cos n\theta + i \sin n\theta)}.$$

Substituting z^n for $\rho^n(\cos n\theta + i \sin n\theta)$ yields

$$z^{-n} = \frac{1}{z^n}.$$

Thus, if we want Equation (1) to be valid for every exponent $n \in J$, z^0 and z^{-n} must be given the following interpretations:

Definition 6.10   *For all $z \neq 0 + 0i$,*

      I. $z^0 = 1 + 0i = 1.$

      II. $z^{-n} = \dfrac{1}{z^n}, \quad n \in N.$

DeMoivre's theorem [Equation (1)] can now be applied to powers with $n \in J$.

Example   Express $(-\sqrt{3} + i)^{-3}$ in the form $a + bi$.

Solution   From Definitions 6.8 and 6.9,

$$\rho = |-\sqrt{3} + i| = \sqrt{3 + 1} = 2;$$

since

$$\cos \theta = -\frac{\sqrt{3}}{2} \quad \text{and} \quad \sin \theta = \frac{1}{2},$$

(continued)

θ is in Quadrant II and $\theta = 150°$. Thus,

$$(-\sqrt{3} + i)^{-3} = [2(\cos 150° + i \sin 150°)]^{-3},$$

and from DeMoivre's theorem we have

$$(-\sqrt{3} + i)^{-3} = \frac{1}{2^3} [\cos(-3 \cdot 150°) + i \sin(-3 \cdot 150°)]$$

$$= \frac{1}{8} [\cos(-450°) + i \sin(-450°)]$$

$$= \frac{1}{8} [0 - 1 \cdot i] = -\frac{1}{8} i.$$

Another extension of DeMoivre's theorem is possible for rational number exponents $1/n$, where $n \in N$. First we define an nth root of z in the same way that an nth root of a real number a is defined, when such a number exists.

Definition 6.11   *For $z \in C$, $n \in N$, the number ω is an nth root of z if $\omega^n = z$.*

We can now state another extension of DeMoivre's theorem applicable to roots of complex numbers:

If $n \in N$ and $z = \rho(\cos \theta + i \sin \theta)$, $z \neq 0$, then

$$\rho^{1/n} \left[\cos \left(\frac{\theta + k \cdot 360°}{n} \right) + i \sin \left(\frac{\theta + k \cdot 360°}{n} \right) \right], \quad k \in J \qquad (2)$$

specifies all nth roots of z.

Using this extension of DeMoivre's theorem, we can now find n distinct complex nth roots for each $z \in C$, where $z \neq 0$. For $k = 0$, one nth root is

$$\rho^{1/n} \left(\cos \frac{\theta}{n} + i \sin \frac{\theta}{n} \right),$$

where θ is the angle with the least positive measure. This root is called the **principal nth root** of z.

Example   Express each of the five fifth roots of $z = \sqrt{2} + \sqrt{2}i$ in trigonometric form.

Solution   From Definition 6.8,

$$\rho = |\sqrt{2} + \sqrt{2}i| = \sqrt{2 + 2} = 2;$$

since, from Definition 6.9,

$$\cos \theta = \frac{\sqrt{2}}{2} \quad \text{and} \quad \sin \theta = \frac{\sqrt{2}}{2},$$

the argument θ is in Quadrant I and $\theta = 45°$. Thus, in trigonometric form,

$$z = 2(\cos 45° + i \sin 45°),$$

and by Equation (2),

$$2^{1/5} \left[\cos \left(\frac{45° + k \cdot 360°}{5} \right) + i \sin \left(\frac{45° + k \cdot 360°}{5} \right) \right], \quad k \in J,$$

is a fifth root of z. Taking $k = 0, 1, 2, 3,$ and 4 in turn yields the roots

$$2^{1/5}(\cos 9° + i \sin 9°),$$
$$2^{1/5}(\cos 81° + i \sin 81°),$$
$$2^{1/5}(\cos 153° + i \sin 153°),$$
$$2^{1/5}(\cos 225° + i \sin 225°),$$
$$2^{1/5}(\cos 297° + i \sin 297°).$$

Notice that the substitution of any other integer for k will simply produce one of these five complex numbers. For example, if $k = 5$,

$$2^{1/5}[\cos(9 + 360)° + i \sin(9 + 360)°] = 2^{1/5}(\cos 9° + i \sin 9°).$$

EXERCISE SET 6.5

A

Express each power in the form a + bi.

Example $(\sqrt{3} + i)^{-2}$

Solution   From Definition 6.8.

$$\rho = |\sqrt{3} + i| = \sqrt{(\sqrt{3})^2 + (1)^2} = \sqrt{4} = 2;$$

(continued)

since, from Definition 6.9,

$$\cos \theta = \frac{\sqrt{3}}{2} \quad \text{and} \quad \sin \theta = \frac{1}{2},$$

the argument θ is in Quadrant I and $\theta = 30°$. Thus,

$$(\sqrt{3} + i)^{-2} = [2(\cos 30° + i \sin 30°)]^{-2}.$$

From DeMoivre's theorem,

$$(\sqrt{3} + i)^{-2} = \frac{1}{2^2} [\cos(-2 \cdot 30°) + i \sin(-2 \cdot 30°)]$$

$$= \frac{1}{4} [\cos(-60°) + i \sin(-60°)]$$

$$= \frac{1}{4} \left(\frac{1}{2} - \frac{\sqrt{3}}{2} i \right) = \frac{1}{8} - \frac{\sqrt{3}}{8} i.$$

1. $[3(\cos 20° + i \sin 20°)]^3$

2. $[2(\cos 42° + i \sin 42°)]^5$

3. $(-1 + i)^6$

4. $(2\sqrt{3} - 2i)^5$

5. $\left(\frac{1}{4} + \frac{\sqrt{3}}{4} i \right)^3$

6. $\left(-\frac{\sqrt{3}}{2} + \frac{1}{2} i \right)^6$

7. $[9(\cos 315° + i \sin 315°)]^{-2}$

8. $[8(\cos 120° + i \sin 120°)]^{-3}$

9. $(2 - 2i)^{-3}$

10. $(\sqrt{3} - i)^{-3}$

11. $(-1 - \sqrt{3}i)^{-5}$

12. $(-2 - 2i)^{-4}$

In Exercises 13–18, find the roots indicated and express each of them in trigonometric form.

Example The two square roots of $\dfrac{\sqrt{3}}{2} - \dfrac{1}{2} i$

Solution

$$\rho = \left| \frac{\sqrt{3}}{2} - \frac{1}{2} i \right| = \sqrt{\frac{3}{4} + \frac{1}{4}} = 1.$$

Thus, $\cos \theta = \sqrt{3}/2$ and $\sin \theta = -1/2$, and θ is in Quadrant IV. Hence $\theta = 330°$ and

$$\frac{\sqrt{3}}{2} - \frac{1}{2} i = \cos(330° + k \cdot 360°) + i \sin(330° + k \cdot 360°).$$

The square roots of $\dfrac{\sqrt{3}}{2} - \dfrac{1}{2} i$, using DeMoivre's theorem, are

$$1^{1/2} \left[\cos \left(\frac{330° + k \cdot 360°}{2} \right) + i \sin \left(\frac{330° + k \cdot 360°}{2} \right) \right],$$

where $k = 0$ and $k = 1$. For $k = 0$, we have

$$\cos 165° + i \sin 165°,$$

and for $k = 1$, we have

$$\cos 345° + i \sin 345°.$$

13. The two square roots of

    a. $\cos 80 + i \sin 80°$ **b.** $\dfrac{1}{2} + \dfrac{\sqrt{3}}{2} i$

14. The two square roots of

    a. $9(\cos 140° + i \sin 140°)$ **b.** $-4i$

15. The three cube roots of

    a. $8(\cos 120° + i \sin 120°)$ **b.** $\dfrac{1}{2} + \dfrac{\sqrt{3}}{2} i$

16. The three cube roots of

    a. $2(\cos 75° + i \sin 75°)$ **b.** $-27i$

17. The four fourth roots of

    a. $\cos 240° + i \sin 240°$ **b.** $\dfrac{1}{2} - \dfrac{\sqrt{3}}{2} i$

18. The four fourth roots of

    a. $81(\cos 60° + i \sin 60°)$ **b.** $-16i$

Solve each equation for all $x \in C$.

19. $x^3 + 1 = 0$.   *Hint:* $x^3 = -1 = -1 + 0i$.
                       Thus, x is a cube root of $-1 + 0i$.

20. $x^5 + 1 = 0$ **21.** $x^3 - 1 = 0$

22. $x^5 - 1 = 0$ **23.** $x^3 = \dfrac{\sqrt{3}}{4} - \dfrac{1}{4} i$

24. $x^5 = 12 - 5i$

B

25. Graph each of the following on a separate Cartesian coordinate system; make a conjecture about the graphs of all nth roots of 1.
    a. The two square roots of 1   **b.** The three cube roots of 1
    c. The four fourth roots of 1   **d.** The five fifth roots of 1
    e. The six sixth roots of 1   **f.** The eight eighth roots of 1

26. Use the results of Exercise 21 to show that the reciprocal of any cube root of unity is itself a cube root of unity.

27. Use DeMoivre's theorem and Definition 6.2 to find an identity for $\cos 3\theta$ in terms of $\cos \theta$.
    Hint: $(\cos \theta + i \sin \theta)^3 = \cos 3\theta + i \sin 3\theta$.

28. Use the hint in Exercise 27 to find an identity for $\sin 3\theta$ in terms of $\sin \theta$.

6.6 Polar Coordinates

The basis that we used to graph functions in Chapter 2 was the fact that we associated a point in the plane with an ordered pair of real numbers (x, y) called the Cartesian coordinates of the point, the first component of the ordered pair being the directed distance of the point from the y-axis and the second component being the directed distance from the x-axis.

Graphing Ordered Pairs (ρ, θ)

The location of a point A in the plane can also be specified by ρ (rho), the distance (a positive number) from the pole O to A and the measure of an angle θ* that the ray through point A makes with a ray called the **polar axis,** as shown in Figure 6.4. If we extend the replacement set of ρ to include the negative real numbers and the replacement set of θ to include the set of all angles, we can specify point A by many ordered pairs of the form (ρ, θ). The two components of each of these ordered pairs are called **polar coordinates** of A. For example, in Figure 6.4a, if (ρ, θ) are polar coordinates of A, then so are $[\rho, (\theta + k \cdot 360)°], k \in J$. Also, if $-\rho$ ($\rho > 0$) denotes the directed distance from O to A along the negative extension of the ray $0A'$, as shown in Figure 6.4b, then $[-\rho, (\theta + 180 + k \cdot 360)°]$ are also acceptable coordinates of A. For example, in Figure 6.5, the point having polar coordinates $(4, 30°)$ also has polar coordinates $(4, 390°)$ and $(4, -330°)$ for positive values of ρ,

---

* The measure of θ can be expressed in degree measure or radian measure.

Figure 6.4

Figure 6.5

and $(-4, 210°)$ for a negative value of ρ. Of course, there are infinitely many other possible polar coordinates for this point.

If point A is at the pole, then $\rho = 0$, and the coordinates of A are $(0, \theta)$, where θ is an arbitrary angle, not necessarily zero. For example, $(0, 90°)$ and $(0, 60°)$ are both coordinates of the pole.

Cartesian and Polar Coordinates

If the pole coincides with the origin, and the polar axis coincides with the positive x-axis, as in Figure 6.6, then for any point on the terminal ray of angle θ with Cartesian coordinates x and y, $\cos \theta = x/\rho$ and $\sin \theta = y/\rho$. Hence, the Cartesian and polar coordinates can be related as follows:

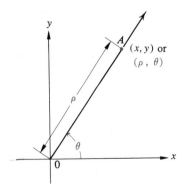

Figure 6.6

$$\left. \begin{array}{l} x = \rho \cos \theta \\ y = \rho \sin \theta \end{array} \right\} \quad (1)$$

$$\left. \begin{array}{l} \rho = \pm \sqrt{x^2 + y^2} \\[2mm] \cos \theta = \dfrac{x}{\rho} \\[2mm] \sin \theta = \dfrac{y}{\rho}, \quad \rho \neq 0 \end{array} \right\} \quad (2)$$

Equations (1) can be used to find the rectangular coordinates for a point if the polar coordinates are known, and Equations (2) can be used to find the polar coordinates for a point if the Cartesian coordinates are known. The positive or negative radical expression is chosen depending on the particular problem.

Example   Find the Cartesian coordinates of the point with polar coordinates (3, 60°).

Solution   From Equations (1), it follows that

$$x = 3 \cos 60°$$

$$= 3 \cdot \frac{1}{2} = \frac{3}{2},$$

$$y = 3 \sin 60°$$

$$= 3 \cdot \frac{\sqrt{3}}{2} = \frac{3\sqrt{3}}{2}.$$

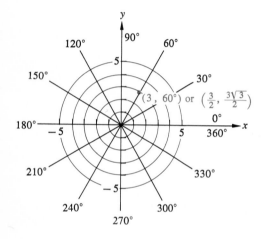

The point and the corresponding ordered pairs are shown in the figure.

Example   Find an approximation for the polar coordinates of the point with Cartesian coordinates (5, −3), where 0° < θ < 360° and ρ > 0. Graph the point.

Solution   From Equations (2) and since ρ > 0,

$$\rho = \sqrt{x^2 + y^2} = \sqrt{25 + 9} = \sqrt{34} \approx 5.831;$$

$$\cos \theta = \frac{5}{5.831} \approx 0.8575.$$

Since the point is in Quadrant IV, then θ ≈ 329.0°. Therefore, the pair of polar coordinates is (√34, 329°). The point and the corresponding ordered pairs are shown in the figure on page 265.

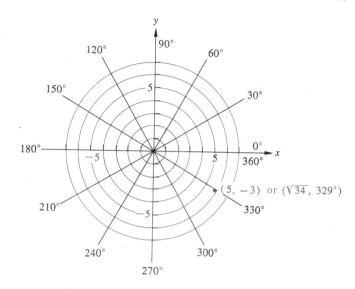

Rewriting Equations

Equations (1) and (2) on page 263 can be used to transform an equation in Cartesian form to polar form, and vice versa.

Example Rewrite $x^2 + y^2 - 4x = 0$ in polar form.

Solution Substituting ρ^2 for $x^2 + y^2$ and $\rho \cos \theta$ for x in

$$x^2 + y^2 - 4x = 0$$

yields

$$\rho^2 - 4\rho \cos \theta = 0,$$

from which

$$\rho(\rho - 4 \cos \theta) = 0.$$

Hence,

$$\rho = 0 \quad \text{or} \quad \rho - 4 \cos \theta = 0.$$

Note that the graph of $\rho = 0$ is the origin and that the graph of $\rho = 4 \cos \theta$ includes the origin as one of its points (for example, for $\theta = 90°$, we have $\rho = 0$). Hence the equation $\rho = 4 \cos \theta$ corresponds to $x^2 + y^2 - 4x = 0$, and it is not necessary to write $\rho = 0$ as part of the answer.

Example Rewrite $\rho(1 - 3 \cos \theta) = 2$ in Cartesian form.

Solution Substituting $\pm\sqrt{x^2 + y^2}$ for ρ and x/ρ, or $x/\pm\sqrt{x^2 + y^2}$, for $\cos \theta$, we have

$$\pm\sqrt{x^2 + y^2}\left[1 - 3\left(\frac{x}{\pm\sqrt{x^2 + y^2}}\right)\right] = 2$$

from which

$$\pm\sqrt{x^2 + y^2} - 3x = 2,$$
$$\pm\sqrt{x^2 + y^2} = 3x + 2.$$

Squaring each member of this equation, we have

$$x^2 + y^2 = 9x^2 + 12x + 4,$$

from which

$$8x^2 - y^2 + 12x + 4 = 0.$$

EXERCISE SET 6.6

A

Find four additional sets of polar coordinates $(-360° < \theta \le 360°)$ *for each point whose coordinates are given.*

1. $(3, 380°)$ **2.** $(6, 840°)$ **3.** $(5, -450°)$

4. $(4, -540°)$ **5.** $(-4, 420°)$ **6.** $(-5, -600°)$

Find the Cartesian coordinates of each point with polar coordinates as given.

7. $\left(4, \frac{\pi^R}{6}\right)$ **8.** $\left(6, \frac{2\pi^R}{3}\right)$ **9.** $\left(3, -\frac{3\pi^R}{4}\right)$

10. $\left(0, \frac{13\pi^R}{3}\right)$ **11.** $\left(-3, \frac{5\pi^R}{6}\right)$ **12.** $\left(-4, \frac{\pi^R}{4}\right)$

Find the pair of polar coordinates $(\theta$ *in radians) using an angle* α *such that* $0^R < \alpha < 2\pi^R$ *and* $\rho > 0$ *for each point with Cartesian coordinates as given.*

13. $(4, 0)$ **14.** $(0, -3)$ **15.** $(2, 2)$

16. $(-1, -\sqrt{3})$ **17.** $\left(-\frac{\sqrt{3}}{2}, \frac{1}{2}\right)$ **18.** $\left(\frac{1}{2}, -\frac{\sqrt{3}}{2}\right)$

Transform each Cartesian equation to an equation in polar form.

Example $y = 3x$

Solution   Substituting $\rho \sin \theta$ for y and $\rho \cos \theta$ for x yields

$$\rho \sin \theta = 3 \rho \cos \theta.$$

Multiplying each member by $1/(\rho \cos \theta)$, $\rho \neq 0$, $\theta \neq 90° + k \cdot 180°$, yields

$$\frac{\sin \theta}{\cos \theta} = 3,$$

$$\tan \theta = 3.$$

Notice that for values of θ for which the equation is satisfied, $\tan \theta$ is a constant, namely 3. Thus the graph of the equation is a straight line with slope 3.

19. $x = 4$ **20.** $y = -3$ **21.** $x^2 = 8y$

22. $y^2 = 4x$ **23.** $x^2 + y^2 = 16$ **24.** $4x^2 + y^2 = 4$

25. $x^2 + y^2 - 3y = 0$ **26.** $x^2 + y^2 + 4x = 0$

Transform each polar equation to an equation in Cartesian form.

Example $\rho = 2 \sec \theta$

Solution   Substituting $1/\cos \theta$ for $\sec \theta$ yields

$$\rho = \frac{2}{\cos \theta},$$

$$\rho \cos \theta = 2.$$

Because $\rho \cos \theta = x$, the Cartesian form of the equation is $x = 2$.

27. $\rho = 6$ **28.** $\rho = 9$ **29.** $\rho = 4 \sin \theta$

30. $\rho = 3 \cos \theta$ **31.** $\rho = 2 \csc \theta$ **32.** $\rho = -4 \sec \theta$

33. $\rho = \dfrac{4}{1 - \sin \theta}$ **34.** $\rho = \dfrac{4}{1 + 2 \cos \theta}$

6.7 Graphing Equations in Polar Form

In our earlier work we have seen that an equation in two variables, say x and y, serves to pair elements from the replacement sets of the variables and has a graph in the geometric plane in a Cartesian coordinate system. An equation in ρ and θ also has a graph in a polar coordinate system.

Example   Graph $\rho = 4 \sin \theta$ in the interval $0° \leq \theta < 360°$.

Solution   Some ordered pairs with commonly used angles 30°, 45°, etc., are first obtained. The tabulation of the data in the arrangement shown is sometimes helpful. The approximations shown for some values of $\sin \theta$ are sufficient for our purpose. These ordered pairs (ρ, θ) are shown in figure (a).

θ	$\sin \theta$	ρ or $4 \sin \theta$
0°	0	0
30°	0.50	2.0
45°	0.71	2.8
60°	0.87	3.5
90°	1.00	4.0
120°	0.87	3.5
135°	0.71	2.8
150°	0.50	2.0
180°	0	0

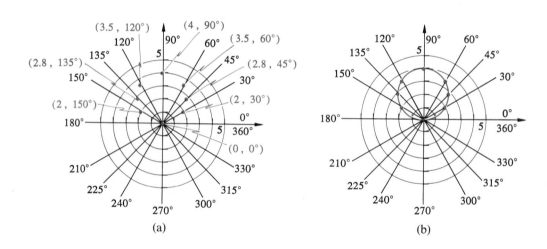

(a)   (b)

The complete curve is obtained for $0° \leq \theta < 180°$. For values of θ where $180° \leq \theta < 360°$, the components of ordered pairs (ρ, θ) are also coordinates of points on the curve shown in figure (b).

Example   Graph $\rho = \dfrac{3}{\sin \theta + \cos \theta}$.

Solution   Ordered pairs are first obtained as shown in the table and in figure (a) on page 269. The graph, a straight line, is shown in figure (b).

θ	$\sin \theta$	$\cos \theta$	$\sin \theta + \cos \theta$	$\rho = \dfrac{3}{\sin \theta + \cos \theta}$
0°	0	1.00	1.00	3.0
30°	0.50	0.87	1.37	2.2
45°	0.71	0.71	1.42	2.1
60°	0.87	0.50	1.37	2.2
90°	1.00	0	1.00	3.0
120°	0.87	−0.50	0.37	8.1
135°	0.71	−0.71	0	undef.

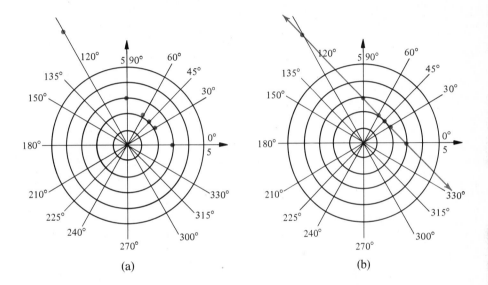

(a)   (b)

Frequently, the polar form of an equation is more useful than the rectangular form; furthermore, its graph may be simpler to sketch from the polar representation.

Excluded Values of θ

By analyzing a polar equation, we can determine what its graph looks like. For example, if

$$\rho^2 = 9 \cos 2\theta \tag{1}$$

and we select $\theta = 60°$, then

$$\rho^2 = 9 \cos 120° = \frac{-9}{2},$$

Figure 6.7

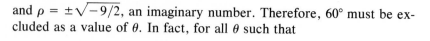

and $\rho = \pm\sqrt{-9/2}$, an imaginary number. Therefore, 60° must be excluded as a value of θ. In fact, for all θ such that

$$(90° + k \cdot 360°) < 2\theta < (270° + k \cdot 360°),$$

or

$$(45° + k \cdot 180°) < \theta < (135° + k \cdot 180°), \ k \in J,$$

it follows that $\cos 2\theta < 0$, and hence these values of θ must be excluded (see Figure 6.7).

Hence, in order to graph $\rho^2 = 9 \cos 2\theta$, it is necessary to select values of θ that are not excluded. Some ordered pairs (ρ, θ) that are solutions of the equation are shown in Table 6.1, and its graph is shown in Figure 6.8. The graph is called a **lemniscate.**

Figure 6.8

TABLE 6.1

θ	2θ	$\cos 2\theta$	ρ^2 or $9 \cos 2\theta$	ρ
0°	0°	1	9	±3
15°	30°	$\dfrac{\sqrt{3}}{2}$	$9\dfrac{\sqrt{3}}{2}$	±2.8
30°	60°	$\dfrac{1}{2}$	$\dfrac{9}{2}$	±2.1
45°	90°	0	0	0
135°	270°	0	0	0
150°	300°	$\dfrac{1}{2}$	$\dfrac{9}{2}$	±2.1
165°	330°	$\dfrac{\sqrt{3}}{2}$	$9\dfrac{\sqrt{3}}{2}$	±2.8
180°	360°	1	9	±3

Tangent Lines at the Pole

If, for some particular value of θ, say α, the value of ρ becomes 0, then the line $\theta = \alpha$ is tangent to the graph at the pole. For example, for the line to be tangent to the graph of $\rho^2 = 9 \cos 2\theta$ at the pole, ρ must be 0. Hence,

$$\cos 2\theta = 0,$$

from which

$$2\theta = \frac{\pi}{2} \quad \text{or} \quad 2\theta = \frac{3\pi}{2},$$

$$\theta = \frac{\pi}{4} \quad \text{or} \quad \theta = \frac{3\pi}{4}.$$

Thus, there are two lines tangent to the graph at the pole as shown in Figure 6.8.

Symmetry

TABLE 6.2

Symmetry with respect to		Replacement for	
		ρ	θ
Polar axis	(a)		$-\theta$
($\theta = 0°$)	(b)	$-\rho$	$\pi - \theta$
Vertical axis	(c)		$\pi - \theta$
($\theta - 90°$)	(d)	$-\rho$	$-\theta$
Pole	(e)		$\pi + \theta$
($\rho = 0$)	(f)	$-\rho$	

The graph of an equation in polar form is often symmetric with respect to a line or a point. In particular, considerations of symmetry with respect to the polar axis ($\theta = 0°$), the vertical line through the pole, sometimes called the vertical axis ($\theta = 90°$), and the pole ($\rho = 0$) are helpful when graphing equations in polar form.

Testing an equation for each of these symmetries consists of making certain replacements of ρ and θ. Then, if the new equation is equivalent to the original, the graph has that particular symmetry. Table 6.2 lists various replacements that are helpful. Note that for each possible symmetry, there are two tests. If either test is successful, the graph has that particular symmetry.

Note that tests (a), (d), and (f) from Table 6.2 are successful when applied to the equation $\rho^2 = 9 \cos 2\theta$. Thus, for test (a), if θ is replaced by $-\theta$,

$$\rho^2 = 9 \cos 2(-\theta) = 9 \cos(-2\theta)$$

$$= 9 \cos 2\theta.$$

Then for test (d), replacing ρ with $-\rho$ and θ with $-\theta$, we have

$$(-\rho)^2 = 9 \cos 2(-\theta)$$

or

$$\rho^2 = 9 \cos 2\theta.$$

Finally, for test (f), replacing ρ with $-\rho$,

$$(-\rho)^2 = 9 \cos 2\theta$$

or

$$\rho^2 = 9 \cos 2\theta.$$

Hence, as indicated in Figure 6.8, the graph is symmetric with respect to the polar axis, the vertical axis, and the pole.

Example   Test the equation $\rho = 1 + \cos\theta$ for the symmetries in Table 6.1.

Test (a):   Replacing θ with $-\theta$:

$$\rho = 1 + \cos(-\theta)$$
$$= 1 + \cos\theta.$$

The new equation is equivalent to the original, hence the graph is symmetric with respect to the polar axis.

Test (c):   Replacing θ with $\pi - \theta$, we have

$$\rho = 1 + \cos(\pi - \theta)$$
$$= 1 - \cos\theta.$$

This is not equivalent to the original equation, so we try the second test.

Test (d):   Replacing ρ with $-\rho$, and θ with $-\theta$, we have

$$-\rho = 1 + \cos(-\theta)$$
$$= 1 + \cos\theta.$$

Since this equation also is not equivalent to the original, we cannot conclude that the graph is symmetric with respect to the vertical axis.

Test (e):   Replacing θ with $\pi + \theta$, we have

$$\rho = 1 + \cos(\pi + \theta)$$
$$= 1 - \cos\theta,$$

which is not equivalent to the original equation. Hence, we try the second test.

Test (f):   Replacing ρ with $-\rho$, we have

$$-\rho = 1 + \cos\theta.$$

This again is not equivalent to the original equation, so we cannot conclude that the graph is symmetric with respect to the pole.

We have shown only that the graph is symmetric with respect to the polar axis. Now, using selected values of θ between $0°$ and $180°$, we first graph the equation in this interval. Then, using the fact that the

θ	$\cos \theta$	ρ or $1 + \cos \theta$
0°	1	2
30°	$\dfrac{\sqrt{3}}{2}$	1.87
60°	$\dfrac{1}{2}$	1.5
90°	0	1
120°	$-\dfrac{1}{2}$	$\dfrac{1}{2}$
150°	$-\dfrac{\sqrt{3}}{2}$	0.13
180°	−1	0

graph is symmetric with respect to the polar axis from test (a), we sketch the entire graph. The graph is known as a **cardioid.**

Several additional interesting types of curves that are graphs of polar equations are shown in Figures 6.9 and 6.10.

LIMAÇONS

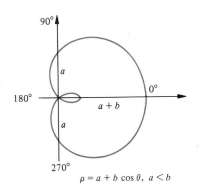

$\rho = a + b \cos \theta, \; a < b$

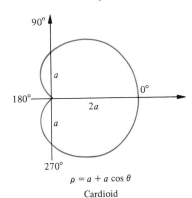

$\rho = a + a \cos \theta$
Cardioid

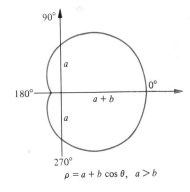

$\rho = a + b \cos \theta, \; a > b$

LEMNISCATES

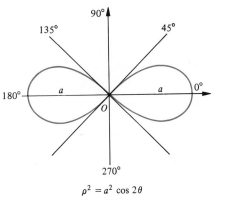

$\rho^2 = a^2 \cos 2\theta$

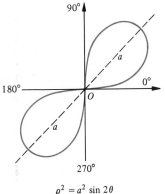

$\rho^2 = a^2 \sin 2\theta$

Figure 6.9

THREE–LEAVED ROSE

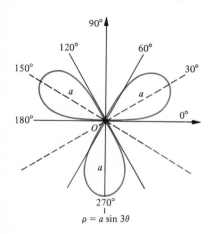

$\rho = a \sin 3\theta$

FOUR–LEAVED ROSE

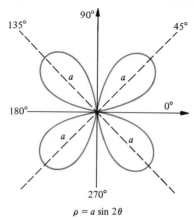

$\rho = a \sin 2\theta$

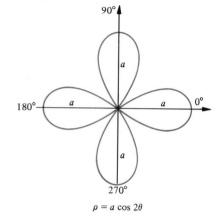

$\rho = a \cos 2\theta$

SPIRAL OF ARCHIMEDES

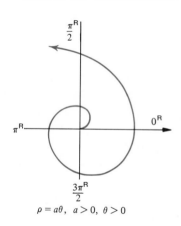

$\rho = a\theta, \quad a > 0, \; \theta > 0$

HYPERBOLIC SPIRAL

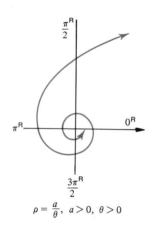

$\rho = \dfrac{a}{\theta}, \quad a > 0, \; \theta > 0$

LOGARITHMIC SPIRAL

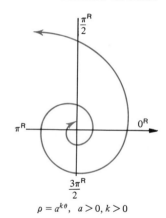

$\rho = a^{k\theta}, \quad a > 0, k > 0$

Figure 6.10

EXERCISE SET 6.7

A

Graph each equation.

1. $\rho = 4 \cos \theta$
(circle)

2. $\rho = 3 \sin \theta$
(circle)

3. $\rho = \cos 3\theta$
(three-leaved rose)

4. $\rho = 2 \sin 3\theta$
(three-leaved rose)

5. $\rho = \sin 2\theta$
(four-leaved rose)

6. $\rho = 2 \cos 2\theta$
(four-leaved rose)

7. $\rho = 1 + 2 \cos \theta$
(limaçon)

8. $\rho = 3 + 3 \cos \theta$
(cardioid)

9. $\rho = 2 + 2 \sin \theta$
(cardioid)

10. $\rho = 2 + \cos \theta$
(limaçon)

11. $\rho^2 = 4 \cos 2\theta$
(lemniscate)

12. $\rho^2 = 4 \sin 2\theta$
(lemniscate)

13. $\rho = 4$ *Hint:* Consider the equation $\rho = 0 \cdot \theta + 4$.

14. $\rho = 5$

15. $\theta = 30°$ *Hint:* Consider the equation $\theta = 0 \cdot \rho + 30°$.

16. $\theta = 45°$

B

Graph each equation for $0^R < \theta < 4\pi^R$.

17. $\rho = \dfrac{1}{\theta}$, $\theta > 0$ (hyperbolic spiral)

18. $\rho = 2\theta$, $\theta > 0$ (spiral of Archimedes)

Graph each of the given pairs of equations and find coordinates for the points of intersection.

19. $\rho = \sin \theta$

$\rho = \cos \theta$

20. $\rho = 1 + \sin \theta$

$\rho = 1$

21. $\rho = 1 + \sin \theta$

$\rho = 1 + \cos \theta$

22. $\rho = 2 \sin \theta$

$\rho = 2 \sin 2\theta$

23. Solve the system in Exercise 19 analytically. Explain why the coordinates of the origin are not in the solution set of the system.

24. Solve the system in Exercise 20 analytically.

25. Solve the system in Exercise 21 analytically.

26. Solve the system in Exercise 22 analytically.

27. Show that the distance between the points with coordinates (ρ_1, θ_1) and (ρ_2, θ_2) is given by $d = \sqrt{\rho_1{}^2 + \rho_2{}^2 - 2\rho_1\rho_2 \cos(\theta_1 - \theta_2)}$.

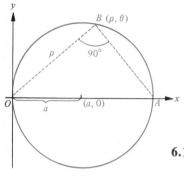

Ex. 28

28. Find an equation in polar form for the circle with center at $(a, 0^R)$ and radius of length a.   *Hint:* Recall that an angle inscribed in a semicircle is a right angle.

Chapter Summary

6.1 A **complex number** is defined by

$$z = a + bi, \quad a, b \in R \text{ and } i^2 = -1.$$

If $z_1 = a_1 + b_1 i$ and $z_2 = a_2 + b_2 i$, then

$$z_1 = z_2 \text{ if and only if } a_1 = a_2 \text{ and } b_1 = b_2.$$

Sums and products of complex numbers are found by treating $a + bi$ as a binomial in the variable i and replacing i^2 with -1.

A complex number $a + bi$ can be identified with a **real number** if $b = 0$; if $b \neq 0$, the number is an **imaginary number,** and for the special case where $a = 0$, the number is a **pure imaginary number.**

For all $b \in R$, $b > 0$,

$$\sqrt{-b} = \sqrt{b}i = i\sqrt{b}.$$

Hence, for a and b positive real numbers,

$$\sqrt{-a}\sqrt{-b} = i^2\sqrt{ab} = -\sqrt{ab}.$$

6.2 The properties used for the set of complex numbers are similar to the corresponding properties of real numbers. Furthermore,

$$z_1 - z_2 = z_1 + (-z_2);$$

$$\frac{z_1}{z_2} = z_1 \cdot \frac{1}{z_2} \quad (z_2 \neq 0).$$

If $z_2, z_3 \neq 0$, then

$$\frac{z_1}{z_2} = \frac{z_1 z_3}{z_2 z_3}.$$

If $z = a + bi$, then the **conjugate** of z is $\bar{z} = a - bi$. The product of $a + bi$ and its conjugate equals $a^2 + b^2$, a real number.

6.3 A plane on which complex numbers are graphed is called a **complex plane.** The x-axis is called the **real axis** and the y-axis is called the **imaginary axis.**

Complex numbers can be added graphically by the parallelogram law applicable to geometric vectors.

The **absolute value** or **modulus** of the complex number z is

$$\rho = |z| = |a + bi| = |(a, b)| = \sqrt{a^2 + b^2}.$$

The modulus is the distance from the origin to the graph of (a, b). An **argument** or **amplitude** of the complex number $z = a + bi = (a, b)$, denoted by **arg($a + bi$)** or **arg(a, b)**, is an angle θ such that

$$\cos \theta = \frac{a}{\rho} \quad \text{and} \quad \sin \theta = \frac{b}{\rho} \quad (a^2 + b^2 \neq 0).$$

If θ is an argument of $a + bi$, then $(\theta + k \cdot 360)°, k \in J$, is also an argument of $a + bi$. The angle θ with the least positive measure is called the **principal argument.**

6.4 A nonzero complex number $a + bi$ can be expressed in **trigonometric form** as

$$a + bi = \rho[\cos(\theta + k \cdot 360°) + i \sin(\theta + k \cdot 360°)], \quad k \in J.$$

If $z_1 = \rho_1(\cos \theta_1 + i \sin \theta_1)$ and $z_2 = \rho_2(\cos \theta_2 + i \sin \theta_2)$, then

$$z_1 \cdot z_2 = \rho_1 \cdot \rho_2[\cos(\theta_1 + \theta_2) + i \sin(\theta_1 + \theta_2)],$$

$$\frac{z_1}{z_2} = \frac{\rho_1}{\rho_2}[\cos(\theta_1 - \theta_2) + i \sin(\theta_1 - \theta_2)].$$

6.5 If $z = \rho(\cos \theta + i \sin \theta)$ and $n \in N$, then

$$z^n = \rho^n(\cos n\theta + i \sin n\theta).$$

This is known as **DeMoivre's theorem.**
If $z \neq 0 + 0i$, then

$$z^0 = 1 + 0i = 1 \quad \text{and} \quad z^{-n} = \frac{1}{z^n}, \quad n \in N.$$

If $n \in N$ and $z = \rho(\cos \theta + i \sin \theta)$, then

$$\rho^{1/n}\left[\cos\left(\frac{\theta + k \cdot 360°}{n}\right) + i \sin\left(\frac{\theta + k \cdot 360°}{n}\right)\right], \quad k \in J$$

is an **nth root of** z. For $k = 0$, the nth root

$$\rho^{1/n}\left(\cos\frac{\theta}{n} + i\sin\frac{\theta}{n}\right)$$

is called the **principal root.**

6.6 The components of an ordered pair $(\rho, \theta°)$ or (ρ, θ^R) that locate a point A in the plane are called the **polar coordinates** of A. Each such ordered pair specifies a unique point; however, each point in the plane corresponds to infinitely many ordered pairs of polar coordinates. Cartesian and polar coordinates are related as follows:

$$x = \rho\cos\theta \qquad\qquad \rho = \pm\sqrt{x^2 + y^2},$$

$$y = \rho\sin\theta$$

$$\cos\theta = \frac{x}{\rho} = \frac{x}{\pm\sqrt{x^2 + y^2}},$$

$$\sin\theta = \frac{y}{\rho} = \frac{y}{\pm\sqrt{x^2 + y^2}} \quad [(x, y) \neq (0, 0)].$$

6.7 Polar equations can be graphed by obtaining a number of ordered pairs (ρ, θ). The notions of excluded values, tangent lines, and symmetry can facilitate the procedures of graphing such equations.

A list of symbols introduced in this chapter is shown inside the front cover, and important properties are shown inside the back cover.

Review Exercises

A

6.1 *Find real numbers x and y for which each statement is true.*

1. $9x - 6yi = -3 + 4i$ 　　　　　　　　**2.** $-8x - 5i = -2y - 5x^2i$

Write each expression in the form $a + bi$.

3. $(-4 - i) + (-4 + 9i)$ 　　　　　　　　**4.** $(-3 + i) + (3 - 2i)$

5. $(8 + 6i)(-2 + 5i)$ 　　　　　　　　**6.** $(5 + 3i)(2 - 4i)$

Write each expression as one of the complex numbers i, -1, $-i$, or 1.

7. i^{13} **8.** i^{23}

Write each expression in the form $a + bi$.

9. $\sqrt{-5}(3 - \sqrt{-2})$ **10.** $(3 - \sqrt{-5})(3 + \sqrt{-5})$

11. Show that $3i$ and $-3i$ satisfy the equation $x^2 + 9 = 0$.

12. Show that $1 + 3i$ and $1 - 3i$ satisfy $x^2 - 2x + 10 = 0$.

6.2 *Express each difference in the form $a + bi$.*

13. $(-7 + 2i) - (8 + 3i)$ **14.** $(6 - 9i) - (3 - 4i)$

Express each quotient in the form $a + bi$.

15. $\dfrac{8 + 3i}{2 + 4i}$ **16.** $\dfrac{-7 + i}{6 - 10i}$

Write each expression in the form bi or $a + bi$.

17. $\dfrac{-2}{\sqrt{-6}}$ **18.** $\dfrac{4}{2 + \sqrt{-5}}$

6.3 *Express each complex number as an ordered pair.*

19. $-4 + i$ **20.** $2\sqrt{3} - 2i$

Express each complex number in the form $a + bi$.

21. $(9, -6)$ **22.** $(3, 4)$

Graph each complex number z, its negative $-z$, and its conjugate $\bar{z}$.

23. $-3 + 5i$ **24.** $(-2, -6)$

Represent each sum graphically and check the results by algebraic methods.

25. $(-4 + 3i) + (8 - 2i)$ **26.** $(-1, -8) + (6, 7)$

Find the absolute value and the principal argument of each complex number.

27. $4 + 2i$ **28.** $(-2, -5)$

6.4 *Represent each complex number in trigonometric form, using the angle with least nonnegative measure.*

29. $1 + i$ **30.** $-3 + 3\sqrt{3}i$

Represent each complex number graphically and write it in the form $a + bi$.

31. $7(\cos 120° + i \sin 120°)$ **32.** $2[\cos(-315°) + i \sin(-315°)]$

Express each product in the form $a + bi$.

33. $3(\cos 200° + i \sin 200°) \cdot 2(\cos 25° + i \sin 25°)$

34. $\sqrt{3}(\cos 50° + i \sin 50°) \cdot \sqrt{12}[\cos(-20°) + i \sin(-20°)]$

Express each quotient in the form $a + bi$.

35. $\dfrac{8(\cos 309° + i \sin 309°)}{9(\cos 129° + i \sin 129°)}$ **36.** $\dfrac{12[\cos(-315°) + i \sin(-315°)]}{3(\cos 270° + i \sin 270°)}$

6.5 *Express each power in the form $a + bi$.*

37. $[3(\cos 15° + i \sin 15°)]^4$ **38.** $(\sqrt{3} - i)^3$

39. $[4(\cos 240° + i \sin 240°)]^{-2}$ **40.** $(4 - 4i)^{-3}$

41. Find the two square roots of $\dfrac{\sqrt{3}}{2} + \dfrac{1}{2}i$.

42. Find the three cube roots of $125(\cos 330° + i \sin 330°)$.

Solve each equation, $x \in C$.

43. $x^4 + 1 = 0$ **44.** $x^5 = -5 - 5\sqrt{3}i$

6.6 *Find four additional sets of polar coordinates $(-360° < \theta \leq 360°)$ for each point.*

45. $(2, 610°)$ **46.** $(-3, 390°)$

Find the Cartesian coordinates for each point.

47. $\left(3, \dfrac{\pi}{3}^{\text{R}}\right)$ **48.** $\left(-2, \dfrac{3\pi}{4}^{\text{R}}\right)$

Find the pair of polar coordinates (θ in radians) using an angle α such that $0^{\text{R}} < \alpha < 2\pi^{\text{R}}$ and $\rho > 0$ for each point.

49. $(2, -2)$ **50.** $(-\sqrt{3}, -1)$

Transform each equation to an equation in polar form.

51. $x = 3$ **52.** $x^2 + 3y^2 = 5$

Transform each equation to an equation in Cartesian form.

53. $\rho = 5 \sin \theta$ **54.** $\rho = \dfrac{2}{1 - \cos \theta}$

6.7 *Graph each equation.*

55. $\rho = 1 + \sin \theta$ **56.** $\rho = 1 - \sin \theta$

57. $\rho = \cos 2\theta$ **58.** $\rho = 2 \cos 3\theta$

ALGEBRA AND GEOMETRY REVIEW

In Appendix A we review the basic ideas of algebra and geometry, using terminology and notation that are needed in the development of various topics in the text.

A.1 Set Notation

Recall that a set is simply a collection of "things." Each "thing" in the set is called a **member** or **element** of the set. The membership can be described by listing the names of the members in braces, { }, or by stating a rule that identifies the members in the set.

Definition A.1 *Two sets are* **equal** *if and only if they have the same members.*

Customarily, the slant bar, /, drawn through symbols for relations, indicates negation. Thus,

$$\{3, 4, 5\} = \{5, 3, 4\} \qquad \text{but} \qquad \{3, 4, 5\} \neq \{4, 5, 6\}.$$

The symbol $\in$ is used to denote membership in a set. For example, we can write

$$3 \in \{3, 4, 5\}$$

to represent the statement "3 is an element of $\{3, 4, 5\}$."

Sets are also designated by means of capital letters, A, B, C, R, etc.

Example   If $A = \{2, 3, 4\}$ and $B = \{4, 5, 6\}$, then

$$3 \in A \qquad \text{but} \qquad 3 \notin B.$$

An unspecified element of a set is usually denoted by a lowercase italic letter such as $a, b, c, x,$ and y or by a lowercase letter from the Greek alphabet such as $\alpha, \beta, \gamma,$ and θ. Such a symbol is called a **variable;** a symbol used to denote a specific element is called a **constant.** Variables are used in conjunction with braces in another symbolism that is often useful in discussing sets. This symbolism, illustrated by

$$\{x \mid x \in A \quad \text{and} \quad x \in B\}$$

and read "the set of all x such that x is an element of A and x is an element of B," is called **set-builder notation.** The vertical line, $\mid$, is read "such that." Set-builder notation names a variable and states conditions on the variable.

Example   If $A = \{2, 3, 4\}$ and $B = \{4, 5, 6\}$, then

$$\{x \mid x \in A \quad \text{or} \quad x \in B\} = \{2, 3, 4, 5, 6\} \tag{1}$$

because 2, 3, 4, 5, 6 are elements of *one or the other* of the two sets, whereas

$$\{x \mid x \in A \quad \text{and} \quad x \in B\} = \{4\} \tag{2}$$

because 4 is an element of *both* sets.

The preceding example is associated with the following two operations on sets.

Definition A.2   *The* **union** *of two sets A and B is the set of all elements that belong to A or to B or to both.*

The symbol $\cup$ is used to denote this operation; $A \cup B$ is read "the union of A and B."

Example   If $A = \{2, 3, 4\}$ and $B = \{4, 5, 6\}$, then

$$A \cup B = \{2, 3, 4, 5, 6\}. \tag{3}$$

Notice that each element in $A \cup B$ is listed only once. Since the symbol 4 denotes only one number, it would be redundant to list the name of the element twice and to write $A \cup B = \{2, 3, 4, 4, 5, 6\}$.

A second useful operation on sets is the following.

Definition A.3   *The* **intersection** *of two sets A and B is the set of all elements that belong to both A and B.*

The symbol ∩ is used to denote this operation; $A \cap B$ is read "the intersection of A and B."

Example   If $A = \{2, 3, 4\}$ and $B = \{4, 5, 6\}$, then

$$A \cap B = \{4\}. \tag{4}$$

Notice from Equations (1) and (3) that the operation of union is associated with the word *or*, and from Equations (2) and (4) that the operation of intersection is associated with the word *and*.

The set that contains no elements is called the **null set** or the **empty set** and is denoted by the symbol ∅.

Example   The intersection of two sets is a set. Therefore, if $C = \{2, 3, 4\}$ and $D = \{5, 6, 7\}$, we can write

$$C \cap D = \{2, 3, 4\} \cap \{5, 6, 7\} = \varnothing.$$

Two sets such as C and D, which do not have any elements in common, are said to be **disjoint.**

A.2 The Set of Real Numbers

Recall from your study of algebra that each real number can be associated with one and only one point on a number line and each point on the line can be associated with one and only one real number. Several examples are shown in Figure A.1. The real number corresponding to a point on the line is called the **coordinate** of the point, and the point is called the **graph** of the number. A number whose graph is to the right of the graph of zero is **positive,** and a number whose graph is to the left is **negative.**

Figure A.1

The following sets of numbers are contained in the set of **real numbers R.** The capital letters shown are the ones that are sometimes associated with the respective sets. These are the symbols that we use in this text.

1. The set N of **natural numbers,** among whose elements are such numbers as 1, 2, 6, 25, and 624.
2. The set J of **integers,** whose elements consist of the natural numbers, their negatives, and zero. Included are such elements as -24, -9, 0, 7, and 314.
3. The set Q of **rational numbers,** whose elements are all those numbers that can be represented in the form $\frac{a}{b}$, or a/b, where a and b are integers and b is not zero. Included are such elements as $-\frac{1}{3}$, 0, $\frac{1}{4}$, and 6.
4. The set H of **irrational numbers,** whose elements are those numbers that are the coordinates of points on the number line that are not the graphs of rational numbers. An irrational number cannot be represented in the form a/b, where a and b are integers.

Figure A.2 summarizes the relationships among these sets of numbers.

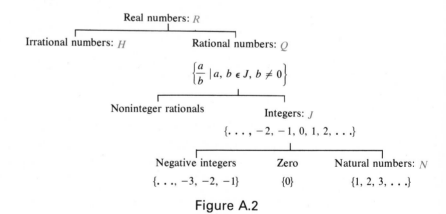

Figure A.2

Radical notation is useful to represent some irrational numbers.

Definition A.4 *For all $a \in R$ where a is positive or zero, $\sqrt{a}$ is the nonnegative number such that*

$$\sqrt{a} \cdot \sqrt{a} = a.$$

Examples

    a. $\sqrt{9}$ is the positive number such that $\sqrt{9}\sqrt{9} = 9$.

    b. $\sqrt{x}$ is the positive number such that $\sqrt{x}\sqrt{x} = x$.

Frequently, rational numbers are used as approximations for irrational numbers. For example, by using the symbol $\approx$ for "approximately equal to," we write $\sqrt{2} \approx 1.414$, $\sqrt{3} \approx 1.732$, $\sqrt{5} \approx 2.236$, etc. Table I in Appendix C gives rational number approximations for some square roots that are irrational numbers.

If *every* element of a set A is also an element of a set B, then A is said to be a **subset** of B. Thus the sets H and Q can be viewed as subsets of R, the set J as a subset of Q or R, and the set N as a subset of J, Q, or R.

If the elements of a set can be paired with the numerals 1, 2, 3, . . . , n for some natural number n so that each element is paired with exactly one numeral and each numeral is paired with exactly one element, then the set is said to be a **finite set.** A set that is not the empty set and is not finite is called an **infinite set.** Some infinite sets can be designated by using three dots and some of the members listed to establish a pattern as shown in Figure A.2.

Often we wish to consider the nonnegative member of the pair of real numbers a and $-a$, where $a \neq 0$. The special notation $|a|$ is used for this purpose. To extend the notation for all $a \in R$, we define $|0| = 0$.

Definition A.5 *For all $a \in R$,*

$$\textit{if } a \textit{ is positive or zero, then } |a| = a;$$

$$\textit{if } a \textit{ is negative, then } |a| = -a.$$

$|a|$ *is called the* **absolute value** *of a.*

Examples

a. $|4| = 4$ b. $|-4| = -(-4) = 4$ c. $|0| = 0$

The order of the elements of the set of real numbers can be established by the following.

Definition A.6 *For all a, $b \in R$, b is **less than** a if for some positive real number c,*

$$b + c = a.$$

*For such conditions, a is said to be **greater than** b.*

Examples

a. 4 is less than 7 because there is a *positive number c* (equal to 3) such that $4 + c = 7$.

b. -9 is less than -5 because there is a *positive number c* (equal to 4) such that $-9 + c = -5$.

The number line shown in Figure A.3 is very helpful in visualizing whether one real number is less than or greater than a second real number. If the graph of b lies to the *left* of the graph of a, then b is less

Figure A.3

than a. The following symbols are used in connection with the property of order:

$<$ read "is less than";

$\leq$ read "is less than or equal to";

$>$ read "is greater than";

$\geq$ read "is greater than or equal to."

Observe that $b < a$ and $a > b$ are equivalent statements.

Examples

a. $4 < 7$ and $7 > 4$

b. $-9 < -5$ and $-5 > -9$

c. $x < 7$ is equivalent to $7 > x$

In your study of arithmetic and algebra, you applied the operations of addition and multiplication to elements of the set of real numbers. You also made assumptions, called **axioms,** about these operations and studied the logical consequences of these axioms. For your reference, we include a list of some of these axioms and properties on page 289.

A.3 Equations in Two Variables; Relations and Functions

Recall from your study of algebra that the ordered pair (2, 9) is called a **solution** of the equation $y = x + 7$ because the replacement of x by

For $a, b, c, d \in R$:

Equality Axioms

1. $a = a$ — Reflexive law

2. If $a = b$, then $b = a$ — Symmetric law

3. If $a = b$ and $b = c$, then $a = c$ — Transitive law

4. If $a = b$, then a may be substituted for b or b for a in any expression. — Substitution law

Order Axioms

1. Exactly one of the following is true: — Trichotomy law

$a < b, \quad a = b, \quad$ or $\quad a > b.$

2. If $a < b$ and $b < c$, then $a < c$. — Transitive law

3. If $a, b > 0$, then — Closure for positive numbers

$a + b > 0 \quad$ and $\quad a \cdot b > 0$

Axioms for Operations

1. $a + b \in R$ — Closure law for addition

2. $a + b = b + a$ — Commutative law of addition

3. $(a + b) + c = a + (b + c)$ — Associative law of addition

4. $a + 0 = 0 + a = a$ — Identity law of addition

5. $a + (-a) = (-a) + a = 0$ — Additive inverse law

6. $a \cdot b \in R$ — Closure law for multiplication

7. $a \cdot b = b \cdot a$ — Commutative law of multiplication

8. $(a \cdot b) \cdot c = a \cdot (b \cdot c)$ — Associative law of multiplication

9. $a \cdot 1 = 1 \cdot a = a$ — Identity law of multiplication

10. $a \cdot \dfrac{1}{a} = \dfrac{1}{a} \cdot a = 1 \quad (a \neq 0)$ — Multiplicative inverse law

11. $a \cdot (b + c) = a \cdot b + a \cdot c$ — Distributive law

Some Properties

1. $a \cdot 0 = 0$

2. $-(-a) = a$

3. $-a = -1 \cdot a$

4. If $a = b$, then $a + c = b + c$

5. If $a + c = b + c$, then $a = b$

6. If $a = b$, then $a \cdot c = b \cdot c$

7. If $a \cdot c = b \cdot c$, then $a = b \quad (c \neq 0)$

8. $a - b = a + (-b)$

9. $\dfrac{a}{b} = \dfrac{c}{d}$ if and only if $a \cdot d = b \cdot c \ (b, d \neq 0)$

10. $\dfrac{a}{b} = \dfrac{a \cdot c}{b \cdot c} \quad (b, c \neq 0)$

11. $\dfrac{a}{c} + \dfrac{b}{c} = \dfrac{a + b}{c} \quad (c \neq 0)$

12. $\dfrac{a}{b} \cdot \dfrac{c}{d} = \dfrac{a \cdot c}{b \cdot d} \quad (b, d \neq 0)$

13. $\dfrac{a}{b} = a \cdot \dfrac{1}{b} \quad (b \neq 0)$

14. $\dfrac{a}{b} \div \dfrac{c}{d} = \dfrac{a}{b} \cdot \dfrac{d}{c} \quad (b, c, d \neq 0)$

15. $\dfrac{a}{b} = \dfrac{-a}{-b} = -\dfrac{a}{-b} = -\dfrac{-a}{b};$

$\dfrac{-a}{b} = \dfrac{a}{-b} = -\dfrac{a}{b} = -\dfrac{-a}{-b} \quad (b \neq 0)$

16. $ab = 0$ if and only if $a = 0$ or $b = 0$

the first component 2 and the replacement of y by the second component 9 results in a true statement, $9 = 2 + 7$. The ordered pair $(2, 9)$ is said to *satisfy* the equation. The set of all such ordered pairs that satisfy an equation is called the **solution set** of the equation.

The equation $y = x + 7$ does not result in a true statement for all ordered pairs of real numbers. For example, $(3, 5)$ is not a solution because $5 \neq 3 + 7$. Such equations are called **conditional equations.** On the other hand, if an equation such as

$$x + y = y + x$$

results in a true statement for every replacement of x and y, for which both members have meaning, the equation is call an **identity.** The left-hand member and the right-hand member of identities are called **equivalent expressions.**

To show that an equation is not an identity, it is necessary only to find one replacement for the variables that will make the equation false. Such a procedure is referred to as showing a **counterexample.**

Example We can show by counterexample that $x^2 - 3y = 3y - x^2$ is not an identity by substituting some arbitrary values for the variables. If we use 1 for x and 1 for y, the left-hand member of the equation equals $1^2 - 3 \cdot 1$, or -2, and the right-hand member equals $3 \cdot 1 - 1^2$, or 2. Hence,

$$x^2 - 3y \neq 3y - x^2$$

for the ordered pair $(1, 1)$, and the equation is not an identity.

Example We can show that the equation

$$(x - y)^2 + 2xy = x^2 + y^2$$

is an identity by simplifying the left-hand member

$$(x - y)^2 + 2xy = x^2 - 2xy + y^2 + 2xy$$
$$= x^2 + y^2.$$

Thus, the left-hand member and the right-hand member are equivalent and the equation is an identity.

Sets of ordered pairs play an important role in mathematics and are given a special name, as follows:

Definition A.7   *A* **relation** *is a set of ordered pairs.*

The set of first components in a set of ordered pairs is called the **domain** of the relation and the set of second components is called the **range.**

Examples
   a. {(5, 8), (6, 9), (7, 10)} is a relation with domain {5, 6, 7} and range {8, 9, 10}.

   b. {(5, 8), (5, 9), (7, 10)} is a relation with domain {5, 7} and range {8, 9, 10}.

The set of ordered pairs exhibited in Example a is a special kind of relation in which each element in the domain is paired with only one element in the range. Such relations are given a special name.

Definition A.8   *A* **function** *is a relation in which each element in the domain is associated with only one element in the range.*

Note that the relation in Example b above is not a function because 5, an element in the domain, is associated with more than one element in the range.

The relations above were exhibited by listing the members in the set of ordered pairs. They can also be described by equations that specify which ordered pairs are in the relation and which are not; those that are in the relation are elements of the solution set. For example,

$$\{(x, y) \mid y = x + 3, \quad x \in \{5, 6, 7\}\}$$

also specifies the function in Example a above:

The elements in the range, 8, 9, and 10, are obtained by replacing x in the equation $y = x + 3$ with 5, 6, and 7 in turn and solving for y. This function consists of three ordered pairs only.

Example   Given the function

$$\{(x, y) \mid y = x - 3, \quad x \in \{1, 2, 3\}\}:$$

1. The domain is $\{1, 2, 3\}$.
2. Replacing x with each element of the domain in turn, you can find the associated values of y to be -2, -1, and 0, respectively. Thus, the range is $\{-2, -1, 0\}$.
3. The function is $\{(1, -2), (2, -1), (3, 0)\}$.

If the domain of a function is the set of real numbers R, rather than a finite set, the function consists of an *infinite set* of ordered pairs and obviously not all its elements can be listed. *If the domain is not specified, we shall assume that it includes all real numbers for which both members of the defining equation are defined.*

Examples

a. The domain of the function defined by $y = x + 3$ is the set R because $x + 3$, and therefore y, are defined for all real number replacements for x.

b. The domain of the function defined by $y = \dfrac{3}{x - 4}$ is the set R with the restriction that $x \neq 4$, because $x - 4 = 0$ and y is undefined for $x = 4$.

Functions are sometimes designated by names (linear, quadratic, etc.) or by means of a single symbol, generally the symbol f. If the discussion includes a consideration of more than one function, other letters such as g, h, F, P, etc., are used.

The symbol for the function can be used in conjunction with the variable representing an element in the domain to represent the associated element in the range. For example, $f(x)$ (read "f of x" or "the value of f at x") is the element in the range of f associated or paired with the element x in the domain. Thus, we can discuss functions defined by an equation such as

$$y = x - 2$$
$$f(x) = x - 2,$$
$$g(x) = x - 2,$$

etc.

where the symbols $f(x)$, $g(x)$, etc., are playing exactly the same role as y. The variable x represents an element in the domain, and y, $f(x)$, $g(x)$, etc., represent an element in the range.

The notation $f(x)$ is especially useful because, by replacing x with a specific real number a in the domain, the notation $f(a)$ will then denote the paired, or corresponding, element in the range of the function.

Example   If $f(x) = 2x - 5,$

$$f(3) = 2(3) - 5 = 6 - 5 = 1,$$
$$f(0) = 2(0) - 5 = 0 - 5 = -5,$$
$$f(-3) = 2(-3) - 5 = -6 - 5 = -11,$$
$$f(a) = 2(a) - 5 = 2a - 5.$$

A.4 Graphs of Relations and Functions

As you probably recall from your study of algebra, an association exists between ordered pairs of real numbers and the points on a geometric plane, sometimes called the **real plane.** If two number lines are drawn perpendicular to each other at their origins as in Figure A.4, they form a rectangular coordinate system. These perpendicular number lines are called **axes** (singular, axis). The horizontal line is usually called the **x-axis,** and the vertical line is usually called the **y-axis.** The x-axis and the y-axis divide the plane into four regions, called **quadrants,** as shown.

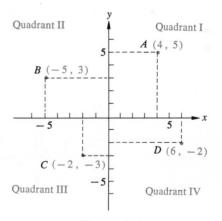

Figure A.4

For a given rectangular coordinate system, any point in the plane can be associated with a unique ordered pair of real numbers. For example, the point A in Quadrant I, in Figure A.4, can be associated with the ordered pair (4, 5), where 4 represents the distance of the point to the right of the y-axis and 5 represents the distance of the point above the

x-axis. The points B, C, and D correspond to the ordered pairs $(-5, 3)$, $(-2, -3)$, and $(6, -2)$, respectively.

The *components* of an ordered pair associated with a point in the plane are called the **coordinates** of the point. The first component is called the **abscissa** of the point; the second component is called the **ordinate** of the point. The *point* is called the **graph** of the ordered pair. An ordered pair is sometimes used as a name for the corresponding point. Thus, we occasionally speak of the point $(2, 3)$ or the point $(4, -3)$ or, in general, the point (x, y).

Recall that in Section A.3, a function was defined in part as a set of ordered pairs. Consequently, a function—or at least a part of a function—can now be displayed as a set of points on the plane. The phrase "part of a function" is used here since the domain or range or both may be the infinite set of real numbers, which cannot be shown on a finite line. For example, consider the function

$$y = x - 4.$$

If arbitrary values are assigned to x, say -3, 0, 3, and 6, and the corresponding values for y are computed, the four ordered pairs

$$(-3, -7), \quad (0, -4), \quad (3, -1), \quad \text{and} \quad (6, 2)$$

are obtained, which are solutions to the equation. These points can be located on a coordinate system as shown in Figure A.5a. These points appear to lie on a straight line, and in fact they do. It can be shown that the coordinates of any point on the line (Figure A.5b) constitute a solu-

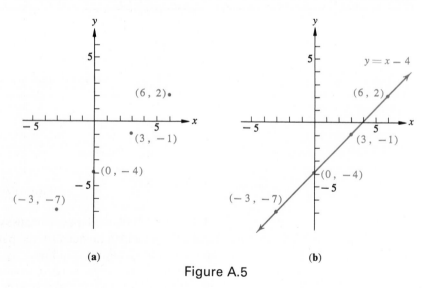

(a)   (b)

Figure A.5

tion of the first-degree equation in two variables, $y = x - 4$ and that, conversely, every solution of $y = x - 4$ corresponds to a point on this line. The line is referred to as the *graph of the function* $y = x - 4$ or, alternatively, as the *graph of the solution set of the equation* or simply as the *graph of the equation*. Obviously, only part of the line can be displayed, so an arrowhead is placed at each end to indicate that the graph, or line, continues in both directions indefinitely. Furthermore, since the graphs of first-degree equations

$$y = mx + b \quad \text{or} \quad ax + by = c$$

are straight lines, it is only necessary to find two ordered pairs in the solution set to sketch the graph. Two pairs that are easy to find are $(0, b)$ and $(a, 0)$, in which the numbers a and b are called the **intercepts.**

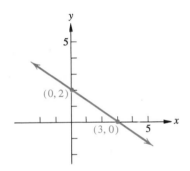

Example The graph of the function $2x + 3y = 6$ can be obtained by first finding the x and y intercepts.

If $y = 0$, then $x = 3$ and $(3, 0)$ is a solution.

If $x = 0$, then $y = 2$ and $(0, 2)$ is a solution.

The x and y intercepts are 3 and 2, respectively. See the graph.

First-degree equations are also called **linear equations,** and the functions defined by these equations are called **linear functions.**

For any two points P_1 and P_2 on a line, the set of points containing P_1 and P_2 and all points lying between P_1 and P_2 is called a **line segment.** We shall designate the line segment by $\overline{P_1P_2}$. A line segment has the important property of length. If we designate the endpoints of a line segment $\overline{P_1P_2}$ with the pairs of coordinates (x_1, y_1) and (x_2, y_2), as in Figure A.6, the length, or measure, of the line segment, which we shall designate by P_1P_2 or some variable such as d, can be determined by an application of the Pythagorean theorem (see Section A.8). From the right triangle shown, we observe that the lengths of the perpendicular sides are $y_2 - y_1$ and $x_2 - x_1$; the square of the distance between P_1 and P_2 is given by

$$d^2 = (x_2 - x_1)^2 + (y_2 - y_1)^2.$$

By considering only the positive square root of the right-hand member, we have that

$$d = \sqrt{(x_2 - x_1)^2 + (y_2 - y_1)^2}.$$

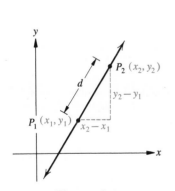

Figure A.6

Example   The distance between the pair of points $(1, 3)$ and $(5, 6)$ is given by

$$d = \sqrt{(5 - 1)^2 + (6 - 3)^2}$$
$$= \sqrt{16 + 9} = \sqrt{25} = 5.$$

As with first-degree equations in two variables, solutions of higher-degree equations in two variables are also ordered pairs, which can be found by arbitrarily assigning values to x and finding the associated values of y. For example, in the equation

$$y = x^2 + 2,$$

if $x = -2$, then

$$y = (-2)^2 + 2 = 6,$$

and $(-2, 6)$ is a solution. Similarly, by replacing x with $-1, 0, 1,$ and 2, we obtain $(-1, 3), (0, 2), (1, 3),$ and $(2, 6)$ as additional solutions. Plotting these points on the plane, we have the graph in Figure A.7a. Clearly, these points do not lie on a straight line. By plotting additional solutions of $y = x^2 + 2$, such as

$$\left(-\frac{3}{2}, \frac{17}{4}\right), \quad \left(-\frac{1}{2}, \frac{9}{4}\right), \quad \left(\frac{1}{2}, \frac{9}{4}\right), \quad \text{and} \quad \left(\frac{3}{2}, \frac{17}{4}\right),$$

we have the additional points in Figure A.7b. These points can now be connected in sequence from left to right by a smooth curve as shown. We assume that this curve is a good approximation to the graph of $y = x^2 + 2$.

More generally, the graph of any equation of the form

$$y = ax^2 + bx + c \quad (a, b, c, x \in R, \ a \neq 0),$$

is called a **parabola.** Notice that such an equation defines a function, since with each x, an equation of this form will associate one and only one y. Such functions are called **quadratic functions.**

The graph of

$$x^2 + y^2 = r^2,$$

where r is a real number greater than zero, is a **circle** with center at the origin and radius of length r. However, although this equation defines a relation, it does not define a function.

(a)

(b)

Figure A.7

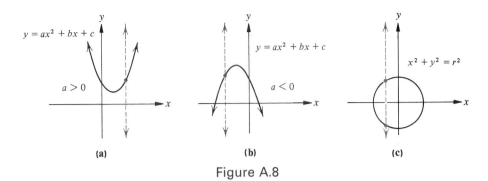

Figure A.8

Whether or not a relation is also a function can be determined by inspecting its graph. For example, consider the graphs of equations $y = ax^2 + bx + c$ and $x^2 + y^2 = r^2$ in Figure A.8. Imagine a vertical line moving across each graph from left to right. Since the line cuts the graph of $y = ax^2 + bx + c$ at *only one point at each position, this equation defines a function;* that is, for each x in this relation, there is only one y. Since the line cuts the graph of $x^2 + y^2 = r^2$ at *more than one point at certain positions, the equation does not define a function,* although it does define a relation. There are ordered pairs in the relation which have the same first components and different second components.

A.5 Zeros of Functions; Equations in One Variable

In any function, the element(s) in the domain that are paired with the element 0 in the range are called **zeros of the function.**

Example   The zeros of

$$f = \{(-3, 1), (-2, 0), (-1, -2), (0, -4), (1, 0)\}$$

are -2 and 1 because each of these first components is paired with a second component 0.

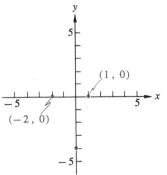

Figure A.9

The graph of each zero in the above example lies on the x-axis, as shown in Figure A.9.

For any function

$$y = f(x),$$

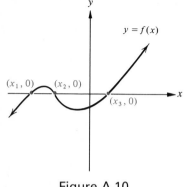

Figure A.10

the zeros of the function are values of x (x_1, x_2, x_3 in Figure A.10) for which

$$y = f(x) = 0.$$

These values of x are the solutions of the equation in one variable, $f(x) = 0$, and the set of such numbers is the solution set of the equation.

Note that the ordered pairs $(x_1, 0)$, $(x_2, 0)$, and $(x_3, 0)$ are the coordinates of the points of intersection of the graph of $y = f(x)$ and the x-axis.

Thus, there are three different names for a single idea:

1. The zeros of $y = f(x)$.
2. The x intercepts of the graph of $y = f(x)$.
3. Solutions of $f(x) = 0$.

In many simple cases, such as

$$x - 2 = 0,$$

the solution set of an equation in one variable is evident by inspection. However, this is not the case for most first-degree equations. Recall from your work in algebra that solutions of first-degree equations in one variable can usually be found by generating **equivalent equations** (a set of equations with the same solution set) until you obtain an equation whose solution set is evident by inspection.

In general, if each member of an equation is multiplied by the same nonzero number, or if the same quantity is added to both members, the result is an equation equivalent to the original equation.

Solutions of quadratic equations in one variable are obtained by various methods. For example if the left-hand member of a quadratic equation of the form

$$ax^2 + bx + c = 0 \quad (a \neq 0)$$

is factorable, the solutions can be obtained from the fact that the left-hand member will equal zero for values of x for which one or both of the factors equals zero. Such a procedure of solving a quadratic equation is called *solution by factoring*.

Example We can solve $x^2 + x = 30$, by first writing the equation equivalently as

$$x^2 + x - 30 = 0, \tag{1}$$

in which form the right-hand member is zero. Factoring the left-hand member yields

$$(x + 6)(x - 5) = 0. \qquad (2)$$

The left-hand member equals zero for values of x for which

$$x + 6 = 0 \qquad \text{or} \qquad x - 5 = 0 \qquad \text{or both.}$$

By inspection, the solution set of (2) and, therefore, of (1) is $\{-6, 5\}$.

Quadratic equations of the form

$$x^2 = a \quad (a \geq 0)$$

can be solved by a method called *extraction of roots*. If the equation has a solution, then x must be a square root of a (see Definition A.4). Since each positive real number a has two square roots, the solution set, for $a > 0$, is $\{\sqrt{a}, -\sqrt{a}\}$. If $a = 0$, the solution set is $\{0\}$.

Example The method of extraction of roots can be used to find the solution set of the equation $4x^2 = 24$. Multiplying each member by $1/4$ yields

$$x^2 = 6$$

Hence, $x = \sqrt{6}$ or $x = -\sqrt{6}$ and the solution set is $\{\sqrt{6}, -\sqrt{6}\}$.

From the method of extraction of roots applied to the equation

$$(x - a)^2 = b \quad (b \geq 0).$$

we obtain

$$x - a = \sqrt{b} \qquad \text{and} \qquad x - a = -\sqrt{b},$$

from which the solution set $\{a + \sqrt{b}, a - \sqrt{b}\}$ is obtained. If $b = 0$, the solution set is $\{a\}$. From this it follows that we can find the solution set of any quadratic equation by first rewriting the equation in the form

$$(x - a)^2 = b.$$

This procedure of solving a quadratic equation is called *completing the square*.

Applying this procedure to the general quadratic equation

$$ax^2 + bx + c = 0 \quad (a \neq 0)$$

results in the formula

$$x = \frac{-b \pm \sqrt{b^2 - 4ac}}{2a},$$

called the **quadratic formula,** which gives us the solutions of any quadratic equation in the form $ax^2 + bx + c = 0$ expressed in terms of a, b, and c. The solution set is

$$\left\{ \frac{-b + \sqrt{b^2 - 4ac}}{2a}, \frac{-b - \sqrt{b^2 - 4ac}}{2a} \right\}.$$

If a, b, $c \in R$, the elements in the solution set are real numbers if and only if $b^2 - 4ac \geq 0$.

Example The equation $x^2 - 5x = 6$ can be solved by using the quadratic formula as follows. First, rewrite the equation as

$$x^2 - 5x - 6 = 0.$$

Then, replacing a with 1, b with -5, and c with -6 in the quadratic formula yields

$$x = \frac{-(-5) \pm \sqrt{(-5)^2 - 4(1)(-6)}}{2(1)},$$

from which

$$x = \frac{5 + \sqrt{25 + 24}}{2} = 6 \quad \text{or} \quad x = \frac{5 - \sqrt{25 + 24}}{2} = -1,$$

and the solution set is $\{6, -1\}$.

A.6 Inverse of a Function

If the components of each ordered pair in a given relation are interchanged, the resulting relation and the given relation are called **inverses** of each other.

Example $\{(1, 3), (5, 7), (11, 13)\}$ and $\{(3, 1), (7, 5), (13, 11)\}$ are inverse relations.

The inverse of a relation $\mathscr{R}$ is denoted by $\mathscr{R}^{-1}$ (read "$\mathscr{R}$ inverse" or "the inverse of $\mathscr{R}$"). It is evident from the above example that the domain and range of $\mathscr{R}^{-1}$ are the range and domain, respectively, of $\mathscr{R}$. We have used the script $\mathscr{R}$ for a relation so that it should not be confused with the R that represents the set of real numbers. Furthermore, it should be understood that -1 in the inverse notation symbol $\mathscr{R}^{-1}$ is not an exponent.

The inverse of the relation

$$\mathscr{R}: y = 3x - 5 \tag{1}$$

can be obtained by replacing x with y and y with x. Hence, the inverse relation of (1) is given by

$$\mathscr{R}^{-1}: x = 3y - 5 \tag{2}$$

or, when y is expressed in terms of x in the defining equation,

$$\mathscr{R}^{-1}: y = \frac{1}{3}(x + 5). \tag{2'}$$

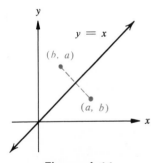

Figure A.11

Notice in the above example that $y = 3x - 5$ and $x = 3y - 5$ from (1) and (2) define inverse relations. The domains and ranges of the relations are interchanged because the variables have been interchanged. However, $x = 3y - 5$ from (2) and $y = \frac{1}{3}(x + 5)$ from (2') are equivalent equations and define the same relation.

The graphs of inverse relations are always located symmetrically with respect to the graph of the linear equation $y = x$. To see this, notice the graphs of the ordered pairs (a, b) and (b, a) in Figure A.11. They are the same distance from, but on opposite sides of, the line that is the graph of the equation $y = x$. The graph of $y = x$ serves as a reflecting line, or mirror, for these points.

Using the example above, Figure A.12 on page 302 shows the graphs of

$$y = 3x - 5$$

and its inverse,

$$x = 3y - 5 \qquad \text{or} \qquad y = \frac{1}{3}(x + 5),$$

together with the graph of $y = x$.

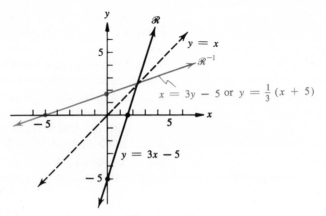

Figure A.12

Because every function is a relation, *every function has an inverse, but the inverse is not always a function.* For example, consider the function

$$y = x^2. \tag{3}$$

Its graph and the graph of its inverse,

$$x = y^2 \quad \text{or} \quad y = \pm\sqrt{x}. \tag{4}$$

are shown in Figure A.13. Since for all but one value of x ($x = 0$), the inverse specified by (4) associates two different values of y (one positive and one negative) in the range, the inverse of (3) is not a function. Observe in Figure A.13 that the graphs of these relations are symmetric with respect to the graph of $y = x$.

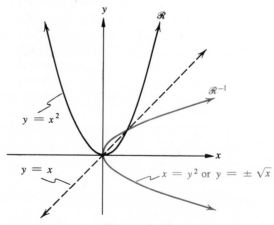

Figure A.13

In order for a function to have an inverse that is also a function, it must be a *one-to-one function;* that is, each element in the domain of the original function must be associated with one and only one element in its range and each element in its range must be associated with one and only one element in its domain.

A.7 Angles and Their Measure

(a)

(b)

Figure A.14

Figure A.15

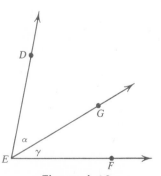

Figure A.16

In geometry, a **ray** is a figure such as that shown in Figure A.14a, where the arrow indicates that the ray extends infinitely far in one direction. The point A (points are usually named with capital letters) in A.14a is the **endpoint** of that ray, and point C is the endpoint of the two rays in A.14b.

A ray is named by naming its endpoint and one other point on the ray. In Figure A.14a the ray is named by $\overrightarrow{AB}$ (read "ray AB"), and in A.14b the rays are named by $\overrightarrow{CD}$ and $\overrightarrow{CE}$.

An **angle** is the union of two rays having a common endpoint called the **vertex** of the angle. The rays are the **sides** of the angle. In Figure A.14b, an angle is formed by $\overrightarrow{CD}$ and $\overrightarrow{CE}$, where $\overrightarrow{CD}$ and $\overrightarrow{CE}$ are the sides, and point C is the vertex.

An angle can be named in several ways. For example, if a point is the vertex of only one angle, as in Figure A.15, then that letter can be used to name the angle; in this case, $\angle B$. Also, an angle can be named using a single letter placed "inside" the angle, such as β (beta), or by using three letters, where the middle letter names the vertex, such as $\angle ABC$ or $\angle CBA$.

If a point is the vertex of more than one angle, as in Figure A.16, each angle can also be named either by using three letters, such as $\angle DEF$, $\angle DEG$, or $\angle GEF$, or by using a single letter "inside" the angle, such as α (alpha), or γ (gamma). However, since three angles have the vertex E, "$\angle E$" cannot be used since it would not clearly name any one of them.

Angles can be measured by various units of measurement, but in geometry they are commonly measured in **degrees.** Such measures can be assigned to an angle by using a circle whose center is at the vertex of the angle. If a circle is divided into 360 arcs of equal length (Figure A.17 on page 304), the number of arcs intercepted by a central angle α is the measure of the angle in degree units and is designated by $\alpha°$ (the measure of the angle is independent of the radius of the measuring circle). From Figure A.17, we have that $\alpha = 40°$.

Each degree is divided into sixty minutes (60′) and each minute of a degree is divided into sixty seconds (60″). To convert from tenths of degrees to minutes, you simply multiply the number of tenths by 60.

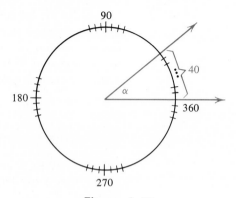

Figure A.17

Examples

a. $0.4° = (0.4 \times 60)'$

$= 24'$

b. $35.2° = 35° + (0.2 \times 60)'$

$= 35° \ 12'$

Conversely, to convert from minutes to tenths of degrees, simply divide the number of minutes by 60.

Examples

a. $36' = \left(\dfrac{36}{60}\right)°$

$= 0.6°$

b. $75° \ 18' = 75° + \left(\dfrac{18}{60}\right)°$

$= 75.3°$

A **protractor,** usually in the shape of a semicircle, as shown in Figure A.18, with 180 equally spaced marks on the semicircle, can be used to measure angles. If an angle is placed with its vertex at the center of the semicircle with one side passing through the 0° mark, the measure of the angle can be read directly.

Examples   In Figure A.18,

$$\angle ABC = 50°,$$

$$\angle ABE = 110°,$$

and

$$\angle DBE = 70°.$$

Also

$$\angle CBE = 110° - 50° = 60°.$$

Figure A.18

If the measure of an angle is less than 90°, the angle is an **acute angle;** if more than 90° and less than 180°, it is an **obtuse angle;** if equal to 90°, it is a **right angle.** If two lines, or rays, form a right angle, the lines, or rays, are **perpendicular,** indicated by the symbol ⊥. Thus $\overrightarrow{DE} \perp \overrightarrow{FG}$ is read "ray DE is perpendicular to ray FG."

Examples   In the figure, α is an acute angle, β is an obtuse angle, and γ is a right angle. Also, $\overrightarrow{AC} \perp \overrightarrow{AB}$.

If the sum of the measures of two angles is 90°, the angles are **complementary;** if the sum is 180°, the angles are **supplementary.**

Examples
   a. If $\angle D = 32°$, $\angle E = 148°$, and $\angle F = 58°$, then $\angle D$ and $\angle F$ are complementary, and $\angle D$ and $\angle E$ are supplementary.

   b. In the figure, angles α and β are complementary, and angles γ and θ (theta) are supplementary.

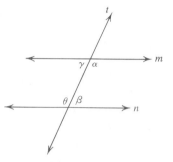

Figure A.19

Frequently, pairs of supplementary angles are introduced through the use of parallel lines. In Figure A.19, in which lines m and n are intersected by a transversal, line t, angles α and β are called interior angles on the same side of the transversal. If lines m and n are parallel, it follows that α and β are supplementary, as are γ and θ.

A.8 Triangles

A **triangle** is a figure formed by three line segments joining three points that are not in the same line. The line segments are the **sides,** and the three points are the **vertices** (plural of **vertex**) of the triangle. The letters assigned to the vertices can be used to name a triangle.

Example In the figure, the points A, B, and C are the vertices of $\triangle ABC$ (read "triangle ABC"), which can also be named by $\triangle ACB$, $\triangle BAC$, $\triangle BCA$, $\triangle CAB$, or $\triangle CBA$. The sides are $\overline{AB}$, $\overline{BC}$, and $\overline{CA}$; their lengths (positive real numbers) can be represented by AB, BC, and CA, respectively.

If each angle of a triangle is acute, the triangle is an **acute triangle;** if one angle is obtuse, it is an **obtuse triangle;** if one angle is a right angle, it is a **right triangle.** In a right triangle, the side opposite the right angle is the **hypotenuse,** and the other sides are the **legs.**

Examples In the figure, $\triangle DEF$ is an acute triangle, $\triangle KGH$ is an obtuse triangle, and $\triangle PQR$ is a right triangle. In $\triangle PQR$, $\overline{PQ}$ and $\overline{PR}$ are the legs, and $\overline{RQ}$ is the hypotenuse.

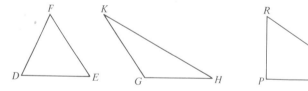

Triangles also have names related to the relative lengths of the sides. If the three sides are of different lengths, the triangle is a **scalene triangle;** if two sides have equal lengths, it is an **isosceles triangle;** if all three sides have equal lengths, it is an **equilateral triangle.**

Examples In the figure, $\triangle ABC$ is scalene, $\triangle DEF$ is isosceles ($FD = FE$), and $\triangle HKL$ is equilateral ($HK = KL = LH$). Note, further, that $\triangle ABC$ is an obtuse triangle, whereas $\triangle DEF$ and $\triangle HKL$ are both acute triangles.

An **altitude** of a triangle is the length of a segment from any vertex of a triangle perpendicular to the opposite side. Sometimes the segment itself is called the altitude.

Examples   In the figure, in $\triangle ABC$, h, or $\overline{CD}$, is the altitude to $\overline{AB}$. In $\triangle EFG$, $\overline{GH}$ is the altitude from G, and $\overline{FL}$ is the altitude from F.

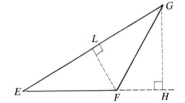

The following properties hold for any triangle (see Figure A.20).

1. The perimeter is $P = a + b + c$.
2. The area is $\mathscr{A} = \frac{1}{2}bh$.
3. $\angle A + \angle B + \angle C = 180°$.

As in Properties 1 and 2, lowercase letters are often used to indicate the lengths of the sides opposite the angles named by the corresponding capital letters.

Figure A.20

Examples
a. The perimeter of $\triangle ABC$ is

$$P = 3 + 5 + 6 = 14.$$

b. If $h = 6$ and $CD = 10$, the area of $\triangle CDE$ is

$$\mathscr{A} = \frac{1}{2}(10)(6) = 30.$$

c. If $\angle G = 70°$ and $\angle K = 50°$,

$$70° + 50° + \angle H = 180°,$$

from which we have that $\angle H = 60°$.

a.

b.

c.

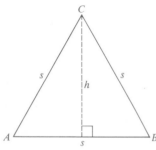

Figure A.21

In addition to Properties 1, 2, and 3, the following properties also apply to certain special triangles.

4. In an isosceles triangle, the angles opposite the equal sides are equal.

Example If $BD = CD$, then $\angle B = \angle C$.

5. If a triangle is equilateral, then (see Figure A.21)

$$\angle A = \angle B = \angle C = 60°, \quad h = \frac{s}{2}\sqrt{3}, \quad \text{and} \quad \mathscr{A} = \frac{\sqrt{3}}{4}s^2.$$

Example If $s = 12$, then

$$h = \frac{12}{2}\sqrt{3} = 6\sqrt{3} \quad \text{and} \quad \mathscr{A} = \frac{\sqrt{3}}{4}(12)^2 = 36\sqrt{3}.$$

6. In a right triangle ($\angle C = 90°$),
   (i) $a^2 + b^2 = c^2$ (the Pythagorean theorem).
   (ii) If $a = b$, then $\angle A = \angle B = 45°$, and $c = a\sqrt{2}$.
   (iii) If one acute angle is 30°, and the length of the opposite side is a, then the other acute angle is 60°, the length of the hypotenuse is $2a$, and the length of the longer leg is $a\sqrt{3}$.

(ii)

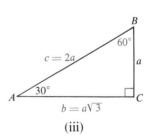

(iii)

Examples Using the measurements of the appropriate triangle:

a.

b.

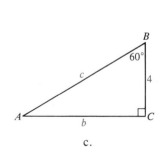

c.

a. $c^2 = 3^2 + 4^2 = 9 + 16 = 25$; $c = 5$

b. $\angle A = \angle B = 45°$; $c = 5\sqrt{2}$

c. $\angle A = 30°$; $c = 2 \cdot 4 = 8$; $b = 4\sqrt{3}$

A.9 Congruent and Similar Triangles

If two triangles are the same size and shape, they are said to be **congruent triangles.** In Figure A.22, the triangles are congruent. This is in-

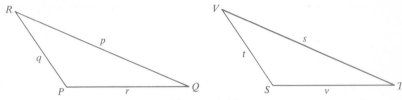

Figure A.22

dicated by use of the symbol $\cong$ (read "is congruent to"). Thus, in Figure A.22, $\triangle PQR \cong \triangle STV$. From this it follows that

$$\angle P = \angle S, \quad p = s,$$
$$\angle Q = \angle T, \quad q = t,$$
$$\angle R = \angle V, \quad r = v.$$

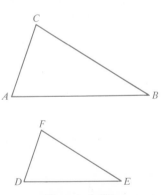

Figure A.23

If two triangles are the same shape, but not necessarily the same size, they are said to be **similar triangles.** In Figure A.23, the triangles are similar. This is written $\triangle ABC \sim \triangle DEF$, where "$\sim$" is read "is similar to." In two similar triangles, the corresponding angles are equal—that is, $\angle A = \angle D$, $\angle B = \angle E$, $\angle C = \angle F$; and the corresponding sides are proportional—that is,

$$\frac{AC}{DF} = \frac{AB}{DE} = \frac{BC}{EF}.$$

Example   Given that $\triangle RST \sim \triangle ADF$, we can find AD as follows. Since the triangles are similar, we have

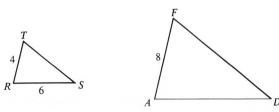

$$\frac{AD}{RS} = \frac{AF}{RT},$$

$$\frac{AD}{6} = \frac{8}{4},$$

from which

$$AD = 12.$$

The following properties can be used to prove that two triangles are similar:

1. two angles of one triangle are equal, respectively, to two angles of the other, or
2. one angle of one triangle is equal to one angle of the other, and the including sides are proportional, or
3. three sides of one triangle are proportional to three sides of the other.

Examples   Using the measurements in the figures:
a. $\angle P = \angle M$ and $\angle Q = \angle N$;

therefore, by Property 1, $\triangle PQR \sim \triangle MNL$.

b. $\angle A = \angle D$ and $\dfrac{AB}{DE} = \dfrac{AC}{DF}$, because $\dfrac{9}{6} = \dfrac{6}{4}$;

therefore, by Property 2, $\triangle ABC \sim \triangle DEF$.

c. $\dfrac{GK}{SW} = \dfrac{KH}{WT} = \dfrac{GH}{ST}$ because $\dfrac{8}{4} = \dfrac{10}{5} = \dfrac{12}{6}$;

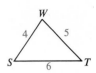

therefore, by Property 3, $\triangle GHK \sim \triangle STW$.

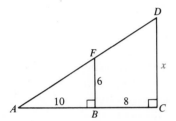

Example To find the length x in the figure, we proceed as follows. $\angle A = \angle A$ and $\angle ABF = \angle ACD$; hence, by Property 1, we have $\triangle ABF \sim \triangle ACD$. Also, $AC = AB + BC = 18$. Because the triangles are similar, the corresponding sides are proportional. Thus,

$$\frac{DC}{FB} = \frac{AC}{AB} \quad \text{and} \quad \frac{x}{6} = \frac{18}{10},$$

from which

$$x = \frac{6 \cdot 18}{10} = \frac{54}{5}.$$

A list of symbols introduced in Appendix A is shown inside the front cover.

B LINEAR INTERPOLATION

If Table II or Table III in Appendix C is used and we wish to obtain approximations for function values between two entries, we can use a method called **linear interpolation** to approximate such values.

The linear interpolation method assumes that differences in function values are directly proportional to the differences of the measures of the angles over small intervals. In fact, the differences are not directly proportional and we are simply obtaining closer rational number approximations for the function values than could be obtained by reading the nearest value from Table II or Table III.

Example Find an approximation for $\sin 0.714^R$ using linear interpolation.

Solution From Table II, we find that

$$\sin 0.71^R \approx 0.6518 \qquad \text{and} \qquad \sin 0.72^R \approx 0.6594.$$

The following arrangement of the data helps us to set up the direct proportion that we assume.

$$0.010 \left\{ 0.004 \left\{ \begin{array}{l} \sin 0.710^R \approx 0.6518 \\ \sin 0.714^R \approx \ ? \\ \sin 0.720^R \approx 0.6594 \end{array} \right\} d \right\} 0.0076 \quad (d = \text{difference}).$$

We have

$$\frac{0.004}{0.010} \approx \frac{d}{0.0076},$$

$$d \approx \frac{4}{10}(0.0076) \approx 0.0030.$$

312

Thus,

$$\sin 0.714 \approx 0.6518 + 0.0030 = 0.6548.$$

The next example illustrates a case where the difference d obtained from the proportion is *subtracted* from one of the values obtained from the table.

Example   Find an approximation for $\cos 0.393^R$.

Solution   From Table II,

$$\cos 0.390^R \approx 0.9249 \qquad \text{and} \qquad \cos 0.400^R \approx 0.9211.$$

By arranging the data for interpolation, we obtain

$$0.010 \left\{ 0.003 \left\{ \begin{array}{l} \cos 0.390^R \approx 0.9249 \\ \cos 0.393^R \approx ? \\ \cos 0.400^R \approx 0.9211 \end{array} \right\} d \right\} 0.0038.$$

We have

$$\frac{0.003}{0.010} \approx \frac{d}{0.0038},$$

$$d \approx \frac{3}{10}(0.0038) \approx 0.0011$$

Thus,

$$\cos 0.393^R \approx 0.9249 - 0.0011 = 0.9238.$$

Notice that we *subtracted* the difference, 0.0011, because in this interval *values for* $\cos \alpha$ *decrease as* α *increases*.

Linear interpolation can also be used to find an approximation for the measure of an angle associated with a given element in the range that is not an entry in the table.

Example   Find an approximation for an angle α in radian measure such that $\tan \alpha = 0.3369$ and $0^R \leq \alpha \leq 1.57^R$.

Solution   From Table II, we observe that

$$\tan 0.320^R \approx 0.3314 \qquad \text{and} \qquad \tan 0.330^R \approx 0.3425.$$

(continued)

By arranging the data for interpolation, we obtain

$$0.010 \left\{ d \left\{ \begin{array}{l} \tan 0.320^R \approx 0.3314 \\ \tan \alpha \quad\;\; \approx 0.3369 \\ \tan 0.330^R \approx 0.3425 \end{array} \right\} 0.0055 \right\} 0.0111.$$

We have

$$\frac{d}{0.010} \approx \frac{0.0055}{0.0111},$$

$$d \approx \frac{55}{111}(0.010) \approx 0.005$$

Thus,

$$\alpha \approx 0.320 + 0.005 = 0.325.$$

In the above examples we used Table II because the measure of the angle was in radians. A similar procedure of linear interpolation is also applicable when the measure of an angle is in degrees. An example is shown in the exercises.

With practice, the computations involved in linear interpolation, as in the examples above, can often be done mentally.

EXERCISE SET B.1

Use linear interpolation to find an approximation for each function value.

Example   cos 9° 14′

Solution   From Table III,

$$\cos 9°\ 12' \approx 0.9871 \qquad \text{and} \qquad \cos 9°\ 18' \approx 0.9869.$$

The data arranged for interpolation appear as

$$6' \left\{ 2' \left\{ \begin{array}{l} \cos 9°\ 12' \approx 0.9871 \\ \cos 9°\ 14' \approx\ ? \\ \cos 9°\ 18' \approx 0.9869 \end{array} \right\} d \right\} 0.0002.$$

Therefore,

$$\frac{2}{6} \approx \frac{d}{0.0002},$$

$$d \approx \frac{1}{3}(0.0002) \approx 0.0001.$$

Thus, $\cos 9° \, 14' \approx 0.9871 - 0.0001 = 0.9870.$

1. $\sin 3° \, 38'$ **2.** $\cos 10° \, 34'$ **3.** $\cot 60° \, 15'$ **4.** $\csc 45° \, 37'$

5. $\tan 42.32°$ **6.** $\cot 17.06°$ **7.** $\cos 15.62°$ **8.** $\sin 82.48°$

9. $\sin 0.255^R$ **10.** $\tan 0.536^R$ **11.** $\sec 0.904^R$ **12.** $\cot 1.362^R$

Use linear interpolation to find an approximation for an acute angle α in degree measure for each of the following.

Example $\sin \alpha = 0.4457$

Solution   From Table III,

$$\sin 26.4° \approx 0.4446 \quad \text{and} \quad \sin 26.5° \approx 0.4462.$$

The data arranged for interpolation appears as

$$0.10 \left\{ d \left\{ \begin{array}{l} \sin 26.4° \approx 0.4446 \\ \sin 26.?° \approx 0.4457 \\ \sin 26.5° \approx 0.4462 \end{array} \right\} 0.0011 \right\} 0.0016.$$

Therefore,

$$\frac{d}{0.10} \approx \frac{0.0011}{0.0016},$$

$$d \approx 0.10 \left(\frac{11}{16}\right) \approx 0.07.$$

Thus, $\alpha \approx 26.4° + 0.07° = 26.47°.$

13. $\sin \alpha = 0.2745$ **14.** $\cos \alpha = 0.9332$ **15.** $\tan \alpha = 0.4819$

16. $\csc \alpha = 1.9461$ **17.** $\sec \alpha = 1.2664$ **18.** $\cot \alpha = 1.0522$

19. $\sin \alpha = 0.7887$ **20.** $\cos \alpha = 0.4605$

Use linear interpolation to find an approximation for an acute angle α in radian measure for each of the following.

21. $\sin \alpha = 0.3099$ **22.** $\cos \alpha = 0.7944$ **23.** $\tan \alpha = 1.578$

24. $\csc \alpha = 2.901$ **25.** $\sec \alpha = 1.440$ **26.** $\cot \alpha = 0.3838$

27. $\sin \alpha = 0.8243$ **28.** $\cos \alpha = 0.7325$

C TABLES

TABLE I Powers, roots, and reciprocals

N	N^2	$\sqrt{N}$	$\sqrt{10N}$	$1/N$	N	N^2	$\sqrt{N}$	$\sqrt{10N}$	$1/N$
1	1	1.0 00	3.1 62	1.00 00	51	2 601	7.1 41	22.5 83	.019 61
2	4	1.4 14	4.4 72	.500 00	52	2 704	7.2 11	22.8 04	.019 23
3	9	1.7 32	5.4 77	.333 33	53	2 809	7.2 80	23.0 22	.018 87
4	16	2.0 00	6.3 25	.250 00	54	2 916	7.3 48	23.2 38	.018 52
5	25	2.2 36	7.0 71	.200 00	55	3 025	7.4 16	23.4 52	.018 18
6	36	2.4 49	7.7 46	.166 67	56	3 136	7.4 83	23.6 64	.017 86
7	49	2.6 46	8.3 67	.142 86	57	3 249	7.5 50	23.8 75	.017 54
8	64	2.8 28	8.9 44	.125 00	58	3 364	7.6 16	24.0 83	.017 24
9	81	3.0 00	9.4 87	.111 11	59	3 481	7.6 81	24.2 90	.016 95
10	100	3.1 62	10.0 00	.100 00	60	3 600	7.7 46	24.4 95	.016 67
11	121	3.3 17	10.4 88	.090 91	61	3 721	7.8 10	24.6 98	.016 39
12	144	3.4 64	10.9 54	.083 33	62	3 844	7.8 74	24.9 00	.016 13
13	169	3.6 06	11.4 02	.076 92	63	3 969	7.9 37	25.1 00	.015 87
14	196	3.7 42	11.8 32	.071 43	64	4 096	8.0 00	25.2 98	.015 62
15	225	3.8 73	12.2 47	.066 67	65	4 225	8.0 62	25.4 95	.015 38
16	256	4.0 00	12.6 49	.062 50	66	4 356	8.1 24	25.6 90	.015 15
17	289	4.1 23	13.0 38	.058 82	67	4 489	8.1 85	25.8 84	.014 93
18	324	4.2 43	13.4 16	.055 56	68	4 624	8.2 46	26.0 77	.014 71
19	361	4.3 59	13.7 84	.052 63	69	4 761	8.3 07	26.2 68	.014 49
20	400	4.4 72	14.1 42	.050 00	70	4 900	8.3 67	26.4 58	.014 29
21	441	4.5 83	14.4 91	.047 62	71	5 041	8.4 26	26.6 46	.014 08
22	484	4.6 90	14.8 32	.045 45	72	5 184	8.4 85	26.8 33	.013 89
23	529	4.7 96	15.1 66	.043 48	73	5 329	8.5 44	27.0 19	.013 70
24	576	4.8 99	15.4 92	.041 67	74	5 476	8.6 02	27.2 03	.013 51
25	625	5.0 00	15.8 11	.040 00	75	5 625	8.6 60	27.3 86	.013 33
26	676	5.0 99	16.1 25	.038 46	76	5 776	8.7 18	27.5 68	.013 16
27	729	5.1 96	16.4 32	.037 04	77	5 929	8.7 75	27.7 49	.012 99
28	784	5.2 92	16.7 33	.035 71	78	6 084	8.8 32	27.9 28	.012 82
29	841	5.3 85	17.0 29	.034 48	79	6 241	8.8 88	28.1 07	.012 66
30	900	5.4 77	17.3 21	.033 33	80	6 400	8.9 44	28.2 84	.012 50
31	961	5.5 68	17.6 07	.032 26	81	6 561	9.0 00	28.4 60	.012 35
32	1 024	5.6 57	17.8 89	.031 25	82	6 724	9.0 55	28.6 36	.012 20
33	1 089	5.7 45	18.1 66	.030 30	83	6 889	9.1 10	28.8 10	.012 05
34	1 156	5.8 31	18.4 39	.029 41	84	7 056	9.1 65	28.9 83	.011 90
35	1 225	5.9 16	18.7 08	.028 57	85	7 225	9.2 20	29.1 55	.011 76
36	1 296	6.0 00	18.9 74	.027 78	86	7 396	9.2 74	29.3 26	.011 63
37	1 369	6.0 83	19.2 35	.027 03	87	7 569	9.3 27	29.4 96	.011 49
38	1 444	6.1 64	19.4 94	.026 32	88	7 744	9.3 81	29.6 65	.011 36
39	1 521	6.2 45	19.7 48	.025 64	89	7 921	9.4 34	29.8 33	.011 24
40	1 600	6.3 25	20.0 00	.025 00	90	8 100	9.4 87	30.0 00	.011 11
41	1 681	6.4 03	20.2 48	.024 39	91	8 281	9.5 39	30.1 66	.010 99
42	1 764	6.4 81	20.4 94	.023 81	92	8 464	9.5 92	30.3 32	.010 87
43	1 849	6.5 57	20.7 36	.023 26	93	8 649	9.6 44	30.4 96	.010 75
44	1 936	6.6 33	20.9 76	.022 73	94	8 836	9.6 95	30.6 59	.010 64
45	2 025	6.7 08	21.2 13	.022 22	95	9 025	9.7 47	30.8 22	.010 53
46	2 116	6.7 82	21.4 48	.021 74	96	9 216	9.7 98	30.9 84	.010 42
47	2 209	6.8 56	21.6 79	.021 28	97	9 409	9.8 49	31.1 45	.010 31
48	2 304	6.9 28	21.9 09	.020 83	98	9 604	9.8 99	31.3 05	.010 20
49	2 401	7.0 00	22.1 36	.020 41	99	9 801	9.9 50	31.4 64	.010 10
50	2 500	7.0 71	22.3 61	.020 00	100	10 000	10.0 00	31.6 23	.010 00
N	N^2	$\sqrt{N}$	$\sqrt{10N}$	$1/N$	N	N^2	$\sqrt{N}$	$\sqrt{10N}$	$1/N$

I

320

TABLE II Values of circular and trigonometric functions

θ radians or Real Number x	θ degrees	$\sin\theta$ or $\sin x$	$\cos\theta$ or $\cos x$	$\tan\theta$ or $\tan x$	$\csc\theta$ or $\csc x$	$\sec\theta$ or $\sec x$	$\cot\theta$ or $\cot x$
0.00	0° 00′	0.0000	1.000	0.0000	No value	1.000	No value
.01	0° 34′	.0100	1.000	.0100	100.0	1.000	100.0
.02	1° 09′	.0200	0.9998	.0200	50.00	1.000	49.99
.03	1° 43′	.0300	0.9996	.0300	33.34	1.000	33.32
.04	2° 18′	.0400	0.9992	.0400	25.01	1.001	24.99
0.05	2° 52′	0.0500	0.9988	0.0500	20.01	1.001	19.98
.06	3° 26′	.0600	.9982	.0601	16.68	1.002	16.65
.07	4° 01′	.0699	.9976	.0701	14.30	1.002	14.26
.08	4° 35′	.0799	.9968	.0802	12.51	1.003	12.47
.09	5° 09′	.0899	.9960	.0902	11.13	1.004	11.08
0.10	5° 44′	0.0998	0.9950	0.1003	10.02	1.005	9.967
.11	6° 18′	.1098	.9940	.1104	9.109	1.006	9.054
.12	6° 53′	.1197	.9928	.1206	8.353	1.007	8.293
.13	7° 27′	.1296	.9916	.1307	7.714	1.009	7.649
.14	8° 01′	.1395	.9902	.1409	7.166	1.010	7.096
0.15	8° 36′	0.1494	0.9888	0.1511	6.692	1.011	6.617
.16	9° 10′	.1593	.9872	.1614	6.277	1.013	6.197
.17	9° 44′	.1692	.9856	.1717	5.911	1.015	5.826
.18	10° 19′	.1790	.9838	.1820	5.586	1.016	5.495
.19	10° 53′	.1889	.9820	.1923	5.295	1.018	5.200
0.20	11° 28′	0.1987	0.9801	0.2027	5.033	1.020	4.933
.21	12° 02′	.2085	.9780	.2131	4.797	1.022	4.692
.22	12° 36′	.2182	.9759	.2236	4.582	1.025	4.472
.23	13° 11′	.2280	.9737	.2341	4.386	1.027	4.271
.24	13° 45′	.2377	.9713	.2447	4.207	1.030	4.086
0.25	14° 19′	0.2474	0.9689	0.2553	4.042	1.032	3.916
.26	14° 54′	.2571	.9664	.2660	3.890	1.035	3.759
.27	15° 28′	.2667	.9638	.2768	3.749	1.038	3.613
.28	16° 03′	.2764	.9611	.2876	3.619	1.041	3.478
.29	16° 37′	.2860	.9582	.2984	3.497	1.044	3.351
0.30	17° 11′	0.2955	0.9553	0.3093	3.384	1.047	3.233
.31	17° 46′	.3051	.9523	.3203	3.278	1.050	3.122
.32	18° 20′	.3146	.9492	.3314	3.179	1.053	3.018
.33	18° 54′	.3240	.9460	.3425	3.086	1.057	2.920
.34	19° 29′	.3335	.9428	.3537	2.999	1.061	2.827
0.35	20° 03′	0.3429	0.9394	0.3650	2.916	1.065	2.740
.36	20° 38′	.3523	.9359	.3764	2.839	1.068	2.657
.37	21° 12′	.3616	.9323	.3879	2.765	1.073	2.578
.38	21° 46′	.3709	.9287	.3994	2.696	1.077	2.504
.39	22° 21′	.3802	.9249	.4111	2.630	1.081	2.433
0.40	22° 55′	0.3894	0.9211	0.4228	2.568	1.086	2.365
.41	23° 29′	.3986	.9171	.4346	2.509	1.090	2.301
.42	24° 04′	.4078	.9131	.4466	2.452	1.095	2.239
.43	24° 38′	.4169	.9090	.4586	2.399	1.100	2.180
.44	25° 13′	.4259	.9048	.4708	2.348	1.105	2.124
0.45	25° 47′	0.4350	0.9004	0.4831	2.299	1.111	2.070

TABLE II (*continued*)

θ radians or Real Number x	θ degrees	sin θ or sin x	cos θ or cos x	tan θ or tan x	csc θ or csc x	sec θ or sec x	cot θ or cot x
0.45	25° 47′	0.4350	0.9004	0.4831	2.299	1.111	2.070
.46	26° 21′	.4439	.8961	.4954	2.253	1.116	2.018
.47	26° 56′	.4529	.8916	.5080	2.208	1.122	1.969
.48	27° 30′	.4618	.8870	.5206	2.166	1.127	1.921
.49	28° 04′	.4706	.8823	.5334	2.125	1.133	1.875
0.50	28° 39′	0.4794	0.8776	0.5463	2.086	1.139	1.830
.51	29° 13′	.4882	.8727	.5594	2.048	1.146	1.788
.52	29° 48′	.4969	.8678	.5726	2.013	1.152	1.747
.53	30° 22′	.5055	.8628	.5859	1.978	1.159	1.707
.54	30° 56′	.5141	.8577	.5994	1.945	1.166	1.668
0.55	31° 31′	0.5227	0.8525	0.6131	1.913	1.173	1.631
.56	32° 05′	.5312	.8473	.6269	1.883	1.180	1.595
.57	32° 40′	.5396	.8419	.6410	1.853	1.188	1.560
.58	33° 14′	.5480	.8365	.6552	1.825	1.196	1.526
.59	33° 48′	.5564	.8309	.6696	1.797	1.203	1.494
0.60	34° 23′	0.5646	0.8253	0.6841	1.771	1.212	1.462
.61	34° 57′	.5729	.8196	.6989	1.746	1.220	1.431
.62	35° 31′	.5810	.8139	.7139	1.721	1.229	1.401
.63	36° 06′	.5891	.8080	.7291	1.697	1.238	1.372
.64	36° 40′	.5972	.8021	.7445	1.674	1.247	1.343
0.65	37° 15′	0.6052	0.7961	0.7602	1.652	1.256	1.315
.66	37° 49′	.6131	.7900	.7761	1.631	1.266	1.288
.67	38° 23′	.6210	.7838	.7923	1.610	1.276	1.262
.68	38° 58′	.6288	.7776	.8087	1.590	1.286	1.237
.69	39° 32′	.6365	.7712	.8253	1.571	1.297	1.212
0.70	40° 06′	0.6442	0.7648	0.8423	1.552	1.307	1.187
.71	40° 41′	.6518	.7584	.8595	1.534	1.319	1.163
.72	41° 15′	.6594	.7518	.8771	1.517	1.330	1.140
.73	41° 50′	.6669	.7452	.8949	1.500	1.342	1.117
.74	42° 24′	.6743	.7385	.9131	1.483	1.354	1.095
0.75	42° 58′	0.6816	0.7317	0.9316	1.467	1.367	1.073
.76	43° 33′	.6889	.7248	.9505	1.452	1.380	1.052
.77	44° 07′	.6961	.7179	.9697	1.436	1.393	1.031
.78	44° 41′	.7033	.7109	.9893	1.422	1.407	1.011
.79	45° 16′	.7104	.7038	1.009	1.408	1.421	0.9908
0.80	45° 50′	0.7174	0.6967	1.030	1.394	1.435	0.9712
.81	46° 25′	.7243	.6895	1.050	1.381	1.450	.9520
.82	46° 59′	.7311	.6822	1.072	1.368	1.466	.9331
.83	47° 33′	.7379	.6749	1.093	1.355	1.482	.9146
.84	48° 08′	.7446	.6675	1.116	1.343	1.498	.8964
0.85	48° 42′	0.7513	0.6600	1.138	1.331	1.515	0.8785
.86	49° 16′	.7578	.6524	1.162	1.320	1.533	.8609
.87	49° 51′	.7643	.6448	1.185	1.308	1.551	.8437
.88	50° 25′	.7707	.6372	1.210	1.297	1.569	.8267
.89	51° 00′	.7771	.6294	1.235	1.287	1.589	.8100
0.90	51° 34′	0.7833	0.6216	1.260	1.277	1.609	0.7936
.91	52° 08′	.7895	.6137	1.286	1.267	1.629	.7774
.92	52° 43′	.7956	.6058	1.313	1.257	1.651	.7615
.93	53° 17′	.8016	.5978	1.341	1.247	1.673	.7458
.94	53° 51′	.8076	.5898	1.369	1.238	1.696	.7303
0.95	54° 26′	0.8134	0.5817	1.398	1.229	1.719	0.7151

TABLE II (*continued*)

θ radians or Real Number x	θ degrees	sin θ or sin x	cos θ or cos x	tan θ or tan x	csc θ or csc x	sec θ or sec x	cot θ or cot x
0.95	54° 26′	0.8134	0.5817	1.398	1.229	1.719	0.7151
.96	55° 00′	.8192	.5735	1.428	1.221	1.744	.7001
.97	55° 35′	.8249	.5653	1.459	1.212	1.769	.6853
.98	56° 09′	.8305	.5570	1.491	1.204	1.795	.6707
.99	56° 43′	.8360	·5487	1.524	1.196	1.823	.6563
1.00	57° 18′	0.8415	0.5403	1.557	1.188	1.851	0.6421
1.01	57° 52′	.8468	.5319	1.592	1.181	1.880	.6281
1.02	58° 27′	.8521	.5234	1.628	1.174	1.911	.6142
1.03	59° 01′	.8573	.5148	1.665	1.166	1.942	.6005
1.04	59° 35′	.8624	.5062	1.704	1.160	1.975	.5870
1.05	60° 10′	0.8674	0.4976	1.743	1.153	2.010	0.5736
1.06	60° 44′	.8724	.4889	1.784	1.146	2.046	.5604
1.07	61° 18′	.8772	.4801	1.827	1.140	2.083	.5473
1.08	61° 53′	.8820	.4713	1.871	1.134	2.122	.5344
1.09	62° 27′	.8866	.4625	1.917	1.128	2.162	.5216
1.10	63° 02′	0.8912	0.4536	1.965	1.122	2.205	0.5090
1.11	63° 36′	.8957	.4447	2.014	1.116	2.249	.4964
1.12	64° 10′	.9001	.4357	2.066	1.111	2.295	.4840
1.13	64° 45′	.9044	.4267	2.120	1.106	2.344	.4718
1.14	65° 19′	.9086	.4176	2.176	1.101	2.395	.4596
1.15	65° 53′	0.9128	0.4085	2.234	1.096	2.448	0.4475
1.16	66° 28′	.9168	.3993	2.296	1.091	2.504	.4356
1.17	67° 02′	.9208	.3902	2.360	1.086	2.563	.4237
1.18	67° 37′	.9246	.3809	2.427	1.082	2.625	.4120
1.19	68° 11′	.9284	.3717	2.498	1.077	2.691	.4003
1.20	68° 45′	0.9320	0.3624	2.572	1.073	2.760	0.3888
1.21	69° 20′	.9356	.3530	2.650	1.069	2.833	.3773
1.22	69° 54′	.9391	.3436	2.733	1.065	2.910	.3659
1.23	70° 28′	.9425	.3342	2.820	1.061	2.992	.3546
1.24	71° 03′	.9458	.3248	2.912	1.057	3.079	.3434
1.25	71° 37′	0.9490	0.3153	3.010	1.054	3.171	0.3323
1.26	72° 12′	.9521	.3058	3.113	1.050	3.270	.3212
1.27	72° 46′	.9551	.2963	3.224	1.047	3.375	.3102
1.28	73° 20′	.9580	.2867	3.341	1.044	3.488	.2993
1.29	73° 55′	.9608	.2771	3.467	1.041	3.609	.2884
1.30	74° 29′	0.9636	0.2675	3.602	1.038	3.738	0.2776
1.31	75° 03′	.9662	.2579	3.747	1.035	3.878	.2669
1.32	75° 38′	.9687	.2482	3.903	1.032	4.029	.2562
1.33	76° 12′	.9711	.2385	4.072	1.030	4.193	.2456
1.34	76° 47′	.9735	.2288	4.256	1.027	4.372	.2350
1.35	77° 21′	0.9757	0.2190	4.455	1.025	4.566	0.2245
1.36	77° 55′	.9779	.2092	4.673	1.023	4.779	.2140
1.37	78° 30′	.9799	.1994	4.913	1.021	5.014	.2035
1.38	79° 04′	.9819	.1896	5.177	1.018	5.273	.1931
1.39	79° 38′	.9837	.1798	5.471	1.017	5.561	.1828
1.40	80° 13′	0.9854	0.1700	5.798	1.015	5.883	0.1725
1.41	80° 47′	.9871	.1601	6.165	1.013	6.246	.1622
1.42	81° 22′	.9887	.1502	6.581	1.011	6.657	.1519
1.43	81° 56′	.9901	.1403	7.055	1.010	7.126	.1417
1.44	82° 30′	.9915	.1304	7.602	1.009	7.667	.1315
1.45	83° 05′	0.9927	0.1205	8.238	1.007	8.299	0.1214

TABLE II *(continued)*

θ radians or Real Number x	θ degrees	sin θ or sin x	cos θ or cos x	tan θ or tan x	csc θ or csc x	sec θ or sec x	cot θ or cot x
1.45	83° 05′	0.9927	0.1205	8.238	1.007	8.299	0.1214
1.46	83° 39′	.9939	.1106	8.989	1.006	9.044	.1113
1.47	84° 13′	.9949	.1006	9.887	1.005	9.938	.1001
1.48	84° 48′	.9959	.0907	10.98	1.004	11.03	.0910
1.49	85° 22′	.9967	.0807	12.35	1.003	12.39	.0810
1.50	85° 57′	0.9975	0.0707	14.10	1.003	14.14	0.0709
1.51	86° 31′	.9982	.0608	16.43	1.002	16.46	.0609
1.52	87° 05′	.9987	.0508	19.67	1.001	19.69	.0508
1.53	87° 40′	.9992	.0408	24.50	1.001	24.52	.0408
1.54	88° 14′	.9995	.0308	32.46	1.000	32.48	.0308
1.55	88° 49′	0.9998	0.0208	48.08	1.000	48.09	0.0208
1.56	89° 23′	.9999	.0108	92.62	1.000	92.63	.0108
1.57	89° 57′	1.000	.0008	1256	1.000	1256	.0008

II

TABLE III   Values of trigonometric functions

θ deg	deg	min	sin θ	cos θ	tan θ	csc θ	sec θ	cot θ			
0.0	0	0	0.0000	1.0000	0.0000	No value	1.0000	No value	90	0	90.0
0.1	0	6	0.0017	1.0000	0.0017	572.96	1.0000	572.96	89	54	89.9
0.2	0	12	0.0035	1.0000	0.0035	286.48	1.0000	286.48	89	48	89.8
0.3	0	18	0.0052	1.0000	0.0052	190.99	1.0000	190.98	89	42	89.7
0.4	0	24	0.0070	1.0000	0.0070	143.24	1.0000	143.24	89	36	89.6
0.5	0	30	0.0087	1.0000	0.0087	114.59	1.0000	114.59	89	30	89.5
0.6	0	36	0.0105	0.9999	0.0105	95.495	1.0001	95.490	89	24	89.4
0.7	0	42	0.0122	0.9999	0.0122	81.853	1.0001	81.847	89	18	89.3
0.8	0	48	0.0140	0.9999	0.0140	71.622	1.0001	71.615	89	12	89.2
0.9	0	54	0.0157	0.9999	0.0157	63.665	1.0001	63.657	89	6	89.1
1.0	1	0	0.0175	0.9998	0.0175	57.299	1.0002	57.290	89	0	89.0
1.1	1	6	0.0192	0.9998	0.0192	52.090	1.0002	52.081	88	54	88.9
1.2	1	12	0.0209	0.9998	0.0209	47.750	1.0002	47.740	88	48	88.8
1.3	1	18	0.0227	0.9997	0.0227	44.077	1.0003	44.066	88	42	88.7
1.4	1	24	0.0244	0.9997	0.0244	40.930	1.0003	40.917	88	36	88.6
1.5	1	30	0.0262	0.9997	0.0262	38.202	1.0003	38.188	88	30	88.5
1.6	1	36	0.0279	0.9996	0.0279	35.815	1.0004	35.801	88	24	88.4
1.7	1	42	0.0297	0.9996	0.0297	33.708	1.0004	33.694	88	18	88.3
1.8	1	48	0.0314	0.9995	0.0314	31.836	1.0005	31.821	88	12	88.2
1.9	1	54	0.0332	0.9995	0.0332	30.161	1.0005	30.145	88	6	88.1
2.0	2	0	0.0349	0.9994	0.0349	28.654	1.0006	28.636	88	0	88.0
2.1	2	6	0.0366	0.9993	0.0367	27.290	1.0007	27.271	87	54	87.9
2.2	2	12	0.0384	0.9993	0.0384	26.050	1.0007	26.031	87	48	87.8
2.3	2	18	0.0401	0.9992	0.0402	24.918	1.0008	24.898	87	42	87.7
2.4	2	24	0.0419	0.9991	0.0419	23.880	1.0009	23.859	87	36	87.6
2.5	2	30	0.0436	0.9990	0.0437	22.926	1.0010	22.904	87	30	87.5
2.6	2	36	0.0454	0.9990	0.0454	22.044	1.0010	22.022	87	24	87.4
2.7	2	42	0.0471	0.9989	0.0472	21.229	1.0011	21.205	87	18	87.3
2.8	2	48	0.0488	0.9988	0.0489	20.471	1.0012	20.446	87	12	87.2
2.9	2	54	0.0506	0.9987	0.0507	19.766	1.0013	19.740	87	6	87.1
3.0	3	0	0.0523	0.9986	0.0524	19.107	1.0014	19.081	87	0	87.0
3.1	3	6	0.0541	0.9985	0.0542	18.492	1.0015	18.464	86	54	86.9
3.2	3	12	0.0558	0.9984	0.0559	17.914	1.0016	17.886	86	48	86.8
3.3	3	18	0.0576	0.9983	0.0577	17.372	1.0017	17.343	86	42	86.7
3.4	3	24	0.0593	0.9982	0.0594	16.862	1.0018	16.832	86	36	86.6
3.5	3	30	0.0610	0.9981	0.0612	16.380	1.0019	16.350	86	30	86.5
3.6	3	36	0.0628	0.9980	0.0629	15.926	1.0020	15.895	86	24	86.4
3.7	3	42	0.0645	0.9979	0.0647	15.496	1.0021	15.464	86	18	86.3
3.8	3	48	0.0663	0.9978	0.0664	15.089	1.0022	15.056	86	12	86.2
3.9	3	54	0.0680	0.9977	0.0682	14.703	1.0023	14.669	86	6	86.1
4.0	4	0	0.0698	0.9976	0.0699	14.336	1.0024	14.301	86	0	86.0
4.1	4	6	0.0715	0.9974	0.0717	13.987	1.0026	13.951	85	54	85.9
4.2	4	12	0.0732	0.9973	0.0734	13.654	1.0027	13.617	85	48	85.8
4.3	4	18	0.0750	0.9972	0.0752	13.337	1.0028	13.300	85	42	85.7
4.4	4	24	0.0767	0.9971	0.0769	13.035	1.0030	12.996	85	36	85.6
4.5	4	30	0.0785	0.9969	0.0787	12.746	1.0031	12.706	85	30	85.5
4.6	4	36	0.0802	0.9968	0.0805	12.469	1.0032	12.429	85	24	85.4
4.7	4	42	0.0819	0.9966	0.0822	12.204	1.0034	12.163	85	18	85.3
4.8	4	48	0.0837	0.9965	0.0840	11.951	1.0035	11.909	85	12	85.2
4.9	4	54	0.0854	0.9963	0.0857	11.707	1.0037	11.665	85	6	85.1
			cos θ	sin θ	cot θ	sec θ	csc θ	tan θ	deg	min	θ deg

TABLE III (*continued*)

θ deg	deg	min	$\sin \theta$	$\cos \theta$	$\tan \theta$	$\csc \theta$	$\sec \theta$	$\cot \theta$			
5.0	5	0	0.0872	0.9962	0.0875	11.474	1.0038	11.430	85	0	85.0
5.1	5	6	0.0889	0.9960	0.0892	11.249	1.0040	11.205	84	54	84.9
5.2	5	12	0.0906	0.9959	0.0910	11.034	1.0041	10.988	84	48	84.8
5.3	5	18	0.0924	0.9957	0.0928	10.826	1.0043	10.780	84	42	84.7
5.4	5	24	0.0941	0.9956	0.0945	10.626	1.0045	10.579	84	36	84.6
5.5	5	30	0.0958	0.9954	0.0963	10.433	1.0046	10.385	84	30	84.5
5.6	5	36	0.0976	0.9952	0.0981	10.248	1.0048	10.199	84	24	84.4
5.7	5	42	0.0993	0.9951	0.0998	10.069	1.0050	10.019	84	18	84.3
5.8	5	48	0.1011	0.9949	0.1016	9.8955	1.0051	9.8448	84	12	84.2
5.9	5	54	0.1028	0.9947	0.1033	9.7283	1.0053	9.6768	84	6	84.1
6.0	6	0	0.1045	0.9945	0.1051	9.5668	1.0055	9.5144	84	0	84.0
6.1	6	6	0.1063	0.9943	0.1069	9.4105	1.0057	9.3573	83	54	83.9
6.2	6	12	0.1080	0.9942	0.1086	9.2593	1.0059	9.2052	83	48	83.8
6.3	6	18	0.1097	0.9940	0.1104	9.1129	1.0061	9.0579	83	42	83.7
6.4	6	24	0.1115	0.9938	0.1122	8.9711	1.0063	8.9152	83	36	83.6
6.5	6	30	0.1132	0.9936	0.1139	8.8337	1.0065	8.7769	83	30	83.5
6.6	6	36	0.1149	0.9934	0.1157	8.7004	1.0067	8.6428	83	24	83.4
6.7	6	42	0.1167	0.9932	0.1175	8.5711	1.0069	8.5126	83	18	83.3
6.8	6	48	0.1184	0.9930	0.1192	8.4457	1.0071	8.3863	83	12	83.2
6.9	6	54	0.1201	0.9928	0.1210	8.3238	1.0073	8.2636	83	6	83.1
7.0	7	0	0.1219	0.9925	0.1228	8.2055	1.0075	8.1444	83	0	83.0
7.1	7	6	0.1236	0.9923	0.1246	8.0905	1.0077	8.0285	82	54	82.9
7.2	7	12	0.1253	0.9921	0.1263	7.9787	1.0079	7.9158	82	48	82.8
7.3	7	18	0.1271	0.9919	0.1281	7.8700	1.0082	7.8062	82	42	82.7
7.4	7	24	0.1288	0.9917	0.1299	7.7642	1.0084	7.6996	82	36	82.6
7.5	7	30	0.1305	0.9914	0.1317	7.6613	1.0086	7.5958	82	30	82.5
7.6	7	36	0.1323	0.9912	0.1334	7.5611	1.0089	7.4947	82	24	82.4
7.7	7	42	0.1340	0.9910	0.1352	7.4635	1.0091	7.3962	82	18	82.3
7.8	7	48	0.1357	0.9907	0.1370	7.3684	1.0093	7.3002	82	12	82.2
7.9	7	54	0.1374	0.9905	0.1388	7.2757	1.0096	7.2066	82	6	82.1
8.0	8	0	0.1392	0.9903	0.1405	7.1853	1.0098	7.1154	82	0	82.0
8.1	8	6	0.1409	0.9900	0.1423	7.0972	1.0101	7.0264	81	54	81.9
8.2	8	12	0.1426	0.9898	0.1441	7.0112	1.0103	6.9395	81	48	81.8
8.3	8	18	0.1444	0.9895	0.1459	6.9273	1.0106	6.8548	81	42	81.7
8.4	8	24	0.1461	0.9893	0.1477	6.8454	1.0108	6.7720	81	36	81.6
8.5	8	30	0.1478	0.9890	0.1495	6.7655	1.0111	6.6912	81	30	81.5
8.6	8	36	0.1495	0.9888	0.1512	6.6874	1.0114	6.6122	81	24	81.4
8.7	8	42	0.1513	0.9885	0.1530	6.6111	1.0116	6.5350	81	18	81.3
8.8	8	48	0.1530	0.9882	0.1548	6.5366	1.0119	6.4596	81	12	81.2
8.9	8	54	0.1547	0.9880	0.1566	6.4637	1.0122	6.3859	81	6	81.1
9.0	9	0	0.1564	0.9877	0.1584	6.3925	1.0125	6.3138	81	0	81.0
9.1	9	6	0.1582	0.9874	0.1602	6.3228	1.0127	6.2432	80	54	80.9
9.2	9	12	0.1599	0.9871	0.1620	6.2547	1.0130	6.1742	80	48	80.8
9.3	9	18	0.1616	0.9869	0.1638	6.1880	1.0133	6.1066	80	42	80.7
9.4	9	24	0.1633	0.9866	0.1655	6.1227	1.0136	6.0405	80	36	80.6
9.5	9	30	0.1650	0.9863	0.1673	6.0589	1.0139	5.9758	80	30	80.5
9.6	9	36	0.1668	0.9860	0.1691	5.9963	1.0142	5.9124	80	24	80.4
9.7	9	42	0.1685	0.9857	0.1709	5.9351	1.0145	5.8502	80	18	80.3
9.8	9	48	0.1702	0.9854	0.1727	5.8751	1.0148	5.7894	80	12	80.2
9.9	9	54	0.1719	0.9851	0.1745	5.8164	1.0151	5.7297	80	6	80.1
			$\cos \theta$	$\sin \theta$	$\cot \theta$	$\sec \theta$	$\csc \theta$	$\tan \theta$	deg	min	θ deg

TABLE III (*continued*)

θ deg	deg	min	sin θ	cos θ	tan θ	csc θ	sec θ	cot θ			
10.0	10	0	0.1736	0.9848	0.1763	5.7588	1.0154	5.6713	80	0	80.0
10.1	10	6	0.1754	0.9845	0.1781	5.7023	1.0157	5.6140	79	54	79.9
10.2	10	12	0.1771	0.9842	0.1799	5.6470	1.0161	5.5578	79	48	79.8
10.3	10	18	0.1788	0.9839	0.1817	5.5928	1.0164	5.5027	79	42	79.7
10.4	10	24	0.1805	0.9836	0.1835	5.5396	1.0167	5.4486	79	36	79.6
10.5	10	30	0.1822	0.9833	0.1853	5.4874	1.0170	5.3955	79	30	79.5
10.6	10	36	0.1840	0.9829	0.1871	5.4362	1.0174	5.3435	79	24	79.4
10.7	10	42	0.1857	0.9826	0.1890	5.3860	1.0177	5.2924	79	18	79.3
10.8	10	48	0.1874	0.9823	0.1908	5.3367	1.0180	5.2422	79	12	79.2
10.9	10	54	0.1891	0.9820	0.1926	5.2883	1.0184	5.1929	79	6	79.1
11.0	11	0	0.1908	0.9816	0.1944	5.2408	1.0187	5.1446	79	0	79.0
11.1	11	6	0.1925	0.9813	0.1962	5.1942	1.0191	5.0970	78	54	78.9
11.2	11	12	0.1942	9.9810	0.1980	5.1484	1.0194	5.0504	78	48	78.8
11.3	11	18	0.1959	0.9806	0.1998	5.1034	1.0198	5.0045	78	42	78.7
11.4	11	24	0.1977	0.9803	0.2016	5.0593	1.0201	4.9595	78	36	78.6
11.5	11	30	0.1994	0.9799	0.2035	5.0159	1.0205	4.9152	78	30	78.5
11.6	11	36	0.2011	0.9796	0.2053	4.9732	1.0209	4.8716	78	24	78.4
11.7	11	42	0.2028	0.9792	0.2071	4.9313	1.0212	4.8288	78	18	78.3
11.8	11	48	0.2045	0.9789	0.2089	4.8901	1.0216	4.7867	78	12	78.2
11.9	11	54	0.2062	0.9785	0.2107	4.8496	1.0220	4.7453	78	6	78.1
12.0	12	0	0.2079	0.9781	0.2126	4.8097	1.0223	4.7046	78	0	78.0
12.1	12	6	0.2096	0.9778	0.2144	4.7706	1.0227	4.6646	77	54	77.9
12.2	12	12	0.2113	0.9774	0.2162	4.7321	1.0231	4.6252	77	48	77.8
12.3	12	18	0.2130	0.9770	0.2180	4.6942	1.0235	4.5864	77	42	77.7
12.4	12	24	0.2147	0.9767	0.2199	4.6569	1.0239	4.5483	77	36	77.6
12.5	12	30	0.2164	0.9763	0.2217	4.6202	1.0243	4.5107	77	30	77.5
12.6	12	36	0.2181	0.9759	0.2235	4.5841	1.0247	4.4737	77	24	77.4
12.7	12	42	0.2198	0.9755	0.2254	4.5486	1.0251	4.4374	77	18	77.3
12.8	12	48	0.2215	0.9751	0.2272	4.5137	1.0255	4.4015	77	12	77.2
12.9	12	54	0.2232	0.9748	0.2290	4.4793	1.0259	4.3662	77	6	77.1
13.0	13	0	0.2250	0.9744	0.2309	4.4454	1.0263	4.3315	77	0	77.0
13.1	13	6	0.2267	0.9740	0.2327	4.4121	1.0267	4.2972	76	54	76.9
13.2	13	12	0.2284	0.9736	0.2345	4.3792	1.0271	4.2635	76	48	76.8
13.3	13	18	0.2300	0.9732	0.2364	4.3469	1.0276	4.2303	76	42	76.7
13.4	13	24	0.2317	0.9728	0.2382	4.3150	1.0280	4.1976	76	36	76.6
13.5	13	30	0.2334	0.9724	0.2401	4.2837	1.0284	4.1653	76	30	76.5
13.6	13	36	0.2351	0.9720	0.2419	4.2528	1.0288	4.1335	76	24	76.4
13.7	13	42	0.2368	0.9715	0.2438	4.2223	1.0293	4.1022	76	18	76.3
13.8	13	48	0.2385	0.9711	0.2456	4.1923	1.0297	4.0713	76	12	76.2
13.9	13	54	0.2402	0.9707	0.2475	4.1627	1.0302	4.0408	76	6	76.1
14.0	14	0	0.2419	0.9703	0.2493	4.1336	1.0306	4.0108	76	0	76.0
14.1	14	6	0.2436	0.9699	0.2512	4.1048	1.0311	3.9812	75	54	75.9
14.2	14	12	0.2453	0.9694	0.2530	4.0765	1.0315	3.9520	75	48	75.8
14.3	14	18	0.2470	0.9690	0.2549	4.0486	1.0320	3.9232	75	42	75.7
14.4	14	24	0.2487	0.9686	0.2568	4.0211	1.0324	3.8947	75	36	75.6
14.5	14	30	0.2504	0.9681	0.2586	3.9939	1.0329	3.8667	75	30	75.5
14.6	14	36	0.2521	0.9677	0.2605	3.9672	1.0334	3.8391	75	24	75.4
14.7	14	42	0.2538	0.9673	0.2623	3.9408	1.0338	3.8118	75	18	75.3
14.8	14	48	0.2554	0.9668	0.2642	3.9147	1.0343	3.7849	75	12	75.2
14.9	14	54	0.2571	0.9664	0.2661	3.8890	1.0348	3.7583	75	6	75.1
			cos θ	sin θ	cot θ	sec θ	csc θ	tan θ	deg	min	θ deg

TABLE III (*continued*)

θ deg	deg	min	sin θ	cos θ	tan θ	csc θ	sec θ	cot θ			
15.0	15	0	0.2588	0.9659	0.2679	3.8637	1.0353	3.7321	75	0	75.0
15.1	15	6	0.2605	0.9655	0.2698	3.8387	1.0358	3.7062	74	54	74.9
15.2	15	12	0.2622	0.9650	0.2717	3.8140	1.0363	3.6806	74	48	74.8
15.3	15	18	0.2639	0.9646	0.2736	3.7897	1.0367	3.6554	74	42	74.7
15.4	15	24	0.2656	0.9641	0.2754	3.7657	1.0372	3.6305	74	36	74.6
15.5	15	30	0.2672	0.9636	0.2773	3.7420	1.0377	3.6059	74	30	74.5
15.6	15	36	0.2689	0.9632	0.2792	3.7186	1.0382	3.5816	74	24	74.4
15.7	15	42	0.2706	0.9627	0.2811	3.6955	1.0388	3.5576	74	18	74.3
15.8	15	48	0.2723	0.9622	0.2830	3.6727	1.0393	3.5339	74	12	74.2
15.9	15	54	0.2740	0.9617	0.2849	3.6502	1.0398	3.5105	74	6	74.1
16.0	16	0	0.2756	0.9613	0.2867	3.6280	1.0403	3.4874	74	0	74.0
16.1	16	6	0.2773	0.9608	0.2886	3.6060	1.0408	3.4646	73	54	73.9
16.2	16	12	0.2790	0.9603	0.2905	3.5843	1.0413	3.4420	73	48	73.8
16.3	16	18	0.2807	0.9598	0.2924	3.5629	1.0419	3.4197	73	42	73.7
16.4	16	24	0.2823	0.9593	0.2943	3.5418	1.0424	3.3977	73	36	73.6
16.5	16	30	0.2840	0.9588	0.2962	3.5209	1.0429	3.3759	73	30	73.5
16.6	16	36	0.2857	0.9583	0.2981	3.5003	1.0435	3.3544	73	24	74.4
16.7	16	42	0.2874	0.9578	0.3000	3.4800	1.0440	3.3332	73	18	73.3
16.8	16	48	0.2890	0.9573	0.3019	3.4598	1.0446	3.3122	73	12	73.2
16.9	16	54	0.2907	0.9568	0.3038	3.4399	1.0451	3.2914	73	6	73.1
17.0	17	0	0.2924	0.9563	0.3057	3.4203	1.0457	3.2709	73	0	73.0
17.1	17	6	0.2940	0.9558	0.3076	3.4009	1.0463	3.2506	72	54	72.9
17.2	17	12	0.2957	0.9553	0.3096	3.3817	1.0468	3.2305	72	48	72.8
17.3	17	18	0.2974	0.9548	0.3115	3.3628	1.0474	3.2106	72	42	72.7
17.4	17	24	0.2990	0.9542	0.3134	3.3440	1.0480	3.1910	72	36	72.6
17.5	17	30	0.3007	0.9537	0.3153	3.3255	1.0485	3.1716	72	30	72.5
17.6	17	36	0.3024	0.9532	0.3172	3.3072	1.0491	3.1524	72	24	72.4
17.7	17	42	0.3040	0.9527	0.3191	3.2891	1.0497	3.1334	72	18	72.3
17.8	17	48	0.3057	0.9521	0.3211	3.2712	1.0503	3.1146	72	12	72.2
17.9	17	54	0.3074	0.9516	0.3230	3.2536	1.0509	3.0961	72	6	72.1
18.0	18	0	0.3090	0.9511	0.3249	3.2361	1.0515	3.0777	72	0	72.0
18.1	18	6	0.3107	0.9505	0.3268	3.2188	1.0521	3.0595	71	54	71.9
18.2	18	12	0.3123	0.9500	0.3288	3.2017	1.0527	3.0415	71	48	71.8
18.3	18	18	0.3140	0.9494	0.3307	3.1848	1.0533	3.0237	71	42	71.7
18.4	18	24	0.3156	0.9489	0.3327	3.1681	1.0539	3.0061	71	36	71.6
18.5	18	30	0.3173	0.9483	0.3346	3.1515	1.0545	2.9887	71	30	71.5
18.6	18	36	0.3190	0.9478	0.3365	3.1352	1.0551	2.9714	71	24	71.4
18.7	18	42	0.3206	0.9472	0.3385	3.1190	1.0557	2.9544	71	18	71.3
18.8	18	48	0.3223	0.9466	0.3404	3.1030	1.0564	2.9375	71	12	71.2
18.9	18	54	0.3239	0.9461	0.3424	3.0872	1.0570	2.9208	71	6	71.1
19.0	19	0	0.3256	0.9455	0.3443	2.0716	1.0576	2.9042	71	0	71.0
19.1	19	6	0.3272	0.9449	0.3463	3.0561	1.0583	2.8878	70	54	70.9
19.2	19	12	0.3289	0.9444	0.3482	3.0407	1.0589	2.8716	70	48	70.8
19.3	19	18	0.3305	0.9438	0.3502	3.0256	1.0595	2.8556	70	42	70.7
19.4	19	24	0.3322	0.9432	0.3522	3.0106	1.0602	2.8397	70	36	70.6
19.5	19	30	0.3338	0.9426	0.3541	· 2.9957	1.0608	2.8239	70	30	70.5
19.6	19	36	0.3355	0.9421	0.3561	2.9811	1.0615	2.8083	70	24	70.4
19.7	19	42	0.3371	0.9415	0.3581	2.9665	1.0622	2.7929	70	18	70.3
19.8	19	48	0.3387	0.9409	0.3600	2.9521	1.0628	2.7776	70	12	70.2
19.9	19	54	0.3404	0.9403	0.3620	2.9379	1.0635	2.7625	70	6	70.1
			cos θ	sin θ	cot θ	sec θ	csc θ	tan θ	deg	min	θ deg

TABLE III (*continued*)

θ deg	deg	min	sin θ	cos θ	tan θ	csc θ	sec θ	cot θ			
20.0	20	0	0.3420	0.9397	0.3640	2.9238	1.0642	2.7475	70	0	70.0
20.1	20	6	0.3437	0.9391	0.3659	2.9099	1.0649	2.7326	69	54	69.9
20.2	20	12	0.3453	0.9385	0.3679	2.8960	1.0655	2.7179	69	48	69.8
20.3	20	18	0.3469	0.9379	0.3699	2.8824	1.0662	2.7034	69	42	69.7
20.4	20	24	0.3486	0.9373	0.3719	2.8688	1.0669	2.6889	69	36	69.6
20.5	20	30	0.3502	0.9367	0.3739	2.8555	1.0676	2.6746	69	30	69.5
20.6	20	36	0.3518	0.9361	0.3759	2.8422	1.0683	2.6605	69	24	69.4
20.7	20	42	0.3535	0.9354	0.3779	2.8291	1.0690	2.6464	69	18	69.3
20.8	20	48	0.3551	0.9348	0.3799	2.8161	1.0697	2.6325	69	12	69.2
20.9	20	54	0.3567	0.9342	0.3819	2.8032	1.0704	2.6187	69	6	69.1
21.0	21	0	0.3584	0.9336	0.3839	2.7904	1.0711	2.6051	69	0	69.0
21.1	21	6	0.3600	0.9330	0.3859	2.7778	1.0719	2.5916	68	54	68.9
21.2	21	12	0.3616	0.9323	0.3879	2.7653	1.0726	2.5782	68	48	68.8
21.3	21	18	0.3633	0.9317	0.3899	2.7529	1.0733	2.5649	68	42	68.7
21.4	21	24	0.3649	0.9311	0.3919	2.7407	1.0740	2.5517	68	36	68.6
21.5	21	30	0.3665	0.9304	0.3939	2.7285	1.0748	2.5386	68	30	68.5
21.6	21	36	0.3681	0.9298	0.3959	2.7165	1.0755	2.5257	68	24	68.4
21.7	21	42	0.3697	0.9291	0.3979	2.7046	1.0763	2.5129	68	18	68.3
21.8	21	48	0.3714	0.9285	0.4000	2.6927	1.0770	2.5002	68	12	68.2
21.9	21	54	0.3730	0.9278	0.4020	2.6811	1.0778	2.4876	68	6	68.1
22.0	22	0	0.3746	0.9272	0.4040	2.6695	1.0785	2.4751	68	0	68.0
22.1	22	6	0.3762	0.9265	0.4061	2.6580	1.0793	2.4627	67	54	67.9
22.2	22	12	0.3778	0.9259	0.4081	2.6466	1.0801	2.4504	67	48	67.8
22.3	22	18	0.3795	0.9252	0.4101	2.6354	1.0808	2.4383	67	42	67.7
22.4	22	24	0.3811	0.9245	0.4122	2.6242	1.0816	2.4262	67	36	67.6
22.5	22	30	0.3827	0.9239	0.4142	2.6131	1.0824	2.4142	67	30	67.5
22.6	22	36	0.3843	0.9232	0.4163	2.6022	1.0832	2.4023	67	24	67.4
22.7	22	42	0.3859	0.9225	0.4183	2.5913	1.0840	2.3906	67	18	67.3
22.8	22	48	0.3875	0.9219	0.4204	2.5805	1.0848	2.3789	67	12	67.2
22.9	22	54	0.3891	0.9212	0.4224	2.5699	1.0856	2.3673	67	6	67.1
23.0	23	0	0.3907	0.9205	0.4245	2.5593	1.0864	2.3559	67	0	67.0
23.1	23	6	0.3923	0.9198	0.4265	2.5488	1.0872	2.3445	66	54	66.9
23.2	23	12	0.3939	0.9191	0.4286	2.5384	1.0880	2.3332	66	48	66.8
23.3	23	18	0.3955	0.9184	0.4307	2.5282	1.0888	2.3220	66	42	66.7
23.4	23	24	0.3971	0.9178	0.4327	2.5180	1.0896	2.3109	66	36	66.6
23.5	23	30	0.3987	0.9171	0.4348	2.5078	1.0904	2.2998	66	30	66.5
23.6	23	36	0.4003	0.9164	0.4369	2.4978	1.0913	2.2889	66	24	66.4
23.7	23	42	0.4019	0.9157	0.4390	2.4879	1.0921	2.2781	66	18	66.3
23.8	23	48	0.4035	0.9150	0.4411	2.4780	1.0929	2.2673	66	12	66.2
23.9	23	54	0.4051	0.9143	0.4431	2.4683	1.0938	2.2566	66	6	66.1
24.0	24	0	0.4067	0.9135	0.4452	2.4586	1.0946	2.2460	66	0	66.0
24.1	24	6	0.4083	0.9128	0.4473	2.4490	1.0955	2.2355	65	54	65.9
24.2	24	12	0.4099	0.9121	0.4494	2.4395	1.0963	2.2251	65	48	65.8
24.3	24	18	0.4115	0.9114	0.4515	2.4301	1.0972	2.2148	65	42	65.7
24.4	24	24	0.4131	0.9107	0.4536	2.4207	1.0981	2.2045	65	36	65.6
24.5	24	30	0.4147	0.9100	0.4557	2.4114	1.0989	2.1943	65	30	65.5
24.6	24	36	0.4163	0.9092	0.4578	2.4022	1.0998	2.1842	65	24	65.4
24.7	24	42	0.4179	0.9085	0.4599	2.3931	1.1007	2.1742	65	18	65.3
24.8	24	48	0.4195	0.9078	0.4621	2.3841	1.1016	2.1642	65	12	65.2
24.9	24	54	0.4210	0.9070	0.4642	2.3751	1.1025	2.1543	65	6	65.1
			cos θ	sin θ	cot θ	sec θ	csc θ	tan θ	deg	min	θ deg

TABLE III (*continued*)

θ deg	deg	min	sin θ	cos θ	tan θ	csc θ	sec θ	cot θ			
25.0	25	0	0.4226	0.9063	0.4663	2.3662	1.1034	2.1445	65	0	65.0
25.1	25	6	0.4242	0.9056	0.4684	2.3574	1.1043	2.1348	64	54	64.9
25.2	25	12	0.4258	0.9048	0.4706	2.3486	1.1052	2.1251	64	48	64.8
25.3	25	18	0.4274	0.9041	0.4727	2.3400	1.1061	2.1155	64	42	64.7
25.4	25	24	0.4289	0.9033	0.4748	2.3314	1.1070	2.1060	64	36	64.6
25.5	25	30	0.4305	0.9026	0.4770	2.3228	1.1079	2.0965	64	30	64.5
25.6	25	36	0.4321	0.9018	0.4791	2.3144	1.1089	2.0872	64	24	64.4
25.7	25	42	0.4337	0.9011	0.4813	2.3060	1.1098	2.0778	64	18	64.3
25.8	25	48	0.4352	0.9003	0.4834	2.2976	1.1107	2.0686	64	12	64.2
25.9	25	54	0.4368	0.8996	0.4856	2.2894	1.1117	2.0594	64	6	64.1
26.0	26	0	0.4384	0.8988	0.4877	2.2812	1.1126	2.0503	64	0	64.0
26.1	26	6	0.4399	0.8980	0.4899	2.2730	1.1136	2.0413	63	54	63.9
26.2	26	12	0.4415	0.8973	0.4921	2.2650	1.1145	2.0323	63	48	63.8
26.3	26	18	0.4431	0.8965	0.4942	2.2570	1.1155	2.0233	63	42	63.7
26.4	26	24	0.4446	0.8957	0.4964	2.2490	1.1164	2.0145	63	36	63.6
26.5	26	30	0.4462	0.8949	0.4986	2.2412	1.1174	2.0057	63	30	63.5
26.6	26	36	0.4478	0.8942	0.5008	2.2333	1.1184	1.9970	63	24	63.4
26.7	26	42	0.4493	0.8934	0.5029	2.2256	1.1194	1.9883	63	18	63.3
26.8	26	48	0.4509	0.8926	0.5051	2.2179	1.1203	1.9797	63	12	63.2
26.9	26	54	0.4524	0.8918	0.5073	2.2103	1.1213	1.9711	63	6	63.1
27.0	27	0	0.4540	0.8910	0.5095	2.2027	1.1223	1.9626	63	0	63.0
27.1	27	6	0.4555	0.8902	0.5117	2.1952	1.1233	1.9542	62	54	62.9
27.2	27	12	0.4571	0.8894	0.5139	2.1877	1.1243	1.9458	62	48	62.8
27.3	27	18	0.4586	0.8886	0.5161	2.1803	1.1253	1.9375	62	42	62.7
27.4	27	24	0.4602	0.8878	0.5184	2.1730	1.1264	1.9292	62	36	62.6
27.5	27	30	0.4617	0.8870	0.5206	2.1657	1.1274	1.9210	62	30	62.5
27.6	27	36	0.4633	0.8862	0.5228	2.1584	1.1284	1.9128	62	24	62.4
27.7	27	42	0.4648	0.8854	0.5250	2.1513	1.1294	1.9047	62	18	62.3
27.8	27	48	0.4664	0.8846	0.5272	2.1441	1.1305	1.8967	62	12	62.2
27.9	27	54	0.4679	0.8838	0.5295	2.1371	1.1315	1.8887	62	6	62.1
28.0	28	0	0.4695	0.8829	0.5317	2.1301	1.1326	1,8807	62	0	62.0
28.1	28	6	0.4710	0.8821	0.5339	2.1231	1.1336	1.8728	61	54	61.9
28.2	28	12	0.4726	0.8813	0.5362	2.1162	1.1347	1.8650	61	48	61.8
28.3	28	18	0.4741	0.8805	0.5384	2.1093	1.1357	1.8572	61	42	61.7
28.4	28	24	0.4756	0.8796	0.5407	2.1025	1.1368	1.8495	61	36	61.6
28.5	28	30	0.4772	0.8788	0.5430	2.0957	1.1379	1.8418	61	30	61.5
28.6	28	36	0.4787	0.8780	0.5452	2.0890	1.1390	1.8341	61	24	61.4
28.7	28	42	0.4802	0.8771	0.5475	2.0824	1.1401	1.8265	61	18	61.3
28.8	28	48	0.4818	0.8763	0.5498	2.0758	1.1412	1.8190	61	12	61.2
28.9	28	54	0.4833	0.8755	0.5520	2.0692	1.1423	1.8115	61	6	61.1
29.0	29	0	0.4848	0.8746	0.5543	2.0627	1.1434	1.8040	61	0	61.0
29.1	29	6	0.4863	0.8738	0.5566	2.0562	1.1445	1.7966	60	54	60.9
29.2	29	12	0.4879	0.8729	0.5589	2.0598	1.1456	1.7893	60	48	60.8
29.3	29	18	0.4894	0.8721	0.5612	2.0434	1.1467	1.7820	60	42	60.7
29.4	29	24	0.4909	0.8712	0.5635	2.0371	1.1478	1.7747	60	36	60.6
29.5	29	30	0.4924	0.8704	0.5658	2.0308	1.1490	1.7675	60	30	60.5
29.6	29	36	0.4939	0.8695	0.5681	2.0245	1.1501	1.7603	60	24	60.4
29.7	29	42	0.4955	0.8686	0.5704	2.0183	1.1512	1.7532	60	18	60.3
29.8	29	48	0.4970	0.8678	0.5727	2.0122	1.1524	1.7461	60	12	60.2
29.9	29	54	0.4985	0.8669	0.5750	2.0061	1.1535	1.7391	60	6	60.1
			cos θ	sin θ	cot θ	sec θ	csc θ	tan θ	deg	min	θ deg

III

TABLE III (*continued*)

θ deg	deg	min	sin θ	cos θ	tan θ	csc θ	sec θ	cot θ			
30.0	30	0	0.5000	0.8660	0.5774	2.0000	1.1547	1.7321	60	0	60.0
30.1	30	6	0.5015	0.8652	0.5797	1.9940	1.1559	1.7251	59	54	59.9
30.2	30	12	0.5030	0.8643	0.5820	1.9880	1.1570	1.7182	59	48	59.8
30.3	30	18	0.5045	0.8634	0.5844	1.9821	1.1582	1.7113	59	42	59.7
30.4	30	24	0.5060	0.8625	0.5867	1.9762	1.1594	1.7045	59	36	59.6
30.5	30	30	0.5075	0.8616	0.5890	1.9703	1.1606	1.6977	59	30	59.5
30.6	30	36	0.5090	0.8607	0.5914	1.9645	1.1618	1.6909	59	24	59.4
30.7	30	42	0.5105	0.8599	0.5938	1.9587	1.1630	1.6842	59	18	59.3
30.8	30	48	0.5120	0.8590	0.5961	1.9530	1.1642	1.6775	59	12	59.2
30.9	30	54	0.5135	0.8581	0.5985	1.9473	1.1654	1.6709	59	6	59.1
31.0	31	0	0.5150	0.8572	0.6009	1.9416	1.1666	1.6643	59	0	59.0
31.1	31	6	0.5165	0.8563	0.6032	1.9360	1.1679	1.6577	58	54	58.9
31.2	31	12	0.5180	0.8554	0.6056	1.9304	1.1691	1.6512	58	48	58.8
31.3	31	18	0.5195	0.8545	0.6080	1.9249	1.1703	1.6447	58	42	58.7
31.4	31	24	0.5210	0.8536	0.6104	1.9194	1.1716	1.6383	58	36	58.6
31.5	31	30	0.5225	0.8526	0.6128	1.9139	1.1728	1.6319	58	30	58.5
31.6	31	36	0.5240	0.8517	0.6152	1.9084	1.1741	1.6255	58	24	58.4
31.7	31	42	0.5255	0.8508	0.6176	1.9031	1.1753	1.6191	58	18	58.3
31.8	31	48	0.5270	0.8499	0.6200	1.8977	1.1766	1.6128	58	12	58.2
31.9	31	54	0.5284	0.8490	0.6224	1.8924	1.1779	1.6066	58	6	58.1
32.0	32	0	0.5299	0.8480	0.6249	1.8871	1.1792	1.6003	58	0	58.0
32.1	32	6	0.5314	0.8471	0.6273	1.8818	1.1805	1.5941	57	54	57.9
32.2	32	12	0.5329	0.8462	0.6297	1.8766	1.1818	1.5880	57	48	57.8
32.3	32	18	0.5344	0.8453	0.6322	1.8714	1.1831	1.5818	57	42	57.7
32.4	32	24	0.5358	0.8443	0.6346	1.8663	1.1844	1.5757	57	36	57.6
32.5	32	30	0.5373	0.8434	0.6371	1.8612	1.1857	1.5697	57	30	57.5
32.6	32	36	0.5388	0.8425	0.6395	1.8561	1.1870	1.5637	57	24	57.4
32.7	32	42	0.5402	0.8415	0.6420	1.8510	1.1883	1.5577	57	18	57.3
32.8	32	48	0.5417	0.8406	0.6445	1.8460	1.1897	1.5517	57	12	57.2
32.9	32	54	0.5432	0.8396	0.6469	1.8410	1.1910	1.5458	57	6	57.1
33.0	33	0	0.5446	0.8387	0.6494	1.8361	1.1924	1.5399	57	0	57.0
33.1	33	6	0.5461	0.8377	0.6519	1.8312	1.1937	1.5340	56	54	56.9
33.2	33	12	0.5476	0.8368	0.6544	1.8263	1.1951	1.5282	56	48	56.8
33.3	33	18	0.5490	0.8358	0.6569	1.8214	1.1964	1.5224	56	42	56.7
33.4	33	24	0.5505	0.8348	0.6594	1.8166	1.1978	1.5166	56	36	56.6
33.5	33	30	0.5519	0.8339	0.6619	1.8118	1.1992	1.5108	56	30	56.5
33.6	33	36	0.5534	0.8329	0.6644	1.8070	1.2006	1.5051	56	24	56.4
33.7	33	42	0.5548	0.8320	0.6669	1.8023	1.2020	1.4994	56	18	56.3
33.8	33	48	0.5563	0.8310	0.6694	1.7976	1.2034	1.4938	56	12	56.2
33.9	33	54	0.5577	0.8300	0.6720	1.7929	1.2048	1.4882	56	6	56.1
34.0	34	0	0.5592	0.8290	0.6745	1.7883	1.2062	1.4826	56	0	56.0
34.1	34	6	0.5606	0.8281	0.6771	1.7837	1.2076	1.4770	55	54	55.9
34.2	34	12	0.5621	0.8271	0.6796	1.7791	1.2091	1.4715	55	48	55.8
34.3	34	18	0.5635	0.8261	0.6822	1.7745	1.2105	1.4659	55	42	55.7
34.4	34	24	0.5650	0.8251	0.6847	1.7700	1.2120	1.4605	55	36	55.6
34.5	34	30	0.5664	0.8241	0.6873	1.7655	1.2134	1.4550	55	30	55.5
34.6	34	36	0.5678	0.8231	0.6899	1.7610	1.2149	1.4496	55	24	55.4
34.7	34	42	0.5693	0.8221	0.6924	1.7566	1.2163	1.4442	55	18	55.3
34.8	34	48	0.5707	0.8211	0.6950	1.7522	1.2178	1.4388	55	12	55.2
34.9	34	54	0.5721	0.8202	0.6976	1.7478	1.2193	1.4335	55	6	55.1
			cos θ	sin θ	cot θ	sec θ	csc θ	tan θ	deg	min	θ deg

TABLE III (*continued*)

θ deg	deg	min	sin θ	cos θ	tan θ	csc θ	sec θ	cot θ			
35.0	35	0	0.5736	0.8192	0.7002	1.7434	1.2208	1.4281	55	0	55.0
35.1	35	6	0.5750	0.8181	0.7028	1.7391	1.2223	1.4229	54	54	54.9
35.2	35	12	0.5764	0.8171	0.7054	1.7348	1.2238	1.4176	54	48	54.8
35.3	35	18	0.5779	0.8161	0.7080	1.7305	1.2253	1.4124	54	42	54.7
35.4	35	24	0.5793	0.8151	0.7107	1.7263	1.2268	1.4071	54	36	54.6
35.5	35	30	0.5807	0.8141	0.7133	1.7221	1.2283	1.4019	54	30	54.5
35.6	35	36	0.5821	0.8131	0.7159	1.7179	1.2299	1.3968	54	24	54.4
35.7	35	42	0.5835	0.8121	0.7186	1.7137	1.2314	1.3916	54	18	54.3
35.8	35	48	0.5850	0.8111	0.7212	1.7095	1.2329	1.3865	54	12	54.2
35.9	35	54	0.5864	0.8100	0.7239	1.7054	1.2345	1.3814	54	6	54.1
36.0	36	0	0.5878	0.8090	0.7265	1.7013	1.2361	1.3764	54	0	54.0
36.1	36	6	0.5892	0.8080	0.7292	1.6972	1.2376	1.3713	53	54	53.9
36.2	36	12	0.5906	0.8070	0.7319	1.6932	1.2392	1.3663	53	48	53.8
36.3	36	18	0.5920	0.8059	0.7346	1.6892	1.2408	1.3613	53	42	53.7
36.4	36	24	0.5934	0.8049	0.7373	1.6852	1.2424	1.3564	53	36	53.6
36.5	36	30	0.5948	0.8039	0.7400	1.6812	1.2440	1.3514	53	30	53.5
36.6	36	36	0.5962	0.8028	0.7427	1.6772	1.2456	1.3465	53	24	53.4
36.7	36	42	0.5976	0.8018	0.7454	1.6733	1.2472	1.3416	53	18	53.3
36.8	36	48	0.5990	0.8007	0.7481	1.6694	1.2489	1.3367	53	12	53.2
36.9	36	54	0.6004	0.7997	0.7508	1.6655	1.2505	1.3319	53	6	53.1
37.0	37	0	0.6018	0.7986	0.7536	1.6616	1.2521	1.3270	53	0	53.0
37.1	37	6	0.6032	0.7976	0.7563	1.6578	1.2538	1.3222	52	54	52.9
37.2	37	12	0.6046	0.7965	0.7590	1.6540	1.2554	1.3175	52	48	52.8
37.3	37	18	0.6060	0.7955	0.7618	1.6502	1.2571	1.3127	52	42	52.7
37.4	37	24	0.6074	0.7944	0.7646	1.6464	1.2588	1.3079	52	36	52.6
37.5	37	30	0.6088	0.7934	0.7673	1.6427	1.2605	1.3032	52	30	52.5
37.6	37	36	0.6101	0.7923	0.7701	1.6390	1.2622	1.2985	52	24	52.4
37.7	37	42	0.6115	0.7912	0.7729	1.6353	1.2639	1.2938	52	18	52.3
37.8	37	48	0.6129	0.7902	0.7757	1.6316	1.2656	1.2892	52	12	52.2
37.9	37	54	0.6143	0.7891	0.7785	1.6279	1.2673	1.2846	52	6	52.1
38.0	38	0	0.6157	0.7880	0.7813	1.6243	1.2690	1.2799	52	0	52.0
38.1	38	6	0.6170	0.7869	0.7841	1.6207	1.2708	1.2753	51	54	51.9
38.2	38	12	0.6184	0.7859	0.7869	1.6171	1.2725	1.2708	51	48	51.8
38.3	38	18	0.6198	0.7848	0.7898	1.6135	1.2742	1.2662	51	42	51.7
38.4	38	24	0.6211	0.7837	0.7926	1.6099	1.2760	1.2617	51	36	51.6
38.5	38	30	0.6225	0.7826	0.7954	1.6064	1.2778	1.2572	51	30	51.5
38.6	38	36	0.6239	0.7815	0.7983	1.6029	1.2796	1.2527	51	24	51.4
38.7	38	42	0.6252	0.7804	0.8012	1.5994	1.2813	1.2482	51	18	51.3
38.8	38	48	0.6266	0.7793	0.8040	1.5959	1.2831	1.2437	51	12	51.2
38.9	38	54	0.6280	0.7782	0.8069	1.5925	1.2849	1.2393	51	6	51.1
39.0	39	0	0.6293	0.7771	0.8098	1.5890	1.2868	1.2349	51	0	51.0
39.1	39	6	0.6307	0.7760	0.8127	1.5856	1.2886	1.2305	50	54	50.9
39.2	39	12	0.6320	0.7749	0.8156	1.5822	1.2904	1.2261	50	48	50.8
39.3	39	18	0.6334	0.7738	0.8185	1.5788	1.2923	1.2218	50	42	50.7
39.4	39	24	0.6347	0.7727	0.8214	1.5755	1.2941	1.2174	50	36	50.6
39.5	39	30	0.6361	0.7716	0.8243	1.5721	1.2960	1.2131	50	30	50.5
39.6	39	36	0.6374	0.7705	0.8273	1.5688	1.2978	1.2088	50	24	50.4
39.7	39	42	0.6388	0.7694	0.8302	1.5655	1.2997	1.2045	50	18	50.3
39.8	39	48	0.6401	0.7683	0.8332	1.5622	1.3016	1.2002	50	12	50.2
39.9	39	54	0.6414	0.7672	0.8361	1.5590	1.3035	1.1960	50	6	50.1
			cos θ	sin θ	cot θ	sec θ	csc θ	tan θ	deg	min	θ deg

TABLE III (*continued*)

θ deg	deg	min	sin θ	cos θ	tan θ	csc θ	sec θ	cot θ			
40.0	40	0	0.6428	0.7660	0.8391	1.5557	1.3054	1.1918	50	0	50.0
40.1	40	6	0.6441	0.7649	0.8421	1.5525	1.3073	1.1875	49	54	49.9
40.2	40	12	0.6455	0.7638	0.8451	1.5493	1.3092	1.1833	49	48	49.8
40.3	40	18	0.6468	0.7627	0.8481	1.5461	1.3112	1.1792	49	42	49.7
40.4	40	24	0.6481	0.7615	0.8511	1.5429	1.3131	1.1750	49	36	49.6
40.5	40	30	0.6494	0.7604	0.8541	1.5398	1.3151	1.1708	49	30	49.5
40.6	40	36	0.6508	0.7593	0.8571	1.5366	1.3171	1.1667	49	24	49.4
40.7	40	42	0.6521	0.7581	0.8601	1.5335	1.3190	1.1626	49	18	49.3
40.8	40	48	0.6534	0.7570	0.8632	1.5304	1.3210	1.1585	49	12	49.2
40.9	40	54	0.6547	0.7559	0.8662	1.5273	1.3230	1.1544	49	6	49.1
41.0	41	0	0.6561	0.7547	0.8693	1.5243	1.3250	1.1504	49	0	49.0
41.1	41	6	0.6574	0.7536	0.8724	1.5212	1.3270	1.1463	48	54	48.9
41.2	41	12	0.6587	0.7524	0.8754	1.5182	1.3291	1.1423	48	48	48.8
41.3	41	18	0.6600	0.7513	0.8785	1.5151	1.3311	1.1383	48	42	48.7
41.4	41	24	0.6613	0.7501	0.8816	1.5121	1.3331	1.1343	48	36	48.6
41.5	41	30	0.6626	0.7490	0.8847	1.5092	1.3352	1.1303	48	30	48.5
41.6	41	36	0.6639	0.7478	0.8878	1.5062	1.3373	1.1263	48	24	48.4
41.7	41	42	0.6652	0.7466	0.8910	1.5032	1.3393	1.1224	48	18	48.3
41.8	41	48	0.6665	0.7455	0.8941	1.5003	1.3414	1.1184	48	12	48.2
41.9	41	54	0.6678	0.7443	0.8972	1.4974	1.3435	1.1145	48	6	48.1
42.0	42	0	0.6691	0.7431	0.9004	1.4945	1.3456	1.1106	48	0	48.0
42.1	42	6	0.6704	0.7420	0.9036	1.4916	1.3478	1.1067	47	54	47.9
42.2	42	12	0.6717	0.7408	0.9067	1.4887	1.3499	1.1028	47	48	47.8
42.3	42	18	0.6730	0.7396	0.9099	1.4859	1.3520	1.0990	47	42	47.7
42.4	42	24	0.6743	0.7385	0.9131	1.4830	1.3542	1.0951	47	36	47.6
42.5	42	30	0.6756	0.7373	0.9163	1.4802	1.3563	1.0913	47	30	47.5
42.6	42	36	0.6769	0.7361	0.9195	1.4774	1.3585	1.0875	47	24	47.4
42.7	42	42	0.6782	0.7349	0.9228	1.4746	1.3607	1.0837	47	18	47.3
42.8	42	48	0.6794	0.7337	0.9260	1.4718	1.3629	1.0799	47	12	47.2
42.9	42	54	0.6807	0.7325	0.9293	1.4690	1.3651	1.0761	47	6	47.1
43.0	43	0	0.6820	0.7314	0.9325	1.4663	1.3673	1.0724	47	0	47.0
43.1	43	6	0.6833	0.7302	0.9358	1.4635	1.3696	1.0686	46	54	46.9
43.2	43	12	0.6845	0.7290	0.9391	1.4608	1.3718	1.0649	46	48	46.8
43.3	43	18	0.6858	0.7278	0.9424	1.4581	1.3741	1.0612	46	42	46.7
43.4	43	24	0.6871	0.7266	0.9457	1.4554	1.3763	1.0575	46	36	46.6
43.5	43	30	0.6884	0.7254	0.9490	1.4527	1.3786	1.0538	46	30	46.5
43.6	43	36	0.6896	0.7242	0.9523	1.4501	1.3809	1.0501	46	24	46.4
43.7	43	42	0.6909	0.7230	0.9556	1.4474	1.3832	1.0464	46	18	46.3
43.8	43	48	0.6921	0.7218	0.9590	1.4448	1.3855	1.0428	46	12	46.2
43.9	43	54	0.6934	0.7206	0.9623	1.4422	1.3878	1.0392	46	6	46.1
44.0	44	0	0.6947	0.7193	0.9657	1.4396	1.3902	1.0355	46	0	46.0
44.1	44	6	0.6959	0.7181	0.9691	1.4370	1.3925	1.0319	45	54	45.9
44.2	44	12	0.6972	0.7169	0.9725	1.4344	1.3949	1.0283	45	48	45.8
44.3	44	18	0.6984	0.7157	0.9759	1.4318	1.3972	1.0247	45	42	45.7
44.4	44	24	0.6997	0.7145	0.9793	1.4293	1.3996	1.0212	45	36	45.6
44.5	44	30	0.7009	0.7133	0.9827	1.4267	1.4020	1.0176	45	30	45.5
44.6	44	36	0.7022	0.7120	0.9861	1.4242	1.4044	1.0141	45	24	45.4
44.7	44	42	0.7034	0.7108	0.9896	1.4217	1.4069	1.0105	45	18	45.3
44.8	44	48	0.7046	0.7096	0.9930	1.4192	1.4093	1.0070	45	12	45.2
44.9	44	54	0.7059	0.7083	0.9965	1.4167	1.4118	1.0035	45	6	45.1
45.0	45	0	0.7071	0.7071	1.0000	1.4142	1.4142	1.0000	45	0	45.0
			cos θ	sin θ	cot θ	sec θ	csc θ	tan θ	deg	min	θ deg

ANSWERS TO ODD-NUMBERED EXERCISES

Exercise Set 1.1

1. II   **3.** IV   **5.** I   **7.** IV   **9.** II   **11.** IV

13. II   **15.** IV   **17.** II   **19.** IV   **21.** III   **23.** III

25. I   **27.** IV   **29.** 4/5   **31.** $-\sqrt{3}/2$

33. a. $\sqrt{3}/2$ **b.** $2/\sqrt{3}$ **c.** 2

Exercise Set 1.2

1. $s = 0, (1, 0); s = \pi/2, (0, 1); s = \pi, (-1, 0); s = 3\pi/2, (0, -1)$

3. 1/4   **5.** 1   **7.** 3/4   **9.** 0   **11.** $1/\sqrt{2}$ **13.** $2/\sqrt{3}$

15. 0   **17.** 1   **19.** 0.9968   **21.** 0.3429   **23.** 0.7518   **25.** 0.3530

27. 0.9992   **29.** 0.8916   **31.** 0.2522   **33.** 0.2838   **35.** 0.3830   **37.** 0.9397

39. 0.5849   **41.** 0.7852   **43.** 0.9612   **45.** 0.0013   **47.** 0.2519   **49.** 0.0997

53. 0.0100   **55.** 0.8776   **57.** 0.8415

Exercise Set 1.3

1. $s = 0, (1, 0); s = \pi/4, (1/\sqrt{2}, 1/\sqrt{2}); s = \pi/2, (0, 1); s = 3\pi/4, (-1/\sqrt{2}, 1/\sqrt{2}); s = \pi, (-1, 0);$
$s = 5\pi/4, (-1/\sqrt{2}, -1/\sqrt{2}); s = 3\pi/2, (0, -1); s = 7\pi/4, (1/\sqrt{2}, -1/\sqrt{2})$

3.

5.

7.

9.   **11.**   **13.**

15. $-1/2$ **17.** $1/2$ **19.** $-\sqrt{3}/2$ **21.** $-1/2$ **23.** $1/\sqrt{2}$ **25.** $1/\sqrt{2}$

27. $-1/\sqrt{2}$ **29.** $\sqrt{3}/2$ **31.** 0.9819 **33.** 0.1994 **35.** -0.2182 **37.** 0.9664

39. -0.5564 **41.** -0.7584 **43.** 0.0001 **45.** 0.0006 **47.** 0.0061

49. $OB = OD$ (equal radii); $\angle AOB = \angle COD$ (equal arcs subtended); $\angle BAO = \angle DCO$ (right angles)

Exercise Set 1.4

1. 1 **3.** $\sqrt{3}$ **5.** $-1/\sqrt{3}$ **7.** 2 **9.** $\sqrt{2}$ **11.** $-\sqrt{2}$

13. $-\sqrt{2}$ **15.** 2 **17.** 2 **19.** $1/\sqrt{3}$ **21.** $1/\sqrt{3}$ **23.** $-\sqrt{3}$

25. $\sqrt{3} + \sqrt{2}$ **27.** -1 **29.** $\dfrac{2\sqrt{6}}{3} + 1$ **31.** 0.5206 **33.** 2.2081 **35.** -4.9131

37. -4.5823 **39.** -3.7591 **41.** -1.2035 **43.** 3.3528 **45.** 0.3388 **47.** -1.4873

49. II   **51.** III   **53.** II   **55.** -1 **57.** $-2/\sqrt{3}$ **59.** $-3/4$

61. $\dfrac{1}{\cos x \sin x}$ **63.** $\cos^2 x$ **65.** $\dfrac{\cos^3 x}{\sin^2 x}$ **67.** $\dfrac{1}{\cos x}$ **69.** $\dfrac{\cos x}{\sin x}$

73. $\tan x = AT/OA = AT/1 = AT$

75. $\csc x = OP/PQ = OC/OB$ (similar triangles) $= OC/1 = OC$

Exercise Set 1.5

1. $\cos\left(\dfrac{3\pi}{4} + 2\pi\right)$ **3.** $\tan\left(\dfrac{\pi}{4} + \pi\right)$ **5.** $\sin\left(\dfrac{5\pi}{4} + 2\pi\right)$

7. $\tan\left(\dfrac{3\pi}{4} + 3\pi\right)$ **9.** $\sin\left(\dfrac{7\pi}{6} + 2\pi\right)$ **11.** $\sin\left(\dfrac{\pi}{3} + 4\pi\right)$

13. 10 centimeters; -10 centimeters   **15.** -8 centimeters; 0 centimeter

17. 22 centimeters   **19.** $40/\sqrt{3}$ centimeters

21. 1.2 volts   **23.** 1.2 volts

25. 0 volt   **27.** -5.89 dynes per square centimeter

29. 0 dyne per square centimeter   **31.** -106 volts

33. -66.7 volts   **35.** 85.2 volts

37. -0.0295 ampere   **39.** 0.002 ampere

41. 0.00993 ampere   **43.** 0.242 foot

Review Exercises

1. II   **2.** I   **3.** IV   **4.** II   **5.** IV   **6.** II

7. III   **8.** II   **9.** $-3/5$ **10.** $4/3$ **11.** $-5/4$ **12.** $-5/3$

13. $-1/\sqrt{2}$ **14.** 2   **15.** 0.5735   **16.** 0.2764   **17.** 0.8820   **18.** 0.2092

19. 3.72   **20.** -0.4122 **21.** 0.3214   **22.** 5.2356

23.

24.

25.

26.
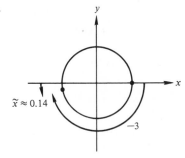

27. $1/\sqrt{2}$ **28.** $-\sqrt{3}/2$ **29.** 1/2   **30.** $-1/\sqrt{2}$ **31.** -0.1304

32. -0.2474 **33.** $-1/\sqrt{3}$ **34.** $-1/\sqrt{3}$ **35.** $-\sqrt{2}$ **36.** $2/\sqrt{3}$

37. -2 **38.** $2/\sqrt{3}$ **39.** 1   **40.** $-\sqrt{3}$ **41.** $3\sqrt{2} + 2$

42. $1/2 + \sqrt{3}$ **43.** 0.9131   **44.** 1.7953   **45.** -1.2475 **46.** -11.0811

47. 0.0382   **48.** -0.3114 **49.** I   **50.** III   **51.** $2/\sqrt{3}$

52. $-1/\sqrt{3}$ **53.** $\dfrac{\sin x}{\cos^2 x}$ **54.** $\dfrac{\cos x}{\sin^2 x}$ **55.** $\cos\left(\dfrac{2\pi}{3} + 2\pi\right)$ **56.** $\sin\left(\dfrac{\pi}{4} + 4\pi\right)$

57. 4 centimeters   **58.** 0 centimeter   **59.** 0 volt   **60.** 0.0259 ampere

Exercise Set 2.1

1.

3.

5.

7. Zeros: $\{x \mid x = k\pi, k \in J\}$;
amplitude: 3

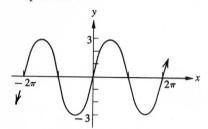

9. Zeros: $\{x \mid x = \pi/2 + k\pi, k \in J\}$;
amplitude: 1/2

11. Zeros: $\{x \mid x = k\pi, k \in J\}$:
amplitude: 1

13. Zeros: $\{x \mid x = k\pi/2, k \in J\}$;
amplitude: 1

15. Zeros: $\{x \mid x = \pi + k \cdot 2\pi, k \in J\}$;
amplitude: 1

17. Zeros: $\{x \mid x = \pi/2 + k\pi, k \in J\}$;
amplitude: 1

19.

21.

23.

As x approaches zero from the left or right, $\dfrac{\sin x}{x}$ approaches
a value of 1. The graph is not periodic because there is no
number a $(a \neq 0)$ such that $\dfrac{\sin(x + a)}{x + a} = \dfrac{\sin x}{x}$.

25.

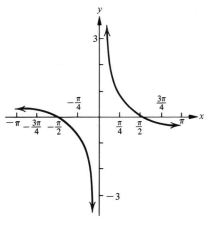

As x approaches zero from the left, $\dfrac{\cos x}{x}$ is negative and its absolute value becomes greater. As x approaches zero from the right, $\dfrac{\cos x}{x}$ is positive and its absolute value becomes greater. The graph is not periodic because there is no number $a(a \neq 0)$ such that $\dfrac{\cos(x + a)}{x + a} = \dfrac{\cos x}{x}$.

27. Period is 1.

29. Period is 1/2.

Exercise Set 2.2

1.

3.

5.

7.

9.

11.

13.

15.

17.

19.

21.

23.

25.

27.

29.

Exercise Set 2.3

1.

3.

5.

7.

9.

11.

13.

15.

17.

19.

21.

Exercise Set 2.4

1.

a. $\{y \mid y \in R\}$

b. $x = \dfrac{\pi}{6} + k \cdot \dfrac{\pi}{3}, \, k \in J$

c. $\left\{ x \mid x = k \cdot \dfrac{\pi}{3}, \, k \in J \right\}$

3.

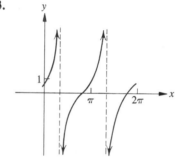

a. $\{y \mid y \in R\}$

b. $x = \pi/3 + k\pi, \, k \in J$

c. $\{x \mid x = 5\pi/6 + k\pi, \, k \in J\}$

5.

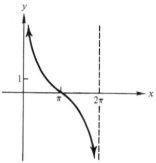

a. $\{y \mid y \in R\}$

b. $x = k \cdot 2\pi, \, k \in J$

c. $\{x \mid x = \pi + k \cdot 2\pi, \, k \in J\}$

7.

9.

11.

13.

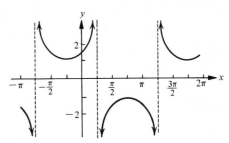

2

Exercise Set 2.5

1. $\{(0, 1), (6.3, 1)\}$

3. $\{(2.1, 0.5)\}$

5. $\{(3\pi/4, -1), (7\pi/4, -1)\}$

7. $\{0, 1.3, \pi, 5.0, 2\pi\}$

9. $\{0.7, 2.6, 3.7, 5.6\}$

11. $2x - 3y = 21$

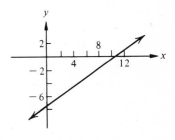

13. $x^2 + y^2 = 4$

15. $x^2 + y = 1$

17. $x^2 + y^2 = 1$

19. $y = \dfrac{8}{x^2 + 4}$

21.

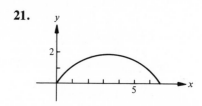

Exercise Set 2.6

1. $\cos y = \sqrt{3}/2;\ \pi/6$ **3.** $\sin y = 1;\ \pi/2$
9. $\pi/4$ **11.** $\pi/3$
17. $\pi/4$ **19.** $-\pi/6$
25. 0.52   **27.** 0.46
33. 1.45   **35.** 1.19

5. $\cot y = 1/\sqrt{3};\ \pi/3$ **7.** $\pi/4$
13. 0   **15.** $\pi/6$
21. $-\pi/3$ **23.** $2\pi/3$
29. 0.36   **31.** 1.24
37. -0.50 **39.** 2.92

41. -1.45

43. $x = \mathrm{Cos}^{-1}\dfrac{3}{4},\ 0 \le x \le \pi$

45. $x = \dfrac{1}{3}\,\mathrm{Sin}^{-1}\dfrac{1}{4},\ -\dfrac{\pi}{6} \le x \le \dfrac{\pi}{6}$

47. $x = \dfrac{1}{2}\,\mathrm{Tan}^{-1}\dfrac{5}{2},\ -\dfrac{\pi}{4} < x < \dfrac{\pi}{4}$

49. $x = \dfrac{1}{3}\,\mathrm{Cos}^{-1} 0.62,\quad 0 \le x \le \dfrac{\pi}{3}$

51. $x = \dfrac{1}{3}\,\mathrm{Tan}^{-1}\dfrac{y}{2},\ -\dfrac{\pi}{6} < x < \dfrac{\pi}{6}$

53. $x = 2\,\mathrm{Sin}^{-1}\dfrac{y}{4},\ -\pi \le x \le \pi$

55. $\sqrt{3}/2$

57. 0   **59.** $-1/\sqrt{2}$ **61.** $\pi/4$ **63.** $\pi/6$ **65.** 0   **67.** π
69. 0.7151   **71.** 2.4482   **73.** 1.0729

Review Exercises

1.

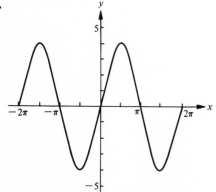

a. amplitude: 4
b. period: 2π
c. no phase shift

2.

a. amplitude: 1/2
b. period: π
c. no phase shift

3.

a. amplitude: 1
b. period: 2π
c. phase shift: $\pi/2$ to the left

4.

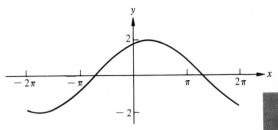

a. amplitude: 2
b. period: 4π
c. phase shift: $\pi/3$ to the right

2

5.

6.

7.

8.

9.

a. range: $\{y \mid y \in R\}$

b. asymptotes: $x = \dfrac{5\pi}{6} + k \cdot \pi, k \in J$

c. zeros: $\left\{x \mid x = \dfrac{\pi}{3} + k \cdot \pi, k \in J\right\}$

10.

a. range: $\{y \mid y \in R\}$

b. asymptotes: $x = k \cdot \dfrac{\pi}{3}, k \in J$

c. zeros: $\left\{ x \mid x = \dfrac{\pi}{6} + k \cdot \dfrac{\pi}{3}, k \in J \right\}$

11.

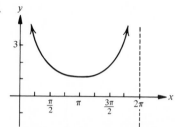

a. range: $\{y \mid y \leq -1 \text{ or } y \geq 1\}$

b. asymptotes: $x = k \cdot 2\pi, k \in J$

c. no zeros

12.

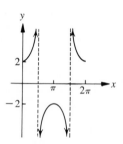

a. range: $\{y \mid y \leq -2 \text{ or } y \geq 2\}$

b. asymptotes: $x = \pi/2 + k \cdot \pi, k \in J$

c. no zeros

13.

Solution set is $\{(1.2, \tfrac{1}{3}), (5.0, \tfrac{1}{3})\}$

14.

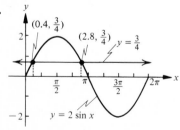

Solution set is $\{(0.4, \tfrac{3}{4}), (2.8, \tfrac{3}{4})\}$

15.

Solution set is
$\{(0.3, 0.5), (1.6, 0), (2.9, -0.5), (4.7, 0)\}$

16.

Solution set is
$\{(0.6, 0.3), (2.5, 0.3), (4.1, -0.3), (5.3, -0.3)\}$

17.

18.

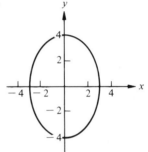

19. $x^2 + 2x - 8y + 1 = 0$ **20.** $\dfrac{x^2}{9} + \dfrac{y^2}{16} = 1$ **21.** $\cos y = 1/\sqrt{2}, \; \pi/4$ **22.** $\cot y = -1; \; -\pi/4$

23. $\csc y = -2; \; -\pi/6$ **24.** $\sec y = 2/\sqrt{3}; \; \pi/6$ **25.** $\pi/2$ **26.** $-\pi/6$

27. $3\pi/4$ **28.** $\pi/6$ **29.** 1.45 **30.** 0.95

31. 0.47 **32.** -1.02

33. $x = \mathrm{Cos}^{-1}\dfrac{3}{5}, \; 0 \le x \le \pi$

34. $x = \dfrac{1}{2} \mathrm{Sin}^{-1}\dfrac{1}{5}, \; -\dfrac{\pi}{4} \le x \le \dfrac{\pi}{4}$

35. $x = \dfrac{1}{2} \mathrm{Tan}^{-1}\dfrac{y}{3}, \; -\dfrac{\pi}{4} < x < \dfrac{\pi}{4}$

36. $x = 2 \mathrm{Cos}^{-1}\dfrac{y}{2}, \; 0 \le x \le 2\pi$

37. $\sqrt{3}$ **38.** $\dfrac{\sqrt{3}}{2}$ **39.** $\dfrac{\pi}{2}$ **40.** $\dfrac{\pi}{4}$

Exercise Set 3.1

1. $m°(\alpha) = (180/\pi)m^R(\alpha); \quad m^R(\alpha) = (\pi/180)m°(\alpha)$

3. $60.0°$ **5.** $240.0°$ **7.** $288.0°$ **9.** $-292.5°$ **11.** $10.3°$ **13.** $-88.2°$

15. 0.52^R **17.** 1.31^R **19.** 0.75^R **21.** -3.52^R **23.** 0.00029^R

25. 0.44^R

27. 19°

29. 4.83^R

31. 288°

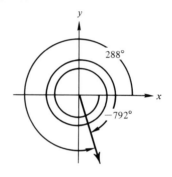

33. $(21 + k \cdot 360)°$, $k \in J$
39. $6\pi^R$; 1080°

35. $(-5\pi/6 + k \cdot 2\pi)^R$, $k \in J$
41. $12\pi^R$; 2160°

37. $(242 + k \cdot 360)°$, $k \in J$
43. $2\pi^R$; 180°

Exercise Set 3.2

1. 6.2 meters
5. $-9\pi/4 \approx -7.07$ feet
9. 280.7°
13. 3,000 radians per minute
17. $-12/\pi \approx -3.82$ degrees per second
21. 1,745 miles
25. 5024 meters per minute
29. 7.17×10^{-4} radians per hour
33. Area of the sector is to the area of the circle as the central angle θ is to 2π radians. Thus,

3. $5\pi^2/6 \approx 8.22$ decimeters
7. 126.9°
11. 3.6 meters per second
15. $-54\pi \approx -169.65$ decimeters per second
19. 104.72 meters
23. 3.98 centimeters
27. 9.39 radians per minute
31. 2.24×10^3 miles per hour

$$\frac{\mathscr{A}(\text{of sector})}{\pi r^2} = \frac{\theta^R}{2\pi}, \qquad \text{from which} \qquad \mathscr{A} = \frac{\pi r^2(\theta^R)}{2\pi} = \tfrac{1}{2}r^2\theta^R.$$

35. 1.92×10^{13} miles

37. 4690^R

Exercise Set 3.3

1. $\cos \alpha = 3/5$ $\sec \alpha = 5/3$
     $\sin \alpha = 4/5$ $\csc \alpha = 5/4$
     $\tan \alpha = 4/3$ $\cot \alpha = 3/4$

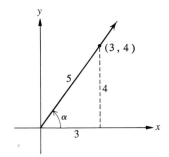

3. $\cos \alpha = -12/13$ $\sec \alpha = -13/12$
     $\sin \alpha = -5/13$ $\csc \alpha = -13/5$
     $\tan \alpha = 5/12$ $\cot \alpha = 12/5$

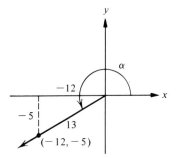

5. $\cos \alpha = 2/\sqrt{13}$ $\sec \alpha = \sqrt{13}/2$
     $\sin \alpha = 3/\sqrt{13}$ $\csc \alpha = \sqrt{13}/3$
     $\tan \alpha = 3/2$ $\cot \alpha = 2/3$

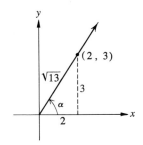

7. $\cos \alpha = -\sqrt{3}/2$ $\sec \alpha = -2/\sqrt{3}$
     $\sin \alpha = -1/2$ $\csc \alpha = -2$
     $\tan \alpha = 1/\sqrt{3}$ $\cot \alpha = \sqrt{3}$

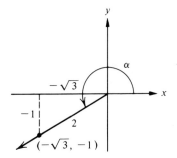

9. $\cos \alpha = \sqrt{3}/2$ $\sec \alpha = 2/\sqrt{3}$
     $\sin \alpha = 1/2$ $\csc \alpha = 2$
     $\tan \alpha = 1/\sqrt{3}$ $\cot \alpha = \sqrt{3}$

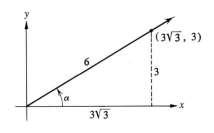

11. $\cos \alpha = 1$ $\sec \alpha = 1$
     $\sin \alpha = 0$ $\csc \alpha$ undefined
     $\tan \alpha = 0$ $\cot \alpha$ undefined

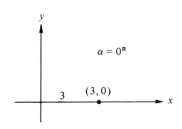

13. a. Not defined for $\alpha = (\pi/2 + k \cdot \pi)^R$, $k \in J$,   **15. a.** Not defined for $\alpha = (\pi/2 + k \cdot \pi)^R$, $k \in J$,
   b. equal to 0 for $\alpha = k \cdot \pi^R$, $k \in J$ **b.** no values equal to 0.

17. III   **19.** I   **21.** III   **23.** I

25. $\cos \alpha = \dfrac{x}{2}$ $\sec \alpha = \dfrac{2}{x}$ **27.** $\cos \alpha = \dfrac{\sqrt{16 - y^2}}{4}$ $\sec \alpha = \dfrac{4}{\sqrt{16 - y^2}}$

$\sin \alpha = \dfrac{\sqrt{4 - x^2}}{2}$ $\csc \alpha = \dfrac{2}{\sqrt{4 - x^2}}$ $\sin \alpha = \dfrac{y}{4}$ $\csc \alpha = \dfrac{4}{y}$

$\tan \alpha = \dfrac{\sqrt{4 - x^2}}{x}$ $\cot \alpha = \dfrac{x}{\sqrt{4 - x^2}}$ $\tan \alpha = \dfrac{y}{\sqrt{16 - y^2}}$ $\cot \alpha = \dfrac{\sqrt{16 - y^2}}{y}$

29. $\cos \alpha = \dfrac{x}{\sqrt{2x^2 - 4}}$ $\sec \alpha = \dfrac{\sqrt{2x^2 - 4}}{x}$

$\sin \alpha = \dfrac{\sqrt{x^2 - 4}}{\sqrt{2x^2 - 4}}$ $\csc \alpha = \dfrac{\sqrt{2x^2 - 4}}{\sqrt{x^2 - 4}}$

$\tan \alpha = \dfrac{\sqrt{x^2 - 4}}{x}$ $\cot \alpha = \dfrac{x}{\sqrt{x^2 - 4}}$

Exercise Set 3.4

1. $1/2$ **3.** $\sqrt{3}$ **5.** $2/\sqrt{3}$ **7.** Undefined   **9.** -1 **11.** -1
13. $-1/2$ **15.** $1/\sqrt{3}$ **17.** $-\sqrt{2}$ **19.** $-1/2$ **21.** $-1/2$ **23.** $-1/2$
25. 0.7379 **27.** 0.9872 **29.** 0.7774 **31.** 0.9857 **33.** 1.0575 **35.** 1.9458
37. 3.7849 **39.** 6.0405 **41.** 0.1132 **43.** $45°$ **45.** $30°$ **47.** $-30°$
49. $73.9°$ **51.** $30.7°$ **53.** $-52.5°$ **55.** $4/5$ **57.** $2/5$ **59.** $3/4$
61. $\dfrac{\sqrt{9 - x^2}}{3}$ **63.** $\sqrt{1 - x^2}$

Exercise Set 3.5

1. $\sin 28°$ **3.** $\cot 10.7°$
5. $\sec 1° 48'$ **7.** $\alpha \approx 33° 42'$, $\beta \approx 56° 18'$, $c \approx 3.61$
9. $\alpha \approx 61° 54'$, $\beta \approx 28° 6'$, $b \approx 8.00$ **11.** $\alpha = 39° 00'$, $a \approx 14.8$, $b \approx 18.3$
13. $\alpha = 67° 48'$, $b \approx 4.49$, $c \approx 11.9$ **15.** $\beta \approx 39° 42'$, $a \approx 18.1$, $c \approx 23.5$
17. $\alpha = 48° 24'$, $a \approx 33.8$, $c \approx 45.2$ **19.** 60.0
21. 24.7 **23.** 360 meters   **25.** $53° 6'$
27. 27.1 decimeters   **29.** 239 meters   **31.** 82.6 feet
33. 12,300 feet   **35.** 5.88 centimeters   **37.** $4\sqrt{3}$
39. $\cos \alpha = \dfrac{l - h}{l}$, from which $l \cos \alpha = l - h$ and $h = l(1 - \cos \alpha)$.

Exercise Set 3.6

1. $\gamma = 85°$, $b \approx 14.1$, $c \approx 14.6$ **3.** $\alpha = 42.8°$, $b \approx 52.0$, $c \approx 84.7$
5. $\beta = 52° 54'$, $a \approx 0.307$, $c \approx 0.526$ **7.** $\gamma = 77° 30'$, $a \approx 7.05$, $b \approx 13.3$

9. One triangle: $\beta \approx 20° 54'$, $\gamma \approx 129° 6'$, $c \approx 10.9$

11. Two triangles: $\gamma \approx 50° 42'$, $\beta \approx 97° 6'$, $b \approx 7.82$ or $\gamma' \approx 129° 18'$, $\beta' \approx 18° 30'$, $b' \approx 2.50$

13. One right triangle: $\alpha = 60° 00'$, $\gamma = 90° 00'$, $a \approx 27.7$

15. Two triangles: $\alpha \approx 60° 24'$, $\gamma \approx 76° 54'$, $c \approx 5.60$ or $\alpha' \approx 119° 36'$, $\gamma' \approx 17° 42'$, $c' \approx 1.75$

17. 1.51

19. 3.049 feet

21. 7.90 centimeters; 14.8 centimeters

23. 78.4 meters

25. 57.8 feet

27. 64.3 meters

29. From the figure, $\tan \gamma = \dfrac{c}{AC}$, or $AC = \dfrac{c}{\tan \gamma}$.

Using the Law of Sines, $\dfrac{AC}{\sin \beta} = \dfrac{a}{\sin[180° - (\alpha + \beta)]} = \dfrac{a}{\sin(\alpha + \beta)}$.

Hence, $AC = \dfrac{a \sin \beta}{\sin(\alpha + \beta)}$, from which $\dfrac{c}{\tan \gamma} = \dfrac{a \sin \beta}{\sin(\alpha + \beta)}$

$$c = \frac{a \sin \beta \tan \gamma}{\sin(\alpha + \beta)}$$

31. From the Law of Sines, $\dfrac{a}{b} = \dfrac{\sin \alpha}{\sin \beta}$. Adding 1 to both members gives $\dfrac{a}{b} + 1 = \dfrac{\sin \alpha}{\sin \beta} + 1$, from which

$\dfrac{a + b}{b} = \dfrac{\sin \alpha + \sin \beta}{\sin \beta}$.

33. From the results of Exercises 31 and 32 and dividing left members and right members respectively gives

$$\frac{\dfrac{a - b}{b}}{\dfrac{a + b}{b}} = \frac{\dfrac{\sin \alpha - \sin \beta}{\sin \beta}}{\dfrac{\sin \alpha + \sin \beta}{\sin \beta}}, \quad \text{from which} \quad \frac{a - b}{a + b} = \frac{\sin \alpha - \sin \beta}{\sin \alpha + \sin \beta}.$$

Exercise Set 3.7

1. $a \approx 4.37$, $\beta \approx 59° 54'$, $\gamma \approx 49° 6'$

3. $c \approx 3.39$, $\alpha \approx 65° 54'$, $\beta \approx 38° 48'$

5. $b \approx 1.42$, $\alpha \approx 17° 54'$, $\gamma \approx 20° 36'$

7. $a \approx 3.83$, $\beta \approx 24° 18'$, $\gamma \approx 55° 18'$

9. $\alpha \approx 95° 42'$, $\beta \approx 50° 42'$, $\gamma \approx 33° 36'$

11. $\alpha \approx 4° 00'$, $\beta \approx 31° 36'$, $\gamma \approx 144° 24'$

13. $\alpha \approx 26° 24'$, $\beta \approx 36° 24'$, $\gamma \approx 117° 12'$

15. $\alpha \approx 41° 24'$, $\beta \approx 55° 48'$, $\gamma \approx 82° 48'$

17. $42° 42'$

19. $82° 30'$

21. 10.9

23. 5.33 kilometers

25. 11.7 centimeters

27. $47.8°$

29. 1,240 feet

31. 875 kilometers

33. Adding 1 to both members of $\cos \alpha = \dfrac{b^2 + c^2 - a^2}{2bc}$ gives

$$1 + \cos \alpha = 1 + \frac{b^2 + c^2 - a^2}{2bc}$$

$$= \frac{2bc + b^2 + c^2 - a^2}{2bc} = \frac{b^2 + 2bc + c^2 - a^2}{2bc}$$

$$= \frac{(b + c)^2 - a^2}{2bc} = \frac{(b + c + a)(b + c - a)}{2bc}.$$

35. $a + b + c = 2s$ and $b + c - a = 2s - 2a = 2(s - a)$. Substituting $2s$ for $a + b + c$ and $2(s - a)$ for $b + c - a$ in the results of Exercise 33 gives

$$1 + \cos \alpha = \frac{(2s)(2)(s - a)}{2bc}, \qquad \text{from which} \qquad \frac{1 + \cos \alpha}{2} = \frac{s(s - a)}{bc}.$$

37. Multiplying left members and right members respectively of the result of Exercise 35 and 36 gives

$$\left(\frac{1 + \cos \alpha}{2}\right)\left(\frac{1 - \cos \alpha}{2}\right) = \left[\frac{s(s - a)}{bc}\right]\left[\frac{(s - b)(s - c)}{bc}\right],$$

$$\frac{1 - \cos^2 \alpha}{4} = \frac{s(s - a)(s - b)(s - c)}{b^2c^2},$$

$$\frac{\sin^2 \alpha}{4} = \frac{s(s - a)(s - b)(s - c)}{b^2c^2}.$$

Taking the square root of both members gives

$$\frac{1}{2}\sin \alpha = \frac{\sqrt{s(s - a)(s - b)(s - c)}}{bc},$$

$$\frac{1}{2}bc \sin \alpha = \sqrt{s(s - a)(s - b)(s - c)}.$$

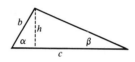

Because $h = b \sin \alpha$ (see the figure), the area $\mathscr{A}$ of a triangle is $\frac{1}{2}$(base × altitude), or $\frac{1}{2}c(b \sin \alpha)$. Thus,

$$\mathscr{A} = \sqrt{s(s - a)(s - b)(s - c)}.$$

39. 3.14

41. Noting in the figure that the radius r is the altitude of the three inner triangles, we have that the total area is $\frac{1}{2}(ra + rb + rc) = \frac{1}{2}(a + b + c)(r) = sr$. From the results of Exercise 37, we have

$$\mathscr{A} = \sqrt{s(s - a)(s - b)(s - c)} = sr,$$

from which

$$r = \sqrt{\frac{s(s - a)(s - b)(s - c)}{s^2}} = \sqrt{\frac{(s - a)(s - b)(s - c)}{s}}.$$

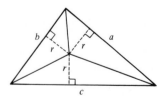

Review Exercises

1. 72.0°

4. 4.49^R

7. $(131 + k \cdot 360)°$, $k \in J$

10. 0.194^R

2. 138.1°

5. 218°

8. $(\pi/4 + k \cdot 2\pi)^R$, $k \in J$

11. 12 decimeters per minute

3. 1.31^R

6. 0.95^R

9. 2.86 meters

12. 0.394 radian per second

13. $\cos \alpha = 4/5$ $\sec \alpha = 5/4$
$\sin \alpha = 3/5$ $\csc \alpha = 5/3$
$\tan \alpha = 3/4$ $\cot \alpha = 4/3$

14. $\cos \alpha = 5/13$ $\sec \alpha = 13/5$
$\sin \alpha = 12/13$ $\csc \alpha = 13/12$
$\tan \alpha = 12/5$ $\cot \alpha = 5/12$

15. $\cos \alpha = -\sqrt{3}/2$ $\sec \alpha = -2/\sqrt{3}$
$\sin \alpha = 1/2$ $\csc \alpha = 2$
$\tan \alpha = -1/\sqrt{3}$ $\cot \alpha = -\sqrt{3}$

16. $\cos \alpha = -2/\sqrt{29}$ $\sec \alpha = -\sqrt{29}/2$
$\sin \alpha = 5/\sqrt{29}$ $\csc \alpha = \sqrt{29}/5$
$\tan \alpha = -5/2$ $\cot \alpha = -2/5$

17. IV   **18.** IV   **19.** III   **20.** IV   **21.** $1/\sqrt{2}$ **22.** $\sqrt{3}$
23. 0   **24.** -1 **25.** $-1/2$ **26.** $\sqrt{2}$ **27.** 0.8196   **28.** -1.8270
29. 0.0854   **30.** -1.0017 **31.** -0.5985 **32.** -1.0372 **33.** $30°$ **34.** $45°$
35. $66.8°$ **36.** $122.3°$
37. $\alpha = 39°$, $a \approx 8.81$, $b \approx 10.9$ **38.** $\alpha \approx 53° 42'$, $\beta \approx 36° 18'$, $b \approx 3.97$
39. $\beta = 57° 24'$, $b \approx 20.2$, $c \approx 24.0$ **40.** $\beta = 18° 42'$, $a \approx 28.7$, $c \approx 30.3$
41. $\gamma = 77.5°$, $a \approx 7.03$, $b \approx 13.3$ **42.** $\beta = 10° 00'$, $a \approx 1.73$, $b \approx 0.425$
43. Two triangles: $\alpha \approx 60.4°$, $\gamma \approx 76.9°$, $c \approx 5.60$
or $\alpha' \approx 119.6°$, $\gamma' \approx 17.7°$, $c' \approx 1.75$
44. One triangle: $\beta \approx 30° 36'$, $\gamma \approx 13° 54'$, $c \approx 17.5$
45. $\alpha \approx 51° 18'$, $\beta \approx 70° 30'$, $c \approx 2.07$ **46.** $\beta \approx 14° 6'$, $\gamma \approx 142° 48'$, $a = 3.7$
47. $\alpha \approx 35° 12'$, $\beta \approx 42° 12'$, $\gamma \approx 102° 36'$ **48.** $\alpha \approx 30° 48'$, $\beta \approx 56° 00'$, $\gamma \approx 93° 12'$

Exercise Set 4.1

1. $\dfrac{1}{\sin \alpha}$ **3.** $\dfrac{1}{\cos^2 \alpha}$ **5.** $\sin^2 \alpha$

7. $\dfrac{1}{\sin \alpha}$ **9.** $\dfrac{1}{\cos \alpha}$ **11.** $\dfrac{1}{\sin \alpha \cos \alpha}$

59. If $x = \pi/4$, then $\sin \dfrac{\pi}{4} + \left(\cos \dfrac{\pi}{4}\right)\left(\tan \dfrac{\pi}{4}\right) = 2$; $\dfrac{1}{\sqrt{2}} + \left(\dfrac{1}{\sqrt{2}}\right) \cdot 1 \neq 2$

61. If $y = \pi/2$, then $2\left(\sin \dfrac{\pi}{2}\right)\left(\cos \dfrac{\pi}{2}\right) + \sin \dfrac{\pi}{2} = 0$; $2(1)(0) + 1 \neq 0$

63. $\csc(-\alpha) = \dfrac{1}{\sin(-\alpha)} = \dfrac{1}{-\sin \alpha} = -\csc \alpha$ **65.** $\cot(-\alpha) = \dfrac{1}{\tan(-\alpha)} = \dfrac{1}{-\tan \alpha} = -\cot \alpha$

Exercise Set 4.2

1. $\dfrac{\sqrt{6} - \sqrt{2}}{4}$ **3.** $-\dfrac{\sqrt{2} + \sqrt{6}}{4}$ **5.** $\dfrac{\sqrt{2} + \sqrt{6}}{4}$ **13.** $\cos 9x$
15. $\cos 2x$ **17.** $\cos x$ **19.** $\cos 2x$ **21.** $16/65$
23. $13/\sqrt{170}$ **25.** $-\cos 60°$ **27.** $-\cos 30°$ **29.** $\cos 45°$
37. If $\alpha = 0°$ and $\beta = 60°$, then

$$\cos(\alpha + \beta) = \cos(0° + 60°) = \cos 60° = \frac{1}{2};$$

$$\cos \alpha + \cos \beta = \cos 0° + \cos 60° = 1 + \frac{1}{2} = \frac{3}{2} \neq \frac{1}{2}.$$

39. Using the difference formula and substituting $\pi/2$ for α and α for β, we obtain

$$\cos\left(\frac{\pi}{2} = \alpha\right) = \cos\frac{\pi}{2}\cos\alpha + \sin\frac{\pi}{2}\sin\alpha$$

$$= 0(\cos\alpha) + 1(\sin\alpha) = \sin\alpha.$$

41. 0   **43.** $\dfrac{\sqrt{3}+1}{2\sqrt{2}}$ **45.** $\dfrac{\sqrt{3}-1}{2\sqrt{2}}$

Exercise Set 4.3

1. $\dfrac{\sqrt{6}+\sqrt{2}}{4}$ **3.** $\dfrac{\sqrt{6}-\sqrt{2}}{4}$ **5.** $\dfrac{\sqrt{2}+\sqrt{6}}{4}$ **13.** $\sin 3x$ **15.** $\sin 4x$ **17.** $\sin 2x$
19. $\sin 2x$ **21.** $-44/125$ **23.** $5/\sqrt{754}$ **25.** $-\sin 60°$ **27.** $\sin 30°$ **29.** $-\sin 30°$
37. If $\alpha = 90°$ and $\beta = 60°$, then

$$\sin(\alpha - \beta) = \sin(90° - 60°) = \sin 30° = \frac{1}{2};$$

$$\sin\alpha - \sin\beta = \sin 90° - \sin 60° = 1 - \frac{\sqrt{3}}{2} \neq \frac{1}{2}.$$

39. 0   **41.** $-\dfrac{1}{2}$ **43.** $\dfrac{\sqrt{3}-1}{2\sqrt{2}}$

Exercise Set 4.4

1. $\dfrac{1+\sqrt{3}}{1-\sqrt{3}}$ **3.** $\dfrac{\sqrt{3}-1}{1+\sqrt{3}}$ **5.** $\dfrac{\sqrt{3}-1}{1+\sqrt{3}}$ **13.** $\tan 9x$ **15.** $\tan 2x$
17. $\tan x$ **19.** $-\tan 60°$ **21.** $\tan 30°$ **23.** $-\tan 45°$

Exercise Set 4.5

1. $\sin 2x$ **3.** $\cos 2x$ **5.** $\sin 4x$ **7.** $\frac{1}{2}\sin x$ **9.** $\cos 10\alpha$ **11.** $2\cos 12\alpha$
13. $\sin\alpha$ **15.** $\cos 2x$ **33.** $24/25$ **35.** $5/\sqrt{34}$ **37.** $-24/7$

Exercise Set 4.6

1. $\sqrt{\dfrac{1-\sqrt{3}/2}{2}}$ **3.** $\dfrac{1-\sqrt{3}/2}{1/2}$ **5.** $\sqrt{\dfrac{1-\sqrt{3}/2}{2}}$ **7.** $\sqrt{\dfrac{1+1/\sqrt{2}}{2}}$

9. $\dfrac{1+\sqrt{3}/2}{1/2}$ **11.** $-\sqrt{\dfrac{1-\sqrt{3}/2}{2}}$ **19.** $\dfrac{1}{\sqrt{3}}$ **21.** $\sqrt{\dfrac{2}{3}}$

23. $\sqrt{\dfrac{1+1/\sqrt{2}}{2}}$ **25.** $\frac{1}{2}(\sin 17° - \sin 7°)$ **27.** $\frac{1}{2}(\sin 3x - \sin x)$ **29.** $\frac{1}{2}(\cos 7x + \cos 3x)$

31. $2 \cos 12° \cos 8°$ **33.** $2 \sin 4\alpha \cos \alpha$ **35.** $2 \cos 3\alpha \sin 2\alpha$

37. $\cos \alpha \cos \beta = \frac{1}{2}[\cos(\alpha + \beta) + \cos(\alpha - \beta)]$
$$= \tfrac{1}{2}[\cos \alpha \cos \beta - \sin \alpha \sin \beta + \cos \alpha \cos \beta + \sin \alpha \sin \beta]$$
$$= \tfrac{1}{2}[2 \cos \alpha \cos \beta] = \cos \alpha \cos \beta$$

39. $\sin \alpha \cos \beta = \frac{1}{2}[\sin(\alpha + \beta) + \sin(\alpha - \beta)]$
$$= \tfrac{1}{2}(\sin \alpha \cos \beta + \cos \alpha \sin \beta + \sin \alpha \cos \beta - \cos \alpha \sin \beta)$$
$$= \tfrac{1}{2}(2 \sin \alpha \cos \beta) = \sin \alpha \cos \beta$$

41. Let $\alpha = x + y$ and $\beta = x - y$. Then,

$$\cos \alpha + \cos \beta = \cos(x + y) + \cos(x - y)$$
$$= \cos x \cos y - \sin x \sin y + \cos x \cos y + \sin x \sin y$$
$$= 2 \cos x \cos y.$$

Solving $\alpha = x + y$ and $\beta = x - y$ for α and β, respectively, gives $x = \dfrac{\alpha + \beta}{2}$ and $y = \dfrac{\alpha - \beta}{2}$. Thus,

$$\cos \alpha + \cos \beta = 2 \cos x \cos y = 2 \cos \frac{\alpha + \beta}{2} \cos \frac{\alpha - \beta}{2}.$$

43. Let $\alpha = x + y$ and $\beta = x - y$. Then,

$$\sin \alpha + \sin \beta = \sin(x + y) + \sin(x - y)$$
$$= \sin x \cos y + \cos x \sin y + \sin x \cos y - \cos x \sin y$$
$$= 2 \sin x \cos y.$$

As in Exercise 41, $x = \dfrac{\alpha + \beta}{2}$ and $y = \dfrac{\alpha - \beta}{2}$. Thus,

$$\sin \alpha + \sin \beta = 2 \sin x \cos y = 2 \sin \frac{\alpha + \beta}{2} \cos \frac{\alpha - \beta}{2}.$$

Exercise Set 4.7

1. $\{\pi/6\}$ **3.** $\{\pi/4\}$ **5.** $\{\pi/2\}$
7. $\{\pi/4, \pi/2\}$ **9.** $\{0, \pi/2\}$ **11.** $\{\pi/4, \pi/2\}$
13. $\{0\}$ **15.** $\{0, 2\pi/3, 4\pi/3\}$ **17.** $\{1.91, 4.37\}$

19. a. $\{270°\}$ **b.** $\{x \mid x = 270° + k \cdot 360°\}, k \in J$

21. a. $\{60°, 180°, 300°\}$
 b. $\{x \mid x = 60° + k \cdot 360°\} \cup \{x \mid x = 180° + k \cdot 360°\} \cup \{x \mid x = 300° + k \cdot 360°\}, k \in J$

23. a. $\{30°, 90°, 150°\}$
 b. $\{x \mid x = 30° + k \cdot 360°\} \cup \{x \mid x = 90° + k \cdot 360°\} \cup \{x \mid x = 150° + k \cdot 360°\}, k \in J$

25. a. $\{218.2°, 321.8°\}$
  b. $\{x \mid x = 218.2° + k \cdot 360°\} \cup \{x \mid x = 321.8° + k \cdot 360°\}, k \in J$

27. a. $\{39.9°, 115.7°, 244.3°, 320.1°\}$
  b. $\{x \mid x = 39.9° + k \cdot 360°\} \cup \{x \mid x = 115.7° + k \cdot 360°\} \cup \{x \mid x = 244.3° + k \cdot 360°\}$
                    $\cup \{x \mid x = 320.1° + k \cdot 360°\}, k \in J$

Exercise Set 4.8

1. $\{0, \pi/3\}$ **3.** $\{\pi/6, 5\pi/12\}$ **5.** $\{\pi/15, \pi/3\}$ **7.** $\{\pi/6\}$ **9.** $\{0\}$
11. $\{\pi/8\}$ **13.** $\{0\}$ **15.** $\{10°, 50°, 130°, 170°, 250°, 290°\}$
17. $\{15°, 75°, 135°, 195°, 255°, 315°\}$ **19.** $\{45°, 135°, 225°, 315°\}$
21. $\{15°, 45°, 75°, 105°, 135°, 165°, 195°, 225°, 255°, 285°, 315°, 345°\}$
23. $\{180°\}$ **25.** $\{60°, 180°, 300°\}$

27. $\{x \mid x = \pi/2 + k \cdot 2\pi\} \cup \{x \mid x = \pi/6 + k \cdot 2\pi\} \cup \{x \mid x = 5\pi/6 + k \cdot 2\pi\}, k \in J$

29. $\{x \mid x = k\pi\} \cup \{x \mid x = \pi/6 + k\pi/3\}, k \in J$

31. $\{x \mid x \approx 1.28 + k\pi/2\} \cup \{x \mid x = \pi/8 + k\pi/2\}, k \in J$

33. $\{x \mid x = \pi/12 + k(2\pi/3)\} \cup \{x \mid x = \pi/4 + k(2\pi/3)\}, k \in J$

35. $\{0.5\}$

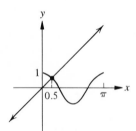

Review Exercises

1. $1/\cos \alpha$ **2.** $1/\sin^2 \alpha$ **3.** $\cos^2 \alpha$ **4.** $1/\sin \alpha$

23. If $\alpha = \dfrac{\pi}{4}$, then $\sin \dfrac{\pi}{4} \sec \dfrac{\pi}{4} = 2 \tan \dfrac{\pi}{4}; \dfrac{1}{\sqrt{2}} \cdot \sqrt{2} \neq 2 \cdot 1$

24. If $\alpha = \dfrac{\pi}{4}$, then $\dfrac{1 - \cos \pi/4}{\sin \pi/4} = \dfrac{1 + \sin \pi/4}{\cos \pi/4}; \dfrac{1 - 1/\sqrt{2}}{1/\sqrt{2}} \neq \dfrac{1 + 1/\sqrt{2}}{1/\sqrt{2}}; \sqrt{2} - 1 \neq \sqrt{2} + 1$

25. $-\sqrt{2} - \sqrt{3}/2$ **26.** $\sqrt{3} - 2$ **29.** $\frac{1}{2}(\cos 6x + \cos 4x)$ **30.** $2 \sin 5x \cos x$
31. $\{\pi/3\}$ **32.** $\{\pi/6\}$ **33.** $\{\pi/4\}$ **34.** $\{\pi/2\}$
35. $\{30°, 150°, 210°, 330°\}$ **36.** $\{45°, 135°, 225°, 315°\}$
37. $\{15°, 105°, 135°, 225°, 255°, 345°\}$ **38.** $\{15°, 30°, 105°, 120°, 195°, 210°, 285°, 300°\}$
39. $\{0°, 45°, 135°, 180°, 225°, 315°\}$ **40.** $\{0°, 180°\}$

Exercise Set 5.1

1. 2.3; 90°   **3.** 3.5; −60°   **5.** 2.4; −90°

7.

9.

11.

13.

15.

17.

19.

21.

23.

25.

27.

29.

31.

33.

35.

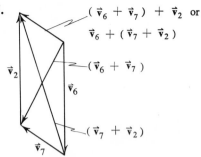

$(\vec{v}_6 + \vec{v}_7) + \vec{v}_2$ or

$\vec{v}_6 + (\vec{v}_7 + \vec{v}_2)$

37.

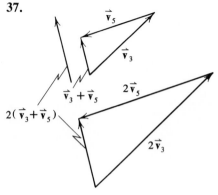

39.

$\frac{1}{3}\vec{v}_1$ $2\vec{v}_1$

$\frac{7}{3}\vec{v}_1$

Exercise Set 5.2

1. $\|\vec{v}_x\| = 5$, $\|\vec{v}_y\| = 5$

3. $\|\vec{v}_x\| = 0$, $\|\vec{v}_y\| = 15$

5. $\|\vec{v}_x\| = 6\sqrt{3}$, $\|\vec{v}_y\| = 6$

7. $\|\vec{v}_x\| = 4$, $\|\vec{v}_y\| = 4\sqrt{3}$

9. $\|\vec{v}_3\| = 5$ pounds; 53° 6′ with 3 pound force, 36° 54′ with 4 pound force.

11. $\|\vec{v}_3\| = 27.9$ kilograms; 43° 48′ with 15 kilogram force, 31° 12′ with 20 kilogram force.

13. 8.72 kilograms, $\alpha \approx 36° 36'$, $\beta \approx 83° 24'$

15. 40 kilograms, 36° 54′

17. 19.7 pounds, 37.1 pounds

19. 248 kilograms

21. 33° 24′

23. $\|\vec{v}_x\| = 1.64$ meters/sec², $\|\vec{v}_y\| = 1.15$ meters/sec²   **25.** 0.967 kilometer per hour

27. Drift angle is 11° 18′ to the right; ground speed is 612 miles per hour; course is 146° 18′

29. Drift angle is 12° to the right; wind direction is 318° measured from true north; wind speed is 106.5 miles per hour

31. Heading is 85° 12′; air speed is 602 kilometers per hour

33. 34.6 nautical miles, 265° 24′

35. 70.7 kilograms on each half

Exercise Set 5.3

1. $x = -3$, $y = 6$

3. $x = -7/2$, $y = -7$

5. $x = -2$, $y = -2$

7. a.

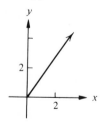

b. 5, 53° 6′

9. a.

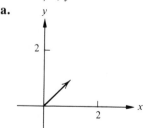

b. $\sqrt{2}$, 45°

11. a.

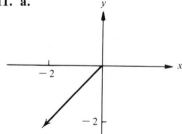

b. $3\sqrt{2}$, 225°

13. a.

b. 4, 0°

15. (2, 2)

17. (0, 1)

19. $(-\frac{5}{2}\sqrt{3}, -\frac{5}{2})$

Exercise Set 5.4

1. (−4, 6)

3. (3, 1)

5. (−4, 1)

7. (−3, −6)

9. (−4, 2)

11. (6, 12)

13. $(-13, -16)$

15. $(-9, 15)$

17. $(16, 10)$

19. $(7, -8)$

21. $(-7, -1)$

23. $(-27, 9)$

25. $(5/2, -1/2)$

27. $(19/6, 8/3)$

29. $(-5/2, 5)$

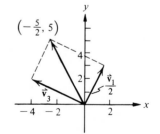

31. $3\mathbf{i} + 5\mathbf{j}$

33. $\mathbf{i} - 4\mathbf{j}$

35. $-3\mathbf{i}$

37. $4\sqrt{2}, -45°$

39. $\sqrt{5}, 26° \ 36'$

41. $\sqrt{10}, -108° \ 24'$

43. $2, 120°$

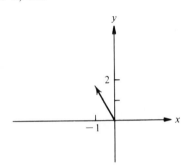

45. Let $\mathbf{v}_1 = (a_1, \ b_1)$ and $\mathbf{v}_2 = (a_2, \ b_2)$. By Definition 5.12, $\mathbf{v}_1 + \mathbf{v}_2 = (a_1, \ b_1) + (a_2, \ b_2) = (a_1 + a_2, b_1 + b_2)$. But $(a_1 + a_2, b_1 + b_2)$ is also a vector. Hence $\mathbf{V}$ is closed for vector addition.

47. Let $\mathbf{v}_1 = (a_1, b_1)$, $\mathbf{v}_2 = (a_2, b_2)$ and $\mathbf{v}_3 = (a_3, b_3)$. Using Definition 5.12 twice,

$$(\mathbf{v}_1 + \mathbf{v}_2) + \mathbf{v}_3 = (a_1 + a_2, b_1 + b_2) + (a_3, b_3)$$
$$= (a_1 + a_2 + a_3, b_1 + b_2 + b_3).$$

Using Definition 5.12 twice again,

$$\mathbf{v}_1 + (\mathbf{v}_2 + \mathbf{v}_3) = (a_1, b_1) + (a_2 + a_3, b_2 + b_3)$$
$$= (a_1 + a_2 + a_3, b_1 + b_2 + b_3).$$

Thus, $(\mathbf{v}_1 + \mathbf{v}_2) + \mathbf{v}_3 = \mathbf{v}_1 + (\mathbf{v}_2 + \mathbf{v}_3)$.

Exercise Set 5.5

1. 48

3. -2

5. 45

7. 13

9. $36\sqrt{2}$

11. $3/4$

13. $156° \ 48'$

15. $90°$

17. $24° \ 00'$

19. $20/\sqrt{29}$, 5

21. $7/\sqrt{41}$, $7/\sqrt{13}$

23. $-14/\sqrt{10}$, $-14/\sqrt{34}$

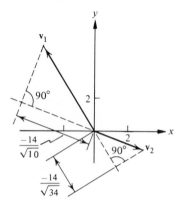

25. 0, 0

33. 24

35. 36

37. $1000\sqrt{3}$ meter-kilograms

39. 1,000,000 meter-kilograms

41. Let $\mathbf{v_1} = (a, b)$. Then $\|\mathbf{v_1}\| = \sqrt{a^2 + b^2}$ and $\|\mathbf{v_1}\|^2 = a^2 + b^2$.
Also, $\mathbf{v_1} \cdot \mathbf{v_1} = (a)(a) + (b)(b) = a^2 + b^2$. Thus, $\mathbf{v_1} \cdot \mathbf{v_1} = \|\mathbf{v_1}\|^2$.

Review Exercises

1. $(\vec{v_1} + \vec{v_2}) + \vec{v_3}$

2.

3.

4.

5. $4\sqrt{3}$; 4

6. 5; 36° 54′

7. 120 kilograms; 22° 36′

8. 6.71 miles per hour; drift of 63° 24′

9. Wind bearing is 23° 00′; wind speed is 183 kilometers per hour

10. 36° 54′   **11.** $x = -1$, $y = 3$ **12.** $x = 4$, $y = 1$

13. 5, 143° 6′   **14.** $5\sqrt{2}$, $-45°$

15. $(-5\sqrt{2}, -5\sqrt{2})$ **16.** $(-\sqrt{3}, 1)$ **17.** $(12, -4)$ **18.** $(-10, 10)$

19. $(8, 2)$ **20.** $(12, 2)$ **21.** $(-1, 3)$ **22.** $(5/2\sqrt{13}, 2/\sqrt{13})$

23. $7\mathbf{i} - 9\mathbf{j}$ **24.** $-8\mathbf{i} - \mathbf{j}$ **25.** $2\sqrt{29}$, 158° 12′   **26.** $\sqrt{130}$, $-52°$ 6′

27. -54 **28.** 75   **29.** $16\sqrt{3}$ **30.** $25\sqrt{3}$

31. 136° 48′   **32.** 56° 30′

33. $3/\sqrt{101}$, $3/5\sqrt{2}$ **34.** $-82/\sqrt{89}$, $-82/\sqrt{85}$

35. $(-4)(4) + (-5)(-16/5) = -16 + 16 = 0$ **36.** $(7)(5) + (6)(-35/6) = 35 - 35 = 0$

Exercise Set 6.1

1. $x = 1$, $y = -3$ **3.** $x = -\dfrac{1}{2}$, $y = 8$ **5.** $1 + 10i$ **7.** $-10 - 11i$

9. $-1 + 6i$ **11.** $0 + 0i$ **13.** $12 - 12i$ **15.** $-36 - 12i$

17. $2 + 3i$ **19.** $-19 + 2i$ **21.** $62 - 39i$ **23.** $26 - 19i$

25. $a^2 + b^2$ **27.** i **29.** -1 **31.** -1

33. $-i$ **35.** $5i$ **37.** $2\sqrt{3}\,i$ **39.** $1 + 3i$

41. $3 - 2\sqrt{5}\,i$ **43.** $8 + 2i$ **45.** $-8 + 8i$ **47.** $-10\sqrt{5} + 2\sqrt{10}\,i$

49. $23 + 2i$ **51.** $9 + \sqrt{3}\,i$

53. If $x = 2i$, then $(2i)^2 + 4 = 4i^2 + 4 = -4 + 4 = 0$;
if $x = -2i$, then $(-2i)^2 + 4 = 4i^2 + 4 = -4 + 4 = 0$

55. a. $\left(-\dfrac{1}{2} + i\dfrac{\sqrt{3}}{2}\right)^2 = \dfrac{1}{4} - i\dfrac{\sqrt{3}}{2} + i^2\left(\dfrac{3}{4}\right) = -\dfrac{1}{2} - i\dfrac{\sqrt{3}}{2}$;

$\left(-\dfrac{1}{2} + i\dfrac{\sqrt{3}}{2}\right)^3 = \left(-\dfrac{1}{2} + i\dfrac{\sqrt{3}}{2}\right)^2\left(-\dfrac{1}{2} + i\dfrac{\sqrt{3}}{2}\right)$

$= \left(-\dfrac{1}{2} - i\dfrac{\sqrt{3}}{2}\right)\left(-\dfrac{1}{2} + i\dfrac{\sqrt{3}}{2}\right) = \dfrac{1}{4} - i^2\left(\dfrac{3}{4}\right) = 1$

b. $\left(-\dfrac{1}{2} - i\dfrac{\sqrt{3}}{2}\right)^2 = \dfrac{1}{4} + i\dfrac{\sqrt{3}}{2} + i^2\left(\dfrac{3}{4}\right) = -\dfrac{1}{2} + i\dfrac{\sqrt{3}}{2}$;

$\left(-\dfrac{1}{2} - i\dfrac{\sqrt{3}}{2}\right)^3 = \left(-\dfrac{1}{2} - i\dfrac{\sqrt{3}}{2}\right)^2\left(-\dfrac{1}{2} - i\dfrac{\sqrt{3}}{2}\right)$

$= \left(-\dfrac{1}{2} + i\dfrac{\sqrt{3}}{2}\right)\left(-\dfrac{1}{2} - i\dfrac{\sqrt{3}}{2}\right) = \dfrac{1}{4} - i^2\left(\dfrac{3}{4}\right) = 1$

57. $a = 0, b = 1$ or $a = 0, b = -1$ **59.** $e^{\pi i} = \cos \pi + i \sin \pi = -1 + i(0) = -1$

61. $\dfrac{e^{ix} - e^{-ix}}{2i} = \dfrac{\cos x + i \sin x - [\cos(-x) + i \sin(-x)]}{2i}$

$$= \dfrac{\cos x + i \sin x - \cos x + i \sin x}{2i} = \dfrac{2i \sin x}{2i} = \sin x$$

63. Using the results of Exercises 61 and 62,

$$\sin^2 x + \cos^2 x = \left(\dfrac{e^{ix} - e^{-ix}}{2i}\right)^2 + \left(\dfrac{e^{ix} + e^{-ix}}{2}\right)^2$$

$$= \dfrac{e^{2ix} - 2e^0 + e^{-2ix}}{4i^2} + \dfrac{e^{2ix} + 2e^0 + e^{-2ix}}{4}$$

$$= \dfrac{-e^{2ix} + 2 - e^{-2ix}}{4} + \dfrac{e^{2ix} + 2 + e^{-2ix}}{4} = \dfrac{4}{4} = 1.$$

Exercise Set 6.2

1. $13 - 4i$ **3.** $2 + 2i$ **5.** $5 - i$ **7.** $6 - 3i$ **9.** $-3 + 3i$

11. $-3i$ **13.** $\frac{3}{2} - \frac{9}{4}i$ **15.** $\frac{8}{85} + \frac{36}{85}i$ **17.** $\frac{9}{17} + \frac{2}{17}i$ **19.** $-\frac{6}{5} + \frac{11}{10}i$

21. $\dfrac{-i}{\sqrt{5}}$ **23.** $-\dfrac{2i}{\sqrt{2}}$ **25.** $\dfrac{4}{7} - \dfrac{\sqrt{5}}{7}i$ **27.** $\dfrac{18}{11} - \dfrac{6\sqrt{2}}{11}i$ **29.** $\dfrac{6\sqrt{2}}{7} - \dfrac{6\sqrt{5}}{7}i$

31. $\dfrac{2\sqrt{5}}{13} - \dfrac{4\sqrt{2}}{13}i$

Exercise Set 6.3

1. $(-1, 6)$ **3.** $(8, 1)$ **5.** $(0, 6)$ **7.** $-8 + 7i$ **9.** $-4 + 0i$ **11.** $7 - \sqrt{2}i$

13.

15.

17.

19.

21. $-1 + 6i$

23. $-4 - 5i$

25. $-1 + 4i$ $-6 + 7i$

27. $\sqrt{29}$; 21° 48′

29. $2\sqrt{2}$; 225°

31. 7; 0°

33. 5; 270°

35. $3\sqrt{10}$; 288° 24′

37. 4; 0°

39. a. $a \neq 0, b = 0$ **b.** $a = 0, b \neq 0$ **c.** $b > 0$ **d.** $b < 0$

41.

43.

45.

Exercise Set 6.4

1. $4(\cos 120° + i \sin 120°)$

3. $10(\cos 210° + i \sin 210°)$

5. $2\sqrt{2}(\cos 315° + i \sin 315°)$

7. $8(\cos 180° + i \sin 180°)$

9. $-1 - \sqrt{3}i$

11. $-\sqrt{2} + \sqrt{2}i$

13. $\dfrac{1}{\sqrt{2}} - \dfrac{1}{\sqrt{2}} i$

15. $-\dfrac{\sqrt{3}}{4} + \dfrac{1}{4} i$

17. $-5\sqrt{2} + 5\sqrt{2}i$ **19.** $\frac{3}{2}\sqrt{3} - \frac{3}{2}i$ **21.** $-\sqrt{2} + \sqrt{2}i$ **23.** $-4 + 0i$

25. $-\frac{1}{5} - \frac{\sqrt{3}}{5}i$ **27.** $\frac{3}{2} - \frac{3\sqrt{3}}{2}i$ **29.** $4 + 4\sqrt{3}i$

31. $(a + bi)^2 = \rho(\cos\theta + i\sin\theta) \cdot \rho(\cos\theta + i\sin\theta)$; using Equation (1) in this section gives

$$(a + bi)^2 = \rho \cdot \rho[\cos(\theta + \theta) + i\sin(\theta + \theta)]$$
$$= \rho^2[\cos 2\theta + i\sin 2\theta].$$

33. $(a + bi)^4 = (a + bi)^3(a + bi)$; using the results of Exercise 32 and Equation (1) in this section, gives

$$\rho^3(\cos 3\theta + i\sin 3\theta) \cdot \rho(\cos\theta + i\sin\theta) = \rho^3 \cdot \rho[\cos(3\theta + \theta) + i\sin(3\theta + \theta)]$$
$$= \rho^4(\cos 4\theta + i\sin 4\theta).$$

35. From Section 4.1, $\sin(-\alpha) = -\sin\alpha$ and $\cos(-\alpha) = \cos\alpha$. Thus, $\cos(-\theta) + i\sin(-\theta) = \cos\theta - i\sin\theta$, the conjugate of $\cos\theta + i\sin\theta$.

Exercise Set 6.5

1. $\frac{27}{2} + \frac{27\sqrt{3}}{2}i$ **3.** $0 + 8i$ **5.** $-\frac{1}{8} + 0i$

7. $0 + \frac{1}{81}i$ **9.** $-\frac{1}{32} + \frac{1}{32}i$ **11.** $-\frac{1}{64} - \frac{\sqrt{3}}{64}i$

13. a. $\cos 40° + i\sin 40°$, $\cos 220° + i\sin 220°$
b. $\cos 30° + i\sin 30°$, $\cos 210° + i\sin 210°$

15. a. $2(\cos 40° + i\sin 40°)$, $2(\cos 160° + i\sin 160°)$, $2(\cos 280° + i\sin 280°)$
b. $\cos 20° + i\sin 20°$, $\cos 140° + i\sin 140°$, $\cos 260° + i\sin 260°$

17. a. $\cos 60° + i\sin 60°$, $\cos 150° + i\sin 150°$, $\cos 240° + i\sin 240°$, $\cos 330° + i\sin 330°$
b. $\cos 75° + i\sin 75°$, $\cos 165° + i\sin 165°$, $\cos 255° + i\sin 255°$, $\cos 345° + i\sin 345°$

19. $\left\{\frac{1}{2} + \frac{\sqrt{3}}{2}i, -1, \frac{1}{2} - \frac{\sqrt{3}}{2}i\right\}$ **21.** $\left\{1, -\frac{1}{2} + \frac{\sqrt{3}}{2}i, -\frac{1}{2} - \frac{\sqrt{3}}{2}i\right\}$

23. $\left\{\frac{1}{2^{1/3}}(\cos 110° + i\sin 110°), \frac{1}{2^{1/3}}(\cos 230° + i\sin 230°), \frac{1}{2^{1/3}}(\cos 350° + i\sin 350°)\right\}$.

25. In all cases, the graphs are spaced equally on the unit circle.

a.

b.

c.

d.

e.

f.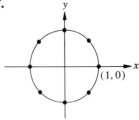

27. $\cos 3\theta = 4 \cos^3 \theta - 3 \cos \theta$

Exercise Set 6.6

1. $(3, 20°), (-3, 200°), (-3, -160°), (3, -340°)$ **3.** $(5, -90°), (-5, -270°), (-5, 90°), (5, 270°)$

5. $(-4, 60°), (4, 240°), (4, -120°), (-4, -300°)$

7. $(2\sqrt{3}, 2)$ **9.** $(-3/\sqrt{2}, -3/\sqrt{2})$ **11.** $(3\sqrt{3}/2, -3/2)$ **13.** $(4, 0^R)$

15. $\left(2\sqrt{2}, \dfrac{\pi^R}{4}\right)$ **17.** $\left(1, \dfrac{5\pi^R}{6}\right)$ **19.** $\rho \cos \theta = 4$ **21.** $\rho = \dfrac{8 \sin \theta}{\cos^2 \theta}$

23. $\rho = 4$ **25.** $\rho = 3 \sin \theta$ **27.** $x^2 + y^2 = 36$ **29.** $x^2 + y^2 = 4y$

31. $y = 2$ **33.** $x^2 - 8y - 16 = 0$

Exercise Set 6.7

1.

3.

6

5.

7.

9.

11.

13.

15.

17.

19.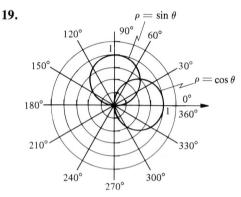

(0.7, 45°) and (0, θ) where θ has any measure

21.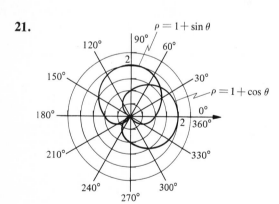

(1.7, 45°), (0.3, 225°) and (0, θ) where θ has any measure

23. $\{(1/\sqrt{2}, 45°)\}$; since ρ is a distance measured from the origin, it may be zero for more than one value of θ. In this case, $\rho = 0$ when $\theta = 0°$ in $\rho = \sin \theta$, and $\rho = 0$ when $\theta = 90°$ in $\rho = \cos \theta$.

25. $\left\{\left(\dfrac{\sqrt{2}+1}{\sqrt{2}}, 45°\right), \left(\dfrac{\sqrt{2}-1}{\sqrt{2}}, 225°\right)\right\}$

27. ρ_1 and ρ_2 are the lengths of sides with included angle $\theta_1 - \theta_2$.
Using the Law of Cosines, $d^2 = \rho_1{}^2 + \rho_2{}^2 - 2\rho_1\rho_2 \cos(\theta_1 - \theta_2)$,

$$d = \sqrt{\rho_1{}^2 + \rho_2{}^2 - 2\rho_1\rho_2 \cos(\theta_1 - \theta_2)}.$$

Review Exercises

1. $x = -\frac{1}{3}, \quad y = -\frac{2}{3}$

2. $x = 1, y = 4; \quad x = -1, \quad y = -4$

3. $-8 + 8i$

4. $0 - i$

5. $-46 + 28i$

6. $22 - 14i$

7. i

8. $-i$

9. $\sqrt{10} + 3\sqrt{5}i$

10. 14

11. If $x = 3i$, then $(3i)^2 + 9 = 9i^2 + 9 = -9 + 9 = 0$;
if $x = -3i$, then $(-3i)^2 + 9 = 9i^2 + 9 = -9 + 9 = 0$.

12. If $x = 1 + 3i$, then $(1 + 3i)^2 - 2(1 + 3i) + 10 = 1 + 6i + 9i^2 - 2 - 6i + 10 = 0$;
if $x = 1 - 3i$, then $(1 - 3i)^2 - 2(1 - 3i) + 10 = 1 - 6i + 9i^2 - 2 + 6i + 10 = 0$.

13. $-15 - i$

14. $3 - 5i$

15. $\frac{7}{5} - \frac{13}{10}i$

16. $-\frac{13}{34} - \frac{8}{17}i$

17. $\frac{2i}{\sqrt{6}}$

18. $\frac{8}{9} - \frac{4\sqrt{5}}{9}i$

19. $(-4, 1)$

20. $(2\sqrt{3}, -2)$

21. $9 - 6i$

22. $3 + 4i$

23.

24.

25. $4 + i$

26. $(5, -1)$

27. $2\sqrt{5}$, 26° 30′

28. $\sqrt{29}$, 248° 10′

29. $\sqrt{2}\,(\cos 45° + i \sin 45°)$

30. $6(\cos 120° + i \sin 120°)$

31. $-\dfrac{7}{2} + \dfrac{7\sqrt{3}}{2}\,i$

32. $\sqrt{2} + \sqrt{2}i$

33. $-3\sqrt{2} - 3\sqrt{2}i$ **34.** $3\sqrt{3} + 3i$

35. $-\frac{8}{9} + 0i$ **36.** $-2\sqrt{2} + 2\sqrt{2}i$

37. $\dfrac{81}{2} + \dfrac{81\sqrt{3}}{2}\,i$ **38.** $0 - 8i$

39. $-\dfrac{1}{32} - \dfrac{\sqrt{3}}{32}\,i$ **40.** $-\dfrac{1}{256} + \dfrac{1}{256}\,i$

41. $\cos 15° + i \sin 15°$, $\cos 195° + i \sin 195°$

42. $5(\cos 110° + i \sin 110°)$, $5(\cos 230° + i \sin 230°)$, $5(\cos 350° + i \sin 350°)$

43. $\{\cos 45° + i \sin 45°, \cos 135° + i \sin 135°, \cos 225° + i \sin 225°, \cos 315° + i \sin 315°\}$

44. $\{10^{1/5}(\cos 48° + i \sin 48°), 10^{1/5}(\cos 120° + i \sin 120°), 10^{1/5}(\cos 192° + i \sin 192°),$
$10^{1/5}(\cos 264° + i \sin 264°), 10^{1/5}(\cos 336° + i \sin 336°)\}$

45. $(2, 250°), (-2, 70°), (2, -110°), (-2, -290°)$ **46.** $(-3, -330°), (-3, 30°), (3, 210°), (3, -150°)$

47. $\left(\dfrac{3}{2}, \dfrac{3\sqrt{3}}{2}\right)$ **48.** $(\sqrt{2}, -\sqrt{2})$ **49.** $\left(2\sqrt{2}, \dfrac{7\pi^{\text{R}}}{4}\right)$ **50.** $\left(2, \dfrac{7\pi^{\text{R}}}{6}\right)$

51. $\rho \cos \theta = 3$ **52.** $\rho^2(\cos^2 \theta + 3 \sin^2 \theta) = 5$

53. $x^2 + y^2 = 5y$ **54.** $y^2 - 4x - 4 = 0$

55.   **56.**

57.

$\rho = \cos 2\theta$

58.

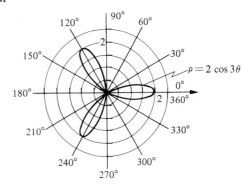

$\rho = 2\cos 3\theta$

Exercise Set B.1

1. 0.0634   **3.** 0.5716   **5.** 0.9105   **7.** 0.9631   **9.** 0.2523   **11.** 1.617

13. 15.93°   **15.** 25.73°   **17.** 37.85°   **19.** 52.06°   **21.** 0.315^R **23.** 1.006^R

25. 0.803^R **27.** 0.969^R

INDEX